Chemistry

Part II
Textbook for Class XII

NCERT

राष्ट्रीय शैक्षिक अनुसंधान और प्रशिक्षण परिषद्
NATIONAL COUNCIL OF EDUCATIONAL RESEARCH AND TRAINING

First Edition
April 2007 Chaitra 1929

Reprinted
November 2007 Kartika 1929
December 2008 Pausa 1930
January 2010 Magha 1931
January 2011 Magha 1932
January 2012 Magha 1933
November 2012 Kartika 1934

PD 350T RNB

© *National Council of Educational Research and Training, 2007*

₹ **95.00**

Printed on 80 GSM paper with NCERT watermark

Published at the Publication Division by the Secretary, National Council of Educational Research and Training, Sri Aurobindo Marg, New Delhi 110 016 and printed at Shagun Offset Pvt. Ltd., B-3, Sector-65, Noida 201 301 (UP)

ISBN 81-7450-648-9 (Part I)
       81-7450-716-7 (Part II)

OFFICES OF THE PUBLICATION DIVISION, NCERT

NCERT Campus
Sri Aurobindo Marg
New Delhi 110 016   Phone : 011-26562708

108, 100 Feet Road
Hosdakere Halli Extension
Banashankari III Stage
Bangalore 560 085   Phone : 080-26725740

Navjivan Trust Building
P.O.Navjivan
Ahmedabad 380 014   Phone : 079-27541446

CWC Campus
Opp. Dhankal Bus Stop
Panihati
Kolkata 700 114   Phone : 033-25530454

CWC Complex
Maligaon
Guwahati 781 021   Phone : 0361-2674869

Publication Team

Head, Publication Division	:	*Ashok Srivastava*
Chief Production Officer	:	*Shiv Kumar*
Chief Editor (Incharge)	:	*Naresh Yadav*
Chief Business Manager	:	*Gautam Ganguly*
Editor	:	*R. N. Bhardwaj*
Assistant Production Officer	:	*Atul Saxena*

Cover and Layout
Blue Fish

FOREWORD

The National Curriculum Framework (NCF), 2005 recommends that children's life at school must be linked to their life outside the school. This principle marks a departure from the legacy of bookish learning which continues to shape our system and causes a gap between the school, home and community. The syllabi and textbooks developed on the basis of NCF signify an attempt to implement this basic idea. They also attempt to discourage rote learning and the maintenance of sharp boundaries between different subject areas. We hope these measures will take us significantly further in the direction of a child-centred system of education outlined in the National Policy on Education (1986).

The success of this effort depends on the steps that school principals and teachers will take to encourage children to reflect on their own learning and to pursue imaginative activities and questions. We must recognise that, given space, time and freedom, children generate new knowledge by engaging with the information passed on to them by adults. Treating the prescribed textbook as the sole basis of examination is one of the key reasons why other resources and sites of learning are ignored. Inculcating creativity and initiative is possible if we perceive and treat children as participants in learning, not as receivers of a fixed body of knowledge.

These aims imply considerable change in school routines and mode of functioning. Flexibility in the daily time-table is as necessary as rigour in implementing the annual calender so that the required number of teaching days are actually devoted to teaching. The methods used for teaching and evaluation will also determine how effective this textbook proves for making children's life at school a happy experience, rather than a source of stress or boredom. Syllabus designers have tried to address the problem of curricular burden by restructuring and reorienting knowledge at different stages with greater consideration for child psychology and the time available for teaching. The textbook attempts to enhance this endeavour by giving higher priority and space to opportunities for contemplation and wondering, discussion in small groups, and activities requiring hands-on experience.

The National Council of Educational Research and Training (NCERT) appreciates the hard work done by the textbook development committee responsible for this book. We wish to thank the Chairperson of the advisory group in science and mathematics, Professor J.V. Narlikar and the Chief Advisor for this book, Professor B. L. Khandelwal for guiding the work of this committee.

Several teachers contributed to the development of this textbook; we are grateful to their principals for making this possible. We are indebted to the institutions and organisations which have generously permitted us to draw upon their resources, material and personnel. As an organisation committed to systemic reform and continuous improvement in the quality of its products, NCERT welcomes comments and suggestions which will enable us to undertake further revision and refinement.

New Delhi
20 November 2006

Director
National Council of Educational
Research and Training

PREFACE

Chemistry has made a profound impact on the society. It is intimately linked to the well-being of human kind. The rate of advancements in chemistry is so high that curriculum developers continuously look for strategies to cope with these advancements. Also, the students have to be inspired to be the future leaders who would make fundamental contributions. The present textbook is a sincere effort in this direction.

The textbook, presented in two parts, comprises of sixteen Units. Although the titles of various Units indicate a sort of compartmentalisation into physical, inorganic and organic chemistry, readers will find that these sub-disciplines have been intermingled, at least to a certain extent, to have a unified approach to the subject. First nine Units covering physical and inorganic chemistry portions are included in Part I while organic chemistry portion comprising of seven Units is included in Part II of the book. The approach of presentation of the subject matter discourages students from rote memorisation. The subject has in fact, been organised around the laws and principles of chemistry. As students master these laws and principles, they will soon get to the point where they can predict much of what will come.

Efforts have been directed towards making the subject stimulating and exciting by references to the historical developments and its usefulness to our lives, wherever appropriate. The text is well illustrated with examples from surrounding environment to facilitate grasping of the qualitative and quantitative aspects of the concept easily. Physical data are given in SI units throughout the book to make comparison of various properties easier. IUPAC system of nomenclature has been followed along with the common names. Structural formulae of chemical compounds showing functional/coordinating groups in different colours are drawn using electronic system. Each Unit has a good number of examples, as illustrations, with their solutions and some intext questions, the answers of some of which are given at the end of the Unit. The end of Unit exercises are designed to apply important principles and provoke thinking process to solve them. Answers of some of these exercises are given at the end of the book.

A variety of materials, e.g., biographical sketches of some scientists, additional information related to a particular topic, etc., is given in boxes with a deep yellow coloured bar. This boxed material with a 'deep yellow bar' is to bring additional life to the topic. However, it is non-evaluative. The structures of some of the more complex compounds incorporated in the book are for understanding their chemistry. As their reproduction would lead to memorisation, it is also a non-evaluative portion of the text.

The information part has been significantly reduced and, wherever possible, it has been substantiated with facts. However, it is necessary for students to be aware of commercially important chemicals, their processes of manufacture and sources of raw materials. This leads to descriptive material in the book. Attempts have been made to make descriptions of such compounds interesting by considering their structures and reactivity. Thermodynamics, kinetics and electrochemical aspects have been applied to a few chemical reactions which should be beneficial to students for understanding why a particular reaction happened and why a particular property is exhibited by the product. There is currently great awareness of environmental and energy issues which are directly related to chemistry. Such issues have been highlighted and dealt with at appropriate places in the book.

A team of experts constituted by the NCERT has developed the manuscript of the book. It gives me great pleasure to acknowledge the valuable contribution of all the members of this team. I also acknowledge the valuable and relentless contribution of the editors in bringing the book to the present shape. I also acknowledge with thanks the dedicated efforts and valuable contribution of Professor Brahm Parkash, who not only coordinated the entire programme but also actively involved in writing and editing of this book. Thanks are also due to the participating teachers and subject experts of the review workshop for their contribution, which has helped us to make the book learner friendly. Also, I thank the technical and administrative staff of the NCERT for their support in the entire process.

The team of this textbook development programme hopes that the book stimulates its readers and makes them feel the excitement and fascination for this subject. Efforts have been made to bring out this book error-free. Nevertheless, it is recognised that in a book of this complexity, there could inevitably be occasional errors. It will always be a pleasure to hear about them from readers to take necessary steps to rectify them.

B.L. KHANDELWAL

Acknowledgments

The National Council of Educational Research and Training (NCERT) gratefully acknowledges the valuable contributions of the individuals and organisations involved in the development of Chemistry textbook for Class XII. The acknowledgements are also due to the following practicing teachers and subject experts for reviewing the draft manuscript and giving useful suggestions for its improvement in a workshop: Dr D.S. Rawat, Department of Chemistry, University of Delhi, Delhi; Dr Mahendra Nath, *Reader*, Chemistry Department, University of Delhi, Delhi; Dr Sulekh Chandra, *Reader*, Zakir Hussain College, New Delhi; Ms Ameeta K., *PGT* (Chemistry), Vidyalaya No. 3, Patiala Cantt (Pb.); Dr G.T. Bhandge, *Professor* and *Head*, DESM, Regional Institute of Education, Mysore; Dr Neeti Misra, *Senior Lecturer*, Department of Chemistry, Acharya Narendra Dev College, New Delhi; Dr S.P.S. Mehta, Department of Chemistry, Kumaun University, Nainital (UA); Dr N.V.S. Naidu, *Assistant Professor* (Chemistry), SVU College of Mathematics and Physical Sciences, S.V. University, Tirupati (A.P.); Dr A.C. Handa, Hindu College, Delhi University, Delhi; Dr A.K. Vashishtha, G.B.S.S.S. Jafrabad, Delhi; Dr Charanjit Kaur, *Head*, Department of Chemistry, Sri Sathya Sai College for Women, Bhopal, P.O. Habibganj; Ms Alka Sharma, *PGT* (Chemistry), S.L.S. DAV Public School, Mausam Vihar, Delhi; Dr H.H. Tripathy, *Reader* (Retired), Regional Institute of Education, Bhubaneswar; Shri C.B. Singh, *PGT* (Chemistry), Kendriya Vidyalaya No. 2, Delhi Cantt, Delhi; and Dr Sunita Hooda, Acharya Narendra Dev College, Delhi University, New Delhi.

The Council also thanks Professor B.L. Khandelwal, Professor Brahm Parkash, Dr K.K. Arora, Dr Vijay Sarda and Professor R.S. Sindhu, members of the Textbook Development Committee for editing the manuscript and bringing it to the present shape.

The Council also acknowledges the contributions of Shri Vijay Singh and Vijay Kaushal *DTP Operators and* Dr K.T. Chitralekha, *Copy Editor* in shaping this book. The efforts of the Publication Department, NCERT are also duly acknowledged.

CONTENTS OF
CHEMISTRY PART I

CONTENTS

Haloalkanes and Haloarenes

Objectives

After studying this Unit, you will be able to

- name haloalkanes and haloarenes according to the IUPAC system of nomenclature from their given structures;
- describe the reactions involved in the preparation of haloalkanes and haloarenes and understand various reactions that they undergo;
- correlate the structures of haloalkanes and haloarenes with various types of reactions;
- use stereochemistry as a tool for understanding the reaction mechanism;
- appreciate the applications of organo-metallic compounds;
- highlight the environmental effects of polyhalogen compounds.

Halogenated compounds persist in the environment due to their resistance to breakdown by soil bacteria.

The replacement of hydrogen atom(s) in a hydrocarbon, aliphatic or aromatic, by halogen atom(s) results in the formation of alkyl halide (haloalkane) and aryl halide (haloarene), respectively. Haloalkanes contain halogen atom(s) attached to the sp^3 hybridised carbon atom of an alkyl group whereas haloarenes contain halogen atom(s) attached to sp^2 hybridised carbon atom(s) of an aryl group. Many halogen containing organic compounds occur in nature and some of these are clinically useful. These classes of compounds find wide applications in industry as well as in day-to-day life. They are used as solvents for relatively non-polar compounds and as starting materials for the synthesis of wide range of organic compounds. Chlorine containing antibiotic, *chloramphenicol,* produced by soil microorganisms is very effective for the treatment of typhoid fever. Our body produces iodine containing hormone, *thyroxine,* the deficiency of which causes a disease called *goiter.* Synthetic halogen compounds, *viz.* chloroquine is used for the treatment of malaria; halothane is used as an anaesthetic during surgery. Certain fully fluorinated compounds are being considered as potential blood substitutes in surgery.

In this Unit, you will study the important methods of preparation, physical and chemical properties and uses of organohalogen compounds.

10.1 Classification

Haloalkanes and haloarenes may be classified as follows:

10.1.1 On the Basis of Number of Halogen Atoms

These may be classified as mono, di, or polyhalogen (tri-,tetra-, etc.) compounds depending on whether they contain one, two or more halogen atoms in their structures. For example,

C_2H_5X

Monohaloalkane

CH_2X
|
CH_2X

Dihaloalkane

CH_2X
|
CHX
|
CH_2X

Trihaloalkane

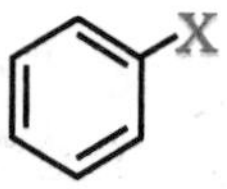

Monohaloarene

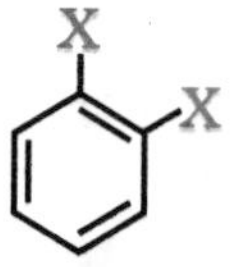

Dihaloarene

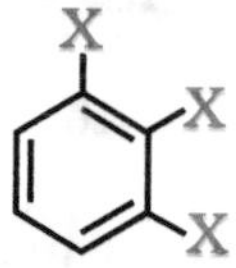

Trihaloarene

Monohalocompounds may further be classified according to the hybridisation of the carbon atom to which the halogen is bonded, as discussed below.

10.1.2 Compounds Containing sp^3 C—X Bond (X= F, Cl, Br, I)

This class includes

(a) Alkyl halides or haloalkanes (R—X)

In alkyl halides, the halogen atom is bonded to an alkyl group (R). They form a homologous series represented by $C_nH_{2n+1}X$. They are further classified as primary, secondary or tertiary according to the nature of carbon to which halogen is attached.

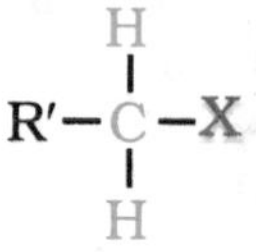

$$R'-\underset{\underset{H}{|}}{\overset{\overset{H}{|}}{C}}-X$$

Primary (1°)

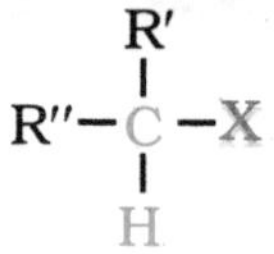

$$R''-\underset{\underset{H}{|}}{\overset{\overset{R'}{|}}{C}}-X$$

Secondary (2°)

$$R''-\underset{\underset{R'''}{|}}{\overset{\overset{R'}{|}}{C}}-X$$

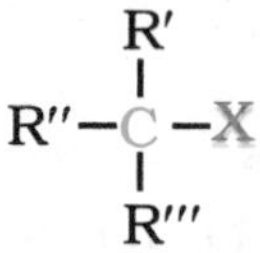

Tertiary (3°)

(b) Allylic halides

These are the compounds in which the halogen atom is bonded to an sp^3-hybridised carbon atom next to carbon-carbon double bond (C=C) *i.e.* to an allylic carbon.

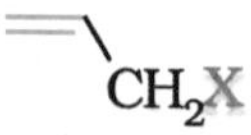

CH_2X

(c) Benzylic halides

These are the compounds in which the halogen atom is bonded to an sp^3-hybridised carbon atom next to an aromatic ring.

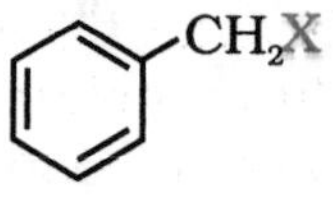

CH_2X

(1°)

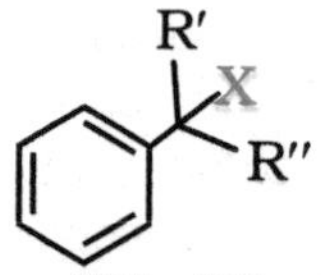

$R' = CH_3, R'' = H (2°)$

$R' = R'' = CH_3 (3°)$

10.1.3 Compounds Containing sp^2 C—X Bond

This class includes:

(a) Vinylic halides

These are the compounds in which the halogen atom is bonded to an sp^2-hybridised carbon atom of a carbon-carbon double bond (C = C).

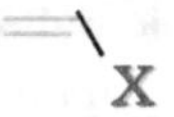

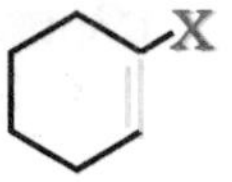

(b) Aryl halides

These are the compounds in which the halogen atom is bonded to the sp^2-hybridised carbon atom of an aromatic ring.

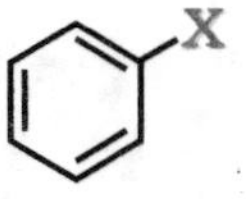

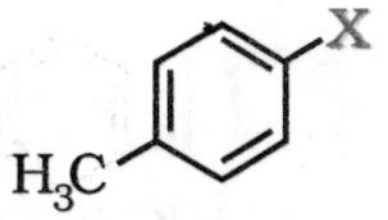

10.2 Nomenclature

Having learnt the classification of halogenated compounds, let us now learn how these are named. The common names of alkyl halides are derived by naming the alkyl group followed by the halide. Alkyl halides are named as halosubstituted hydrocarbons in the IUPAC system of nomenclature. Haloarenes are the common as well as IUPAC names of aryl halides. For dihalogen derivatives, the prefixes o-, m-, p- are used in common system but in IUPAC system, the numerals 1,2; 1,3 and 1,4 are used.

$CH_3CH_2CH_2Br$

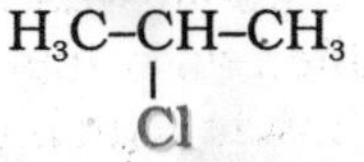

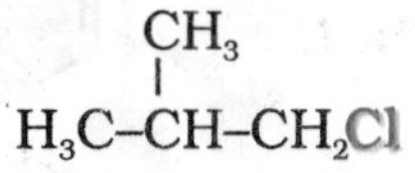

Common name: n-Propyl bromide
IUPAC name: 1-Bromopropane

$H_3C–CH–CH_3$
   $|$
   Cl

Isopropyl chloride
2-Chloropropane

CH_3
 $|$
$H_3C–CH–CH_2Cl$

Isobutyl chloride
1-Chloro-2-methylpropane

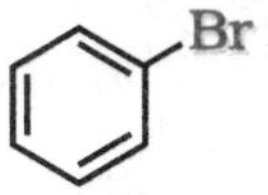

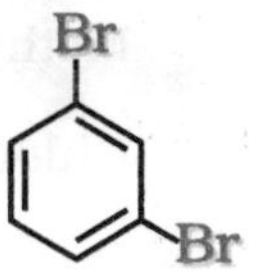

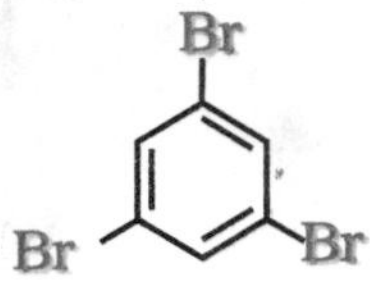

Common name: Bromobenzene
IUPAC name: Bromobenzene

m-Dibromobenzene
1,3-Dibromobenzene

sym-Tribromobenzene
1,3,5-Tribromobenzene

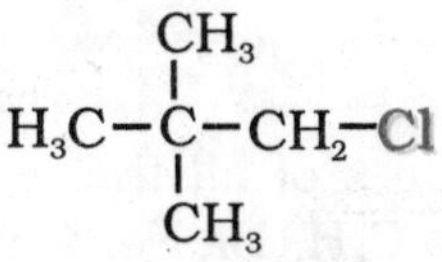

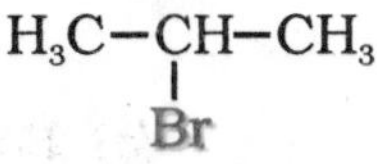

CH_3
 $|$
$H_3C–C–CH_2–Cl$
 $|$
CH_3

IUPAC name: 1-Chloro-2,2-dimethylpropane

$H_3C–CH–CH_3$
   $|$
   Br

2-Bromopropane

The dihaloalkanes having the same type of halogen atoms are named as alkylidene or alkylene dihalides. The dihalo-compounds having same type of halogen atoms are further classified as geminal halides (halogen atoms are present on the same carbon atom) and vicinal halides (halogen atoms are present on the adjacent carbon atoms). In common name system, *gem*-dihalides are named as alkylidene halides and *vic*-dihalides are named as alkylene dihalides. In IUPAC system, they are named as dihaloalkanes.

$$H_3C-CHCl_2 \qquad\qquad \underset{\underset{Cl\;\;\;Cl}{|\quad\;\;|}}{H_2C-CH_2}$$

Common name: Ethylidene chloride   Ethylene dichloride
               (*gem*-dihalide)   (*vic-dihalide*)

IUPAC name: 1, 1-Dichloroethane   1, 2-Dichloroethane

Some common examples of halocompounds are mentioned in Table **10.1**.

Table 10.1: Common and IUPAC names of some Halides

Structure	Common name	IUPAC name
$CH_3CH_2CH(Cl)CH_3$	sec-Butyl chloride	2-Chlorobutane
$(CH_3)_3CCH_2Br$	neo-Pentyl bromide	1-Bromo-2,2-dimethyl**propane**
$(CH_3)_3CBr$	tert-Butyl bromide	2-Bromo-2-methylpropane
$CH_2 = CHCl$	Vinyl chloride	Chloroethene
$CH_2 = CHCH_2Br$	Allyl bromide	3-Bromopropene
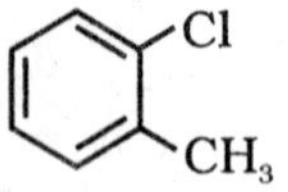 ![o-chlorotoluene structure] Cl / CH₃	o-Chlorotoluene	1-Chloro-2-methylbenzene or 2-Chlorotoluene
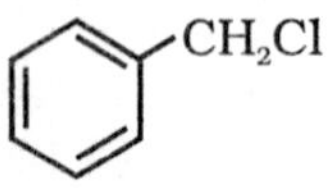 ![benzyl chloride structure] CH₂Cl	Benzyl chloride	Chlorophenylmethane
CH_2Cl_2	Methylene chloride	Dichloromethane
$CHCl_3$	Chloroform	Trichloromethane
$CHBr_3$	Bromoform	Tribromomethane
CCl_4	Carbon tetrachloride	Tetrachloromethane
$CH_3CH_2CH_2F$	n-Propyl fluoride	1-Fluoropropane

Example 10.1   Draw the structures of all the eight structural isomers that have the molecular formula $C_5H_{11}Br$. Name each isomer according to IUPAC system and classify them as primary, secondary or tertiary bromide.

Solution $CH_3CH_2CH_2CH_2CH_2Br$ 1-Bromopentane (1°)

$CH_3CH_2CH_2CH(Br)CH_3$ 2-Bromopentane(2°)

$CH_3CH_2CH(Br)CH_2CH_3$ 3-Bromopentane (2°)

$(CH_3)_2CHCH_2CH_2Br$ 1-Bromo-3-methylbutane (1°)

$(CH_3)_2CHCHBrCH_3$ 2-Bromo-3-methylbutane(2°)

$(CH_3)_2CBrCH_2CH_3$ 2-Bromo-2-methylbutane (3°)

$CH_3CH_2CH(CH_3)CH_2Br$ 1-Bromo-2-methylbutane(1°)

$(CH_3)_3CCH_2Br$ 1-Bromo-2,2-dimethylpropane (1°)

Write IUPAC names of the following:

Example 10.2

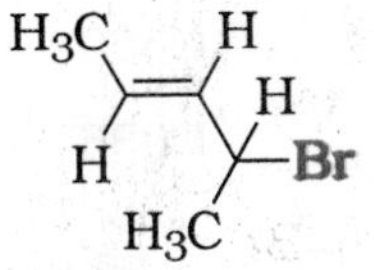

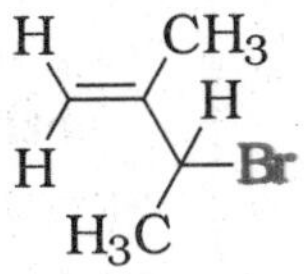

(i) 4-Bromopent-2-ene

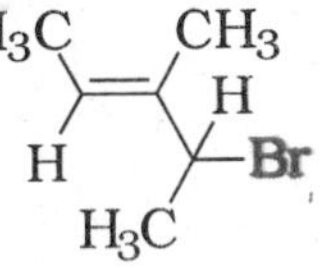

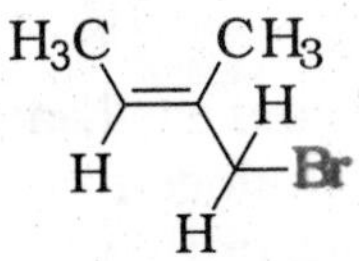

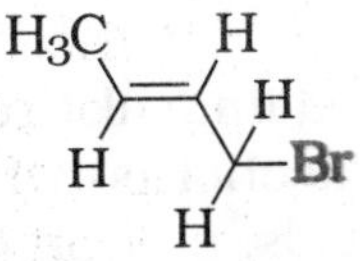

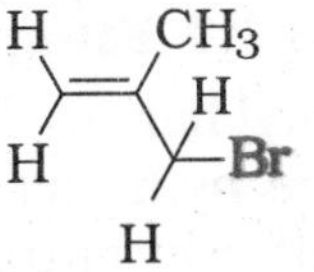

(iii) 4-Bromo-3-methylpent-2-ene

(v) 1-Bromobut-2-ene

(ii) 3-Bromo-2-methylbut-1-ene

(iv) 1-Bromo-2-methylbut-2-ene

(vi) 3-Bromo-2-methylpropene

Solution

10.1 Write structures of the following compounds:

    (i) 2-Chloro-3-methylpentane

    (ii) 1-Chloro-4-ethylcyclohexane

    (iii) 4-tert. Butyl-3-iodoheptane

    (iv) 1,4-Dibromobut-2-ene

    (v) 1-Bromo-4-sec. butyl-2-methylbenzene.

10.3 Nature of C–X Bond

Since halogen atoms are more electronegative than carbon, the carbon-halogen bond of alkyl halide is polarised; the carbon atom bears a partial positive charge whereas the halogen atom bears a partial negative charge.

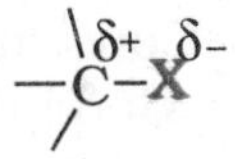

$$-\overset{|}{\underset{|}{C}}{}^{\delta+}\!\!-X^{\delta-}$$

Since the size of halogen atom increases as we go down the group in the periodic table, fluorine atom is the smallest and iodine atom, the largest. Consequently the carbon-halogen bond length also increases from C—F to C—I. Some typical bond lengths, bond enthalpies and dipole moments are given in Table 10.2.

Table 10.2: Carbon-Halogen (C—X) Bond Lengths, Bond Enthalpies and Dipole Moments

Bond	Bond length/pm	C-X Bond enthalpies/ kJmol^{-1}	Dipole moment/Debye
CH_3-F	139	452	1.847
CH_3-Cl	178	351	1.860
CH_3-Br	193	293	1.830
CH_3-I	214	234	1.636

10.4 Methods of Preparation

10.4.1 From Alcohols

Alkyl halides are best prepared from alcohols, which are easily accessible. The hydroxyl group of an alcohol is replaced by halogen on reaction with concentrated halogen acids, phosphorus halides or thionyl chloride. Thionyl chloride is preferred because the other two products are escapable gases. Hence the reaction gives pure alkyl halides. Phosphorus tribromide and triiodide are usually generated *in situ* (produced in the reaction mixture) by the reaction of red phosphorus with bromine and iodine respectively. The preparation of alkyl chloride is carried out either by passing dry hydrogen chloride gas through a solution of alcohol or by heating a solution of alcohol in concentrated aqueous acid.

$$R-OH + HCl \xrightarrow{ZnCl_2} R-Cl + H_2O$$

$$R-OH + NaBr + H_2SO_4 \longrightarrow R-Br + NaHSO_4 + H_2O$$

$$3R-OH + PX_3 \longrightarrow 3R-X + H_3PO_3 \quad (X = Cl \ Br)$$

$$R-OH + PCl_5 \longrightarrow R-Cl + POCl_3 + HCl$$

$$R-OH \xrightarrow[X_2=Br_2,I_2]{red\ P/X_2} R-X$$

$$R-OH + SOCl_2 \longrightarrow R-Cl + SO_2 + HCl$$

The reactions of primary and secondary alcohols with HX require the presence of a catalyst, $ZnCl_2$. With tertiary alcohols, the reaction is conducted by simply shaking with concentrated HCl at room temperature. Constant boiling with HBr (48%) is used for preparing alkyl bromide. Good yields of R—I may be obtained by heating alcohols with sodium or potassium iodide in 95% phosphoric acid. The order of reactivity of alcohols with a given haloacid is 3°>2°>1°. The above method is not applicable for the preparation of aryl halides because the carbon-oxygen bond in phenols has a partial double bond character and is difficult to break being stronger than a single bond (Unit 11, Class XI).

10.4.2 From Hydrocarbons

(a) By free radical halogenation

Free radical chlorination or bromination of alkanes gives a complex mixture of isomeric mono- and polyhaloalkanes, which is difficult to separate as pure compounds. Consequently, the yield of any one compound is low (Unit 13, Class XI).

$$CH_3CH_2CH_2CH_3 \xrightarrow[\text{or heat}]{Cl_2/\text{UV light}} CH_3CH_2CH_2CH_2Cl + CH_3CH_2CHClCH_3$$

Example 10.3

Identify all the possible monochloro structural isomers expected to be formed on free radical monochlorination of $(CH_3)_2CHCH_2CH_3$.

Solution

In the given molecule, there are four different types of hydrogen atoms. Replacement of these hydrogen atoms will give the following

$(CH_3)_2CHCH_2CH_2Cl$ $(CH_3)_2CHCH(Cl)CH_3$

$(CH_3)_2C(Cl)CH_2CH_3$ $CH_3CH(CH_2Cl)CH_2CH_3$

(b) By electrophilic substitution

Aryl chlorides and bromides can be easily prepared by electrophilic substitution of arenes with chlorine and bromine respectively in the presence of Lewis acid catalysts like iron or iron(III) chloride.

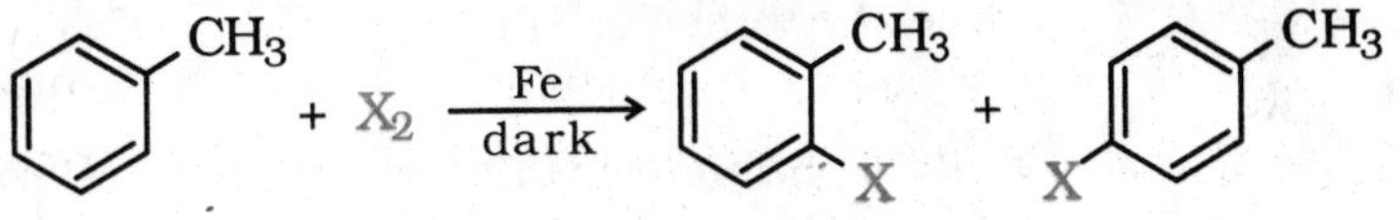

o-Halotoluene   p-Halotoluene

The *ortho* and *para* isomers can be easily separated due to large difference in their melting points. Reactions with iodine are reversible in nature and require the presence of an oxidising agent (HNO_3, HIO_4) to oxidise the HI formed during iodination. Fluoro compounds are not prepared by this method due to high reactivity of fluorine.

(c) Sandmeyer's reaction

When a primary aromatic amine, dissolved or suspended in cold aqueous mineral acid, is treated with sodium nitrite, a diazonium salt is formed (Unit 13, Class XII). Mixing the solution of freshly prepared diazonium salt with cuprous chloride or cuprous bromide results in the replacement of the diazonium group by –Cl or –Br.

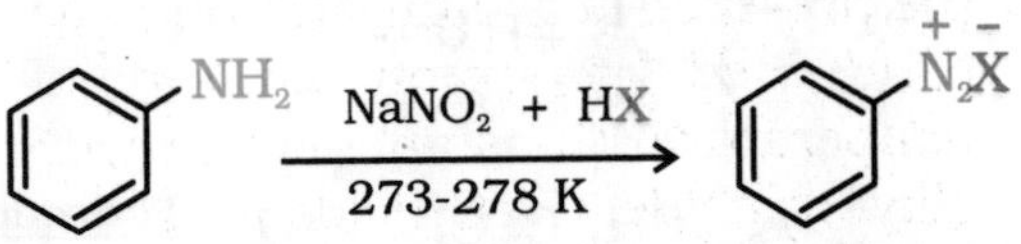

Benzene diazonium
halide

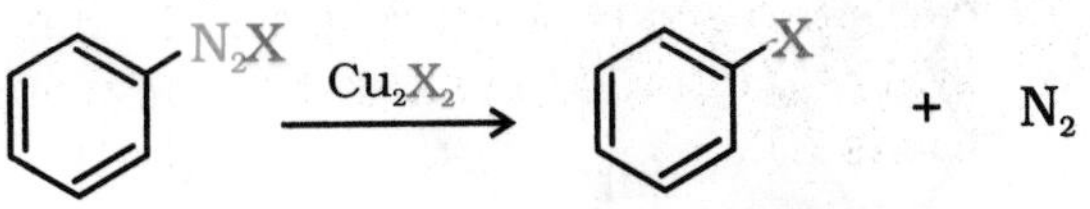

Aryl halide

X = Cl, Br

Replacement of the diazonium group by iodine does not require the presence of cuprous halide and is done simply by shaking the diazonium salt with potassium iodide.

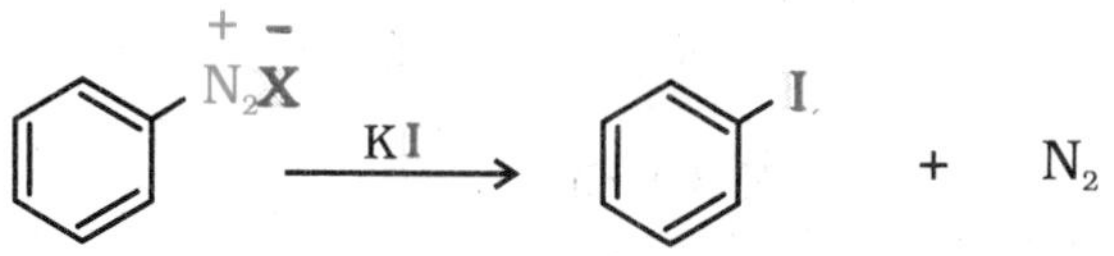

$$\text{C}_6\text{H}_5\overset{+}{\text{N}_2}\overset{-}{\text{X}} \xrightarrow{\text{KI}} \text{C}_6\text{H}_5\text{I} + \text{N}_2$$

(d) From alkenes

(i) *Addition of hydrogen halides*: An alkene is converted to corresponding alkyl halide by reaction with hydrogen chloride, hydrogen bromide or hydrogen iodide.

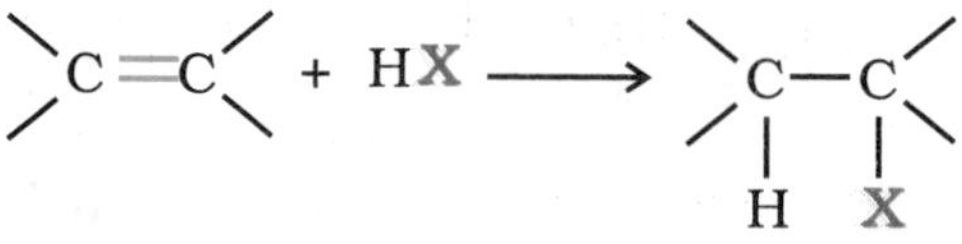

$$\underset{}{>}\!\text{C}=\text{C}\!\underset{}{<} + \text{HX} \longrightarrow \underset{\text{H}}{>}\!\text{C}-\text{C}\!\underset{\text{X}}{<}$$

Propene yields two products, however only one predominates as per Markovnikov's rule. (Unit 13, Class XI)

$$\text{CH}_3\text{CH}=\text{CH}_2 + \text{H–I} \longrightarrow \underset{\text{minor}}{\text{CH}_3\text{CH}_2\text{CH}_2\text{I}} + \underset{\text{major}}{\text{CH}_3\text{CHICH}_3}$$

(ii) *Addition of halogens:* In the laboratory, addition of bromine in CCl_4 to an alkene resulting in discharge of reddish brown colour of bromine constitutes an important method for the detection of double bond in a molecule. The addition results in the synthesis of *vic*-dibromides, which are colourless (Unit 13, Class XI).

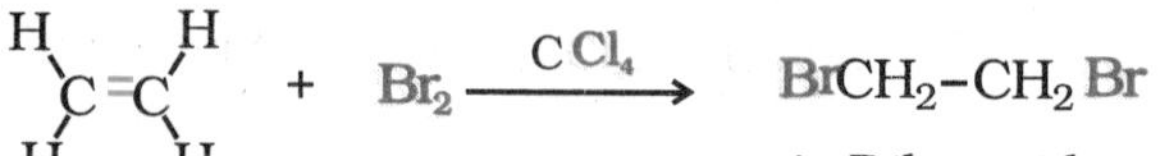

$$\underset{\text{H}\quad\text{H}}{\overset{\text{H}\quad\text{H}}{\text{C}=\text{C}}} + \text{Br}_2 \xrightarrow{\text{CCl}_4} \underset{\textit{vic}\text{-Dibromide}}{\text{BrCH}_2-\text{CH}_2\text{Br}}$$

Example 10.4 Write the products of the following reactions:

(i) 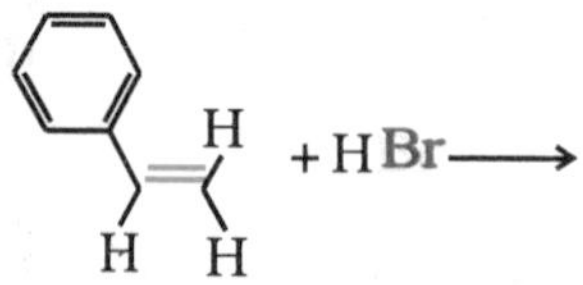 C_6H_5–CH=CH$_2$ + HBr $\longrightarrow$ (ii) $\text{CH}_3\text{–CH}_2\text{–CH}=\text{CH}_2 + \text{HCl} \longrightarrow$

(iii) 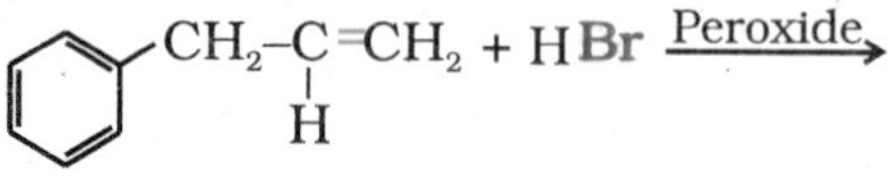 C_6H_5–CH$_2$–C(H)=CH$_2$ + HBr $\xrightarrow{\text{Peroxide}}$

Solution

(i) 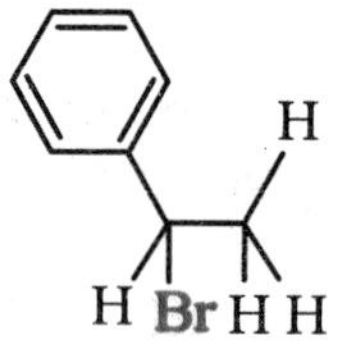 C_6H_5–CH(Br)–CH$_3$ (ii) $\text{CH}_3\text{–CH}_2\text{–CH(Cl)–CH}_3$ (iii) 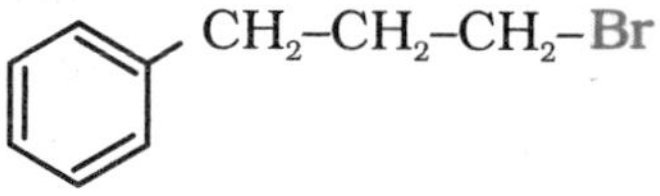 C_6H_5–CH$_2$–CH$_2$–CH$_2$–Br

10.4.3 Halogen Exchange

Alkyl iodides are often prepared by the reaction of alkyl chlorides/bromides with NaI in dry acetone. This reaction is known as **Finkelstein** reaction.

$$R\text{--}X \ + \ NaI \longrightarrow R\text{--}I \ + \ NaX$$

$$X = Cl, Br$$

NaCl or NaBr thus formed is precipitated in dry acetone. It facilitates the forward reaction according to Le Chatelier's Principle.

The synthesis of alkyl fluorides is best accomplished by heating an alkyl chloride/bromide in the presence of a metallic fluoride such as AgF, Hg_2F_2, CoF_2 or SbF_3. The reaction is termed as **Swarts** reaction.

$$H_3C\text{--}Br + AgF \longrightarrow H_3C\text{--}F \ + \ AgBr$$

Intext Questions

10.2 Why is sulphuric acid not used during the reaction of alcohols with KI?

10.3 Write structures of different dihalogen derivatives of propane.

10.4 Among the isomeric alkanes of molecular formula C_5H_{12}, identify the one that on photochemical chlorination yields

(i) A single monochloride.

(ii) Three isomeric monochlorides.

(iii) Four isomeric monochlorides.

10.5 Draw the structures of major monohalo products in each of the following reactions:

(i)  cyclohexanol with OH + SOCl₂ →

(ii) 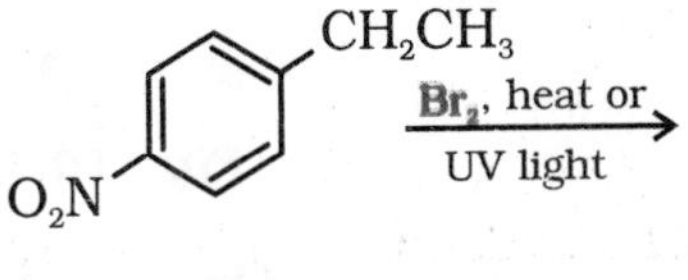 p-ethylnitrobenzene (CH₂CH₃, O₂N) + Br₂, heat or UV light →

(iii) 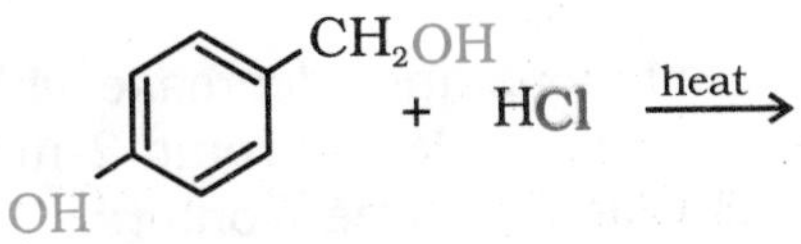 4-hydroxybenzyl alcohol (CH₂OH, OH) + HCl heat →

(iv) 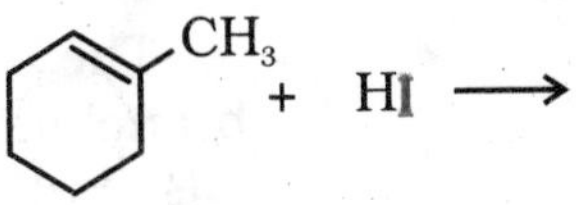 1-methylcyclohexene (CH₃) + HI →

(v) CH₃CH₂Br + NaI →

(vi) 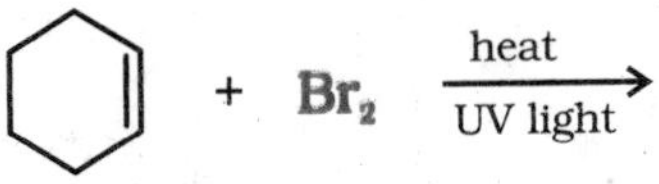 cyclohexene + Br₂ heat / UV light →

10.5 Physical Properties

Alkyl halides are colourless when pure. However, bromides and iodides develop colour when exposed to light. Many volatile halogen compounds have sweet smell.

Melting and boiling points

Methyl chloride, methyl bromide, ethyl chloride and some chlorofluoromethanes are gases at room temperature. Higher members are liquids or solids. As we have already learnt, molecules of organic halogen compounds are generally polar. Due to greater polarity as well as higher molecular mass as compared to the parent hydrocarbon, the intermolecular forces of attraction (dipole-dipole and van der Waals) are stronger in the halogen derivatives. That is why the boiling points of chlorides, bromides and iodides are considerably higher than those of the hydrocarbons of comparable molecular mass.

The attractions get stronger as the molecules get bigger in size and have more electrons. The pattern of variation of boiling points of different halides is depicted in Fig. 10.1. For the same alkyl group, the boiling points of alkyl halides decrease in the order: RI> RBr> RCl> RF. This is because with the increase in size and mass of halogen atom, the magnitude of van der Waal forces increases.

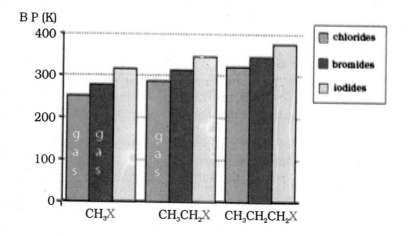

Fig. 10.1: *Comparison of boiling points of some alkyl halides*

The boiling points of isomeric haloalkanes decrease with increase in branching (Unit 12, Class XI). For example, 2-bromo-2-methylpropane has the lowest boiling point among the three isomers.

$$CH_3CH_2CH_2CH_2Br \qquad CH_3CH_2\underset{\underset{Br}{|}}{CH}CH_3 \qquad H_3C-\underset{\underset{Br}{|}}{\overset{\overset{CH_3}{|}}{C}}-CH_3$$

b.p./K	375	364	346

Boiling points of isomeric dihalobenzenes are very nearly the same. However, the *para*-isomers are high melting as compared to their *ortho*- and *meta*-isomers. It is due to symmetry of *para*-isomers that fits in crystal lattice better as compared to *ortho*- and *meta*-isomers.

	Cl structure	Cl structure	Cl structure
b.p/K	453	446	448
m.p/K	256	249	323

Density

Bromo, iodo and polychloro derivatives of hydrocarbons are heavier than water. The density increases with increase in number of carbon atoms, halogen atoms and atomic mass of the halogen atoms (Table 10.3).

Table 10.3: Density of some Haloalkanes

Compound	Density (g/mL)	Compound	Density (g/mL)
n–C_3H_7Cl	0.89	CH_2Cl_2	1.336
n–C_3H_7Br	1.335	$CHCl_3$	1.489
n–C_3H_7I	1.747	CCl_4	1.595

Solubility

The haloalkanes are only very slightly soluble in water. In order for a haloalkane to dissolve in water, energy is required to overcome the attractions between the haloalkane molecules and break the hydrogen bonds between water molecules. Less energy is released when new attractions are set up between the haloalkane and the water molecules as these are not as strong as the original hydrogen bonds in water. As a result, the solubility of haloalkanes in water is low. However, haloalkanes tend to dissolve in organic solvents because the new intermolecular attractions between haloalkanes and solvent molecules have much the same strength as the ones being broken in the separate haloalkane and solvent molecules.

Intext Question

10.6 Arrange each set of compounds in order of increasing boiling points.

    (i) Bromomethane, Bromoform, Chloromethane, Dibromomethane.

    (ii) 1-Chloropropane, Isopropyl chloride, 1-Chlorobutane.

10.6 Chemical Reactions

10.6.1 Reactions of Haloalkanes

The reactions of haloalkanes may be divided into the following categories:

    (i) Nucleophilic substitution

    (ii) Elimination reactions

    (iii) Reaction with metals.

(i) Nucleophilic substitution reactions

In this type of reaction, a nucleophile reacts with haloalkane (the substrate) having a partial positive charge on the carbon atom bonded to halogen. A substitution reaction takes place and halogen atom, called leaving group departs as halide ion. Since the substitution reaction is initiated by a nucleophile, it is called nucleophilic substitution reaction.

$$\overset{-}{Nu} + \overset{\delta^+}{-}\overset{|}{\underset{|}{C}}\overset{\delta^-}{-X} \longrightarrow \overset{|}{\underset{|}{C}}-Nu + \overset{-}{X}$$

It is one of the most useful classes of organic reactions of alkyl halides in which halogen is bonded to sp^3 hybridised carbon. The products formed by the reaction of haloalkanes with some common nucleophiles are given in Table 10.4.

Table 10.4: Nucleophilic Substitution of Alkyl Halides (R-X)

$$R - X + Nu^- \rightarrow R - Nu + X^-$$

Reagent	Nucleophile (Nu^-)	Substitution product R–Nu	Class of main product
NaOH (KOH)	HO^-	ROH	Alcohol
H_2O	H_2O	ROH	Alcohol
NaOR′	$R'O^-$	ROR′	Ether
NaI	I^-	R—I	Alkyl iodide
NH_3	NH_3	RNH_2	Primary amine
$R'NH_2$	$R'NH_2$	RNHR′	Sec. amine
R′R″NH	R′R″NH	RNR′R″	Tert. amine
KCN	$\bar{C}{\equiv}N:$	RCN	Nitrile (cyanide)
AgCN	Ag-CN:	RNC (isocyanide)	Isonitrile
KNO_2	O=N—O	R—O—N=O	Alkyl nitrite
$AgNO_2$	Ag—Ö—N=O	$R—NO_2$	Nitroalkane
R′COOAg	$R'COO^-$	R′COOR	Ester
$LiAlH_4$	H	RH	Hydrocarbon
$R'^- M^+$	R'^-	RR′	Alkane

Groups like cyanides and nitrites possess two nucleophilic centres and are called *ambident nucleophiles*. Actually cyanide group is a hybrid of two contributing structures and therefore can act as a nucleophile in two different ways [$^\ominus C{\equiv}N \leftrightarrow :C=N^\ominus$], *i.e.,* linking through carbon atom resulting in alkyl cyanides and through nitrogen atom leading to isocyanides. Similarly nitrite ion also represents an ambident nucleophile with two different points of linkage [$^-O—\ddot{N}=O$]. The linkage through oxygen results in alkyl nitrites while through nitrogen atom, it leads to nitroalkanes.

Mechanism: This reaction has been found to proceed by two different mechanims which are described below:

(a) Substitution nucleophilic bimolecular (S$_N$2)

The reaction between CH_3Cl and hydroxide ion to yield methanol and chloride ion follows a second order kinetics, i.e., the rate depends upon the concentration of both the reactants.

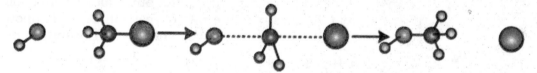

As you have already learnt in Section 12.3.2 of Class XI, the solid wedge represents the bond coming out of the paper, dashed line going down the paper and a straight line representing bond in the plane of the paper.

This can be represented diagrammatically as shown in Fig. 10.2.

Fig. 10.2: *Red dot represents the incoming hydroxide ion and green dot represents the outgoing halide ion*

It depicts a bimolecular nucleophilic displacement (S$_N$2) reaction; the incoming nucleophile interacts with alkyl halide causing the carbon-halide bond to break while forming a new carbon-OH bond. These two processes take place simultaneously in a single step and no intermediate is formed. As the reaction progresses and the bond between the nucleophile and the carbon atom starts forming, the bond between carbon atom and leaving group weakens. As this happens, the configuration of carbon atom under attack inverts in much the same way as an umbrella is turned inside out when caught in a strong wind, while the leaving group is pushed away. This process is called as **inversion of configuration**. In the transition state, the carbon atom is simultaneously bonded to incoming nucleophile and the outgoing leaving

In the year 1937, Edward Davies Hughes and Sir Christopher Ingold proposed a mechanism for an S$_N$2 reaction.

group and such structures are unstable and cannot be isolated. This is because the carbon atom in the transition state is simultaneously bonded to five atoms and therefore is unstable.

Hughes worked under Ingold and earned a D.Sc. degree from the University of London.

Since this reaction requires the approach of the nucleophile to the carbon bearing the leaving group, the presence of bulky substituents on or near the carbon atom have a dramatic inhibiting effect. Of the simple alkyl halides, methyl halides react most rapidly in S_N2 reactions because there are only three small hydrogen atoms. Tertiary halides are the least reactive because bulky groups hinder the approaching nucleophiles. Thus the order of reactivity followed is:

Primary halide > Secondary halide > Tertiary halide.

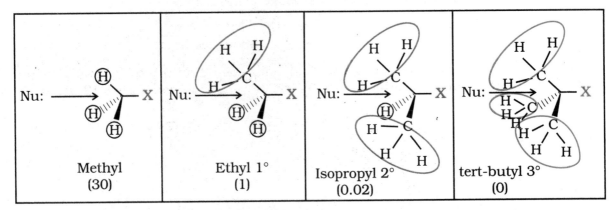

| Methyl (30) | Ethyl 1° (1) | Isopropyl 2° (0.02) | tert-butyl 3° (0) |

Fig.10.3: *Steric effects in S_N2 reaction. The relative rate of S_N2 reaction is given in parenthesis*

(b) Substitution nucleophilic unimolecular (S_N1)

S_N1 reactions are generally carried out in polar protic solvents (like water, alcohol, acetic acid, etc.). The reaction between *tert*-butyl bromide and hydroxide ion yields *tert*-butyl alcohol and follows the first order kinetics, *i.e.*, the rate of reaction depends upon the concentration of only one reactant, which is *tert*- butyl bromide.

$$(CH_3)_3CBr \ + \ ^-OH \longrightarrow (CH_3)_3COH \ + \ Br^-$$

2-Bromo-2-methylpropane   2-Methylpropan-2-ol

It occurs in two steps. In step I, the polarised C—Br bond undergoes slow cleavage to produce a carbocation and a bromide ion. The carbocation thus formed is then attacked by nucleophile in step II to complete the substitution reaction.

Step I is the slowest and reversible. It involves the C–Br bond breaking for which the energy is obtained through solvation of halide ion with the proton of protic solvent. Since the rate of reaction depends upon the slowest step, the rate of reaction depends only on the concentration of alkyl halide and not on the concentration of hydroxide ion. Further, greater the stability of carbocation, greater will be its ease of formation from alkyl halide and faster will be the rate of reaction. In case of alkyl halides, 3^0 alkyl halides undergo S_N1 reaction very fast because of the high stability of 3^0 carbocations. We can sum up the order of reactivity of alkyl halides towards S_N1 and S_N2 reactions as follows:

For S_N2 reaction

⟶

Tertiary halide; Secondary halide; Primary halide; CH_3X

⟵

For S_N1 reaction

For the same reasons, allylic and benzylic halides show high reactivity towards the S_N1 reaction. The carbocation thus formed gets stabilised through resonance (Unit 12, Class XI) as shown below:

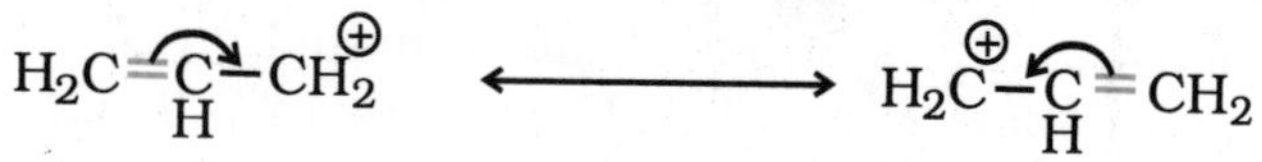

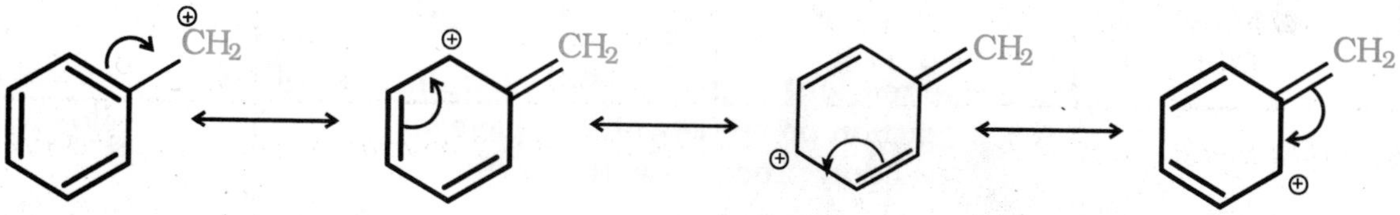

For a given alkyl group, the reactivity of the halide, R-X, follows the same order in both the mechanisms R–I> R–Br>R–Cl>>R–F.

In the following pairs of halogen compounds, which would undergo S_N2 reaction faster? *Example 10.6*

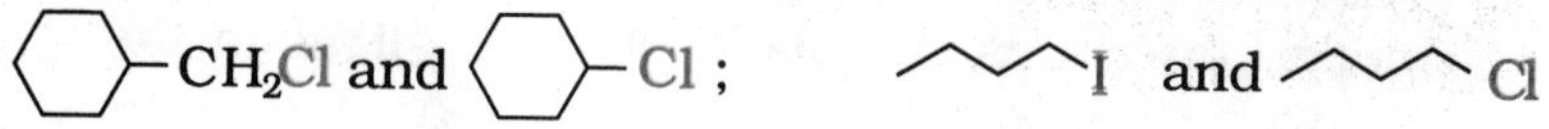

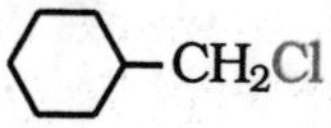

It is primary halide and therefore undergoes S_N2 *Solution* reaction faster.

As iodine is a better leaving group because of its large size, it will be released at a faster rate in the presence of incoming nucleophile.

Predict the order of reactivity of the following compounds in S_N1 and *Example 10.7* S_N2 reactions:

(i) The four isomeric bromobutanes

(ii) $C_6H_5CH_2Br$, $C_6H_5CH(C_6H_5)Br$, $C_6H_5CH(CH_3)Br$, $C_6H_5C(CH_3)(C_6H_5)Br$

<u>*Solution*</u> (i) $CH_3CH_2CH_2CH_2Br < (CH_3)_2CHCH_2Br < CH_3CH_2CH(Br)CH_3 < (CH_3)_3CBr$ (S_N1)

$CH_3CH_2CH_2CH_2Br > (CH_3)_2CHCH_2Br > CH_3CH_2CH(Br)CH_3 > (CH_3)_3CBr$ (S_N2)

Of the two primary bromides, the carbocation intermediate derived from $(CH_3)_2CHCH_2Br$ is more stable than derived from $CH_3CH_2CH_2CH_2Br$ because of greater electron donating inductive effect of $(CH_3)_2CH-$ group. Therefore, $(CH_3)_2CHCH_2Br$ is more reactive than $CH_3CH_2CH_2CH_2Br$ in S_N1 reactions. $CH_3CH_2CH(Br)CH_3$ is a secondary bromide and $(CH_3)_3CBr$ is a tertiary bromide. Hence the above order is followed in S_N1. The reactivity in S_N2 reactions follows the reverse order as the steric hinderance around the electrophilic carbon increases in that order.

(ii) $C_6H_5C(CH_3)(C_6H_5)Br > C_6H_5CH(C_6H_5)Br > C_6H_5CH(CH_3)Br > C_6H_5CH_2Br$ (S_N1)

$C_6H_5C(CH_3)(C_6H_5)Br < C_6H_5CH(C_6H_5)Br < C_6H_5CH(CH_3)Br < C_6H_5CH_2Br$ (S_N2)

Of the two secondary bromides, the carbocation intermediate obtained from $C_6H_5CH(C_6H_5)Br$ is more stable than obtained from $C_6H_5CH(CH_3)Br$ because it is stabilised by two phenyl groups due to resonance. Therefore, the former bromide is more reactive than the latter in S_N1 reactions. A phenyl group is bulkier than a methyl group. Therefore, $C_6H_5CH(C_6H_5)Br$ is less reactive than $C_6H_5CH(CH_3)Br$ in S_N2 reactions.

(c) **Stereochemical aspects of nucleophilic substitution reactions**
A S_N2 reaction proceeds with complete stereochemical inversion while a S_N1 reaction proceeds with racemisation.

In order to understand this concept, we need to learn some basic stereochemical principles and notations (**optical activity, chirality, retention, inversion, racemisation,** etc.).

(i) *Plane polarised light and optical activity*: Certain compounds rotate the plane polarised light (produced by passing ordinary light through Nicol prism) when it is passed through their solutions. Such compounds are called **optically active** compounds. The angle by which the plane polarised light is rotated is measured by an instrument called polarimeter. If the compound rotates the plane polarised light to the right, i.e., clockwise direction, it is called *dextrorotatory* (Greek for right rotating) or the d-form and is indicated by placing a positive (+) sign before the degree of rotation. If the light is rotated towards left (anticlockwise direction), the compound is said to be laevo-rotatory or the l-form and a negative (–) sign is placed before the degree of rotation. Such (+) and (–) isomers of a compound are called **optical isomers** and the phenomenon is termed as **optical isomerism**.

(ii) *Molecular asymmetry, chirality and enantiomers*: The observation of Louis Pasteur (1848) that crystals of certain compounds exist in the form of mirror images laid the foundation of modern stereochemistry. He demonstrated that aqueous solutions of both types of crystals showed optical rotation, equal in magnitude (for solution of equal concentration) but opposite in direction. He believed that this difference in

William Nicol (1768-1851) developed the first prism that produced plane polarised light.

Jacobus Hendricus Van't Hoff (1852-1911) received the first Nobel Prize in Chemistry in 1901 for his work on solutions.

optical activity was associated with the three dimensional arrangements of atoms (**configurations**) in two types of crystals. Dutch scientist, *J. Van't Hoff* and French scientist, *C. Le Bel* in the same year (1874), independently argued that the spatial arrangement of four groups (valencies) around a central carbon is tetrahedral and if all the substituents attached to that carbon are different, such a carbon is called **asymmetric carbon** or **stereocentre**. The resulting molecule would lack symmetry and is referred to as asymmetric molecule. The asymmetry of the molecule is responsible for the optical activity in such organic compounds.

The symmetry and asymmetry are also observed in many day to day objects: a sphere, a cube, a cone, are all identical to their mirror images and can be superimposed. However, many objects are non superimposable on their mirror images. For example, your left and right hand look similar but if you put your left hand on your right hand, they do not coincide. The objects which are non-superimposable on their mirror image (like a pair of hands) are said to be **chiral** and this property is known as **chirality**. While the objects, which are, superimposable on their mirror images are called **achiral**.

The above test of molecular chirality can be applied to organic molecules by constructing models and its mirror images or by drawing three dimensional structures and attempting to superimpose them in our minds. There are other aids, however, that can assist us in recognising chiral molecules. One such aid is the presence of a single asymmetric carbon atom. Let us consider two simple molecules propan-2-ol and butan-2-ol and their mirror images.

CHIRALITY

An object that cannot be superimposed on its mirror image is called chiral

Chiral objects
Nonsuperimposable
mirror images

Nonchiral objects
Superimposable
mirror images

Fig 10.4: Some common examples of chiral and achiral objects

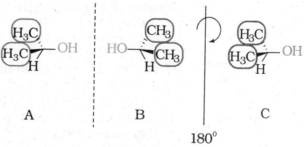

C obtained by rotating B by 180^0
C is superimposable on its mirror image A

As you can see very clearly, propan-2-ol does not contain an asymmetric carbon, as all the four groups attached to the tetrahedral carbon are not different. Thus it is an **achiral** molecule.

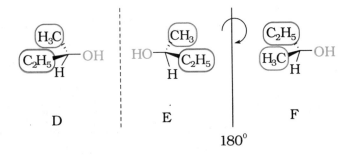

D

E

F

$180°$

F obtained by rotating E by $180°$
F is non superimposable on its mirror image D

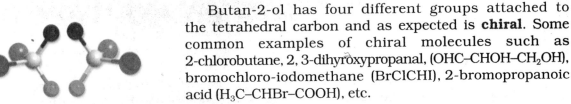

Fig. 10.5: A chiral molecule
and its mirror image

Butan-2-ol has four different groups attached to the tetrahedral carbon and as expected is **chiral**. Some common examples of chiral molecules such as 2-chlorobutane, 2, 3-dihyroxypropanal, (OHC–CHOH–CH$_2$OH), bromochloro-iodomethane (BrClCHI), 2-bromopropanoic acid (H$_3$C–CHBr–COOH), etc.

The stereoisomers related to each other as non-superimposable mirror images are called **enantiomers** (Fig. 10.5).

Enantiomers possess identical physical properties namely, melting point, boiling point, refractive index, etc. They only differ with respect to the rotation of plane polarised light. If one of the enantiomer is *dextro rotatory*, the other will be *laevo rotatory*.

> However, the sign of optical rotation is not necessarily related to the absolute configuration of the molecule.

A mixture containing two enantiomers in equal proportions will have zero optical rotation, as the rotation due to one isomer will be cancelled by the rotation due to the other isomer. Such a mixture is known as **racemic mixture** or **racemic modification**. A racemic mixture is represented by prefixing *dl* or (±) before the name, for example (±) butan-2-ol. The process of conversion of enantiomer into a racemic mixture is known as **racemisation**.

Example 10.8 Identify chiral and achiral molecules in each of the following pair of compounds. (Wedge and Dash representations according to Class XI, Fig 12.1).

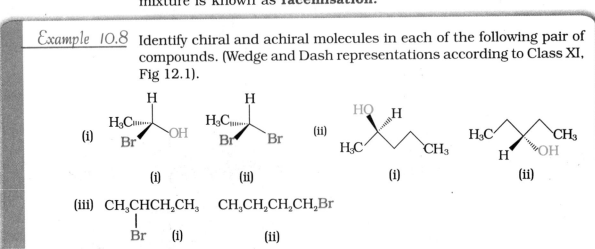

(iii) CH$_3$CHCH$_2$CH$_3$ CH$_3$CH$_2$CH$_2$CH$_2$Br
       |
       Br   (i)   (ii)

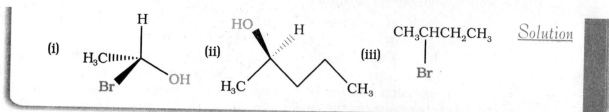

(i) (ii) (iii) *Solution*

(iii) *Retention:* Retention of configuration is the preservation of integrity of the spatial arrangement of bonds to an asymmetric centre during a chemical reaction or transformation. It is also the configurational correlation when a chemical species XCabc is converted into the chemical species YCabc having the same *relative configuration.*

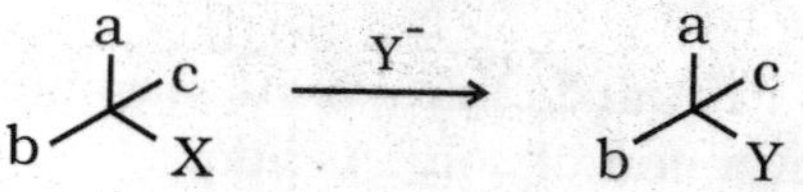

$$\underset{b}{\overset{a}{\diagup}}\overset{c}{\underset{X}{\diagdown}} \quad \xrightarrow{Y^-} \quad \underset{b}{\overset{a}{\diagup}}\overset{c}{\underset{Y}{\diagdown}}$$

In general, if during a reaction, no bond to the stereocentre is broken, the product will have the same general configuration of groups around the stereocentre as that of reactant. Such a reaction is said to proceed with retention of the configuration. Consider as an example, the reaction that takes place when (–)-2-methylbutan-1-ol is heated with concentrated hydrochloric acid.

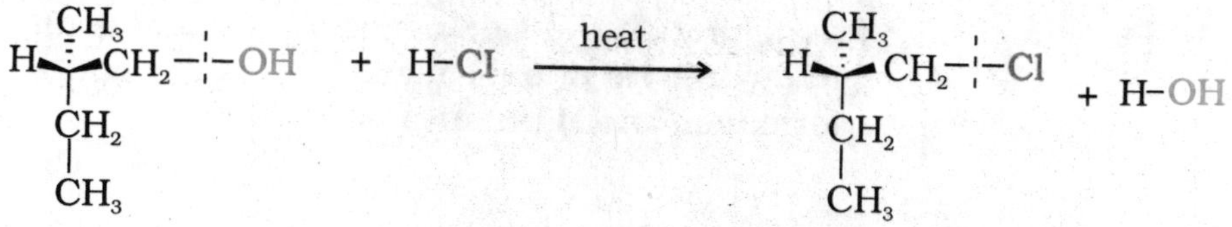

$$\underset{\substack{| \\ CH_2 \\ | \\ CH_3}}{\overset{CH_3}{H-\overset{|}{C}}}\!-CH_2-\overset{|}{\underset{|}{C}}-OH \;+\; H-Cl \;\;\xrightarrow{\text{heat}}\;\; \underset{\substack{| \\ CH_2 \\ | \\ CH_3}}{\overset{CH_3}{H-\overset{|}{C}}}\!-CH_2-\overset{|}{\underset{|}{C}}-Cl \;+\; H-OH$$

(–)–2-Methylbutan-1-ol   (+)-1-Chloro-2-methylbutane

(iv) *Inversion, retention and racemisation:* There are three outcomes for a reaction at an asymmetric carbon atom. Consider the replacement of a group X by Y in the following reaction;

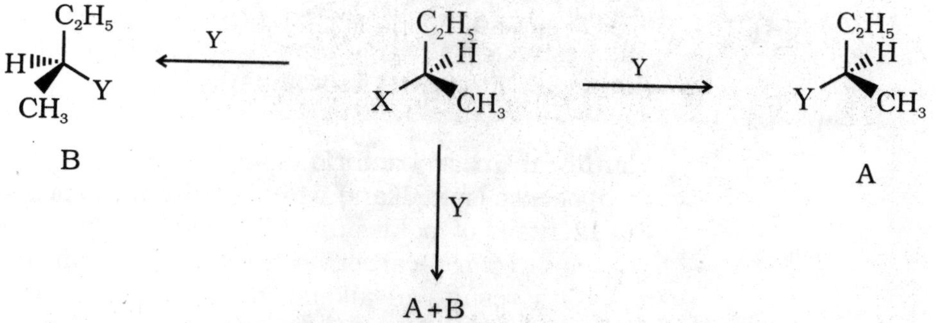

$$\underset{CH_3}{\overset{C_2H_5}{H\cdots C}}\!\!-Y \quad \xleftarrow{Y} \quad \underset{X}{\overset{C_2H_5}{C}}\!\!\overset{H}{\underset{CH_3}{}} \quad \xrightarrow{Y} \quad \underset{Y}{\overset{C_2H_5}{C}}\!\!\overset{H}{\underset{CH_3}{}}$$

B   A

$\downarrow Y$

A+B

If (A) is the only compound obtained, the process is called retention of configuration.

If (B) is the only compound obtained, the process is called inversion of configuration.

If a 50:50 mixture of the above two is obtained then the process is called racemisation and the product is optically inactive, as one isomer will rotate light in the direction opposite to another.

Now let us have a fresh look at S_N1 and S_N2 mechanisms by taking examples of optically active alkyl halides.

In case of optically active alkyl halides, the product formed as a result of S_N2 mechanism has the inverted configuration as compared to the reactant. This is because the nucleophile attaches itself on the side opposite to the one where the halogen atom is present. When (–)-2-bromooctane is allowed to react with sodium hydroxide, (+)-octan-2-ol is formed with the –OH group occupying the position opposite to what bromide had occupied.

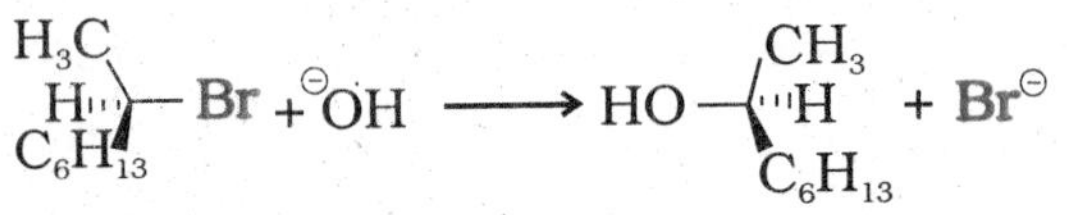

Thus, S_N2 reactions of optically active halides are accompanied by inversion of configuration.

In case of optically active alkyl halides, S_N1 reactions are accompanied by racemisation. Can you think of the reason why it happens? Actually the carbocation formed in the slow step being sp^2 hybridised is planar (achiral). The attack of the nucleophile may be accomplished from either side resulting in a mixture of products, one having the same configuration (the –OH attaching on the same position as halide ion) and the other having opposite configuration (the –OH attaching on the side opposite to halide ion). This may be illustrated by hydrolysis of optically active 2-bromobutane, which results in the formation of (±)-butan-2-ol.

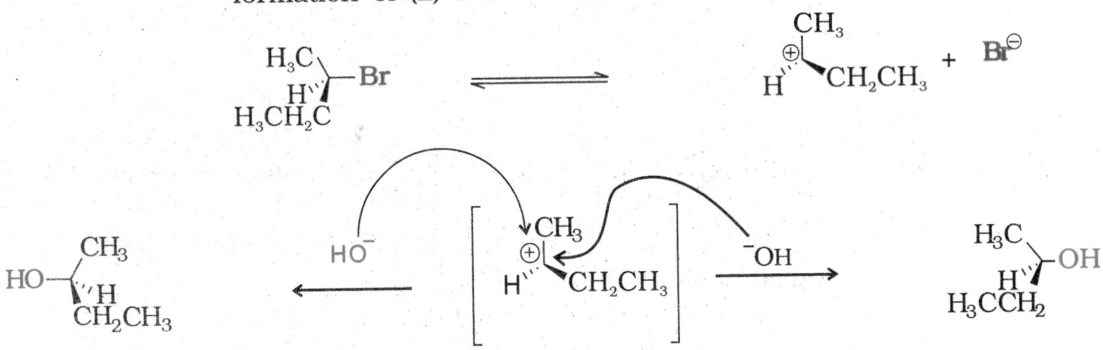

(+)-Butan-2-ol

(–)Butan-2-ol

2. *Elimination reactions*

When a haloalkane with β-hydrogen atom is heated with alcoholic solution of potassium hydroxide, there is elimination of hydrogen atom from β-carbon and a halogen atom from the α-carbon atom. As a result, an alkene is formed as a product. Since β-hydrogen atom is involved in elimination, it is often called β-**elimination**.

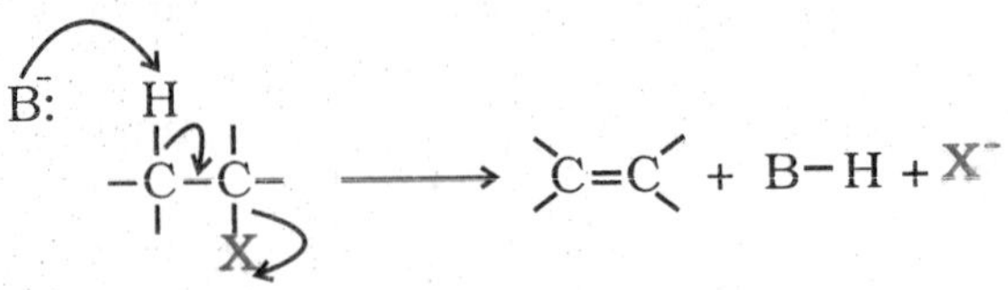

B=Base ; X=Leaving group

If there is possibility of formation of more than one alkene due to the availability of more than one β-hydrogen atoms, usually one alkene is formed as the major product. These form part of a pattern first observed by Russian chemist, Alexander Zaitsev (also pronounced as Saytzeff) who in 1875 formulated a rule which can be summarised as "*in dehydrohalogenation reactions, the preferred product is that alkene which has the greater number of alkyl groups attached to the doubly bonded carbon atoms.*" Thus, 2-bromopentane gives pent-2-ene as the major product.

$$H_3C-CH_2-CH=CH-CH_3 \xleftarrow{\ ^-OH\ } H_3C-CH_2-CH_2-\overset{\overset{\displaystyle Br}{|}}{\underset{\underset{\displaystyle H}{|}}{C}}H-CH_2 \xrightarrow{\ ^-OH\ } H_3C-CH_2-CH_2-CH=CH_2$$

Pent-2-ene   (81%)   2-Bromopentane   Pent-l-ene   (19%)

Elimination versus substitution

A chemical reaction is the result of competition; it is a race that is won by the fastest runner. A collection of molecules tend to do, by and large, what is easiest for them. An alkyl halide with α-hydrogen atoms when reacted with a base or a nucleophile has two competing routes: substitution (S_N1 and S_N2) and elimination. Which route will be taken up depends upon the nature of alkyl halide, strength and size of base/nucleophile and reaction conditions. Thus, a bulkier nucleophile will prefer to act as a base and abstracts a proton rather than approach a tetravalent carbon atom (steric reasons) and *vice versa.* Similarly, a primary alkyl halide will prefer a S_N2 reaction, a secondary halide- S_N2 or elimination depending upon the strength of base/nucleophile and a tertiary halide- S_N1 or elimination depending upon the stability of carbocation or the more substituted alkene.

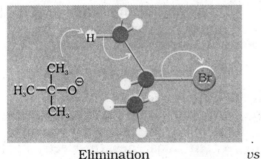 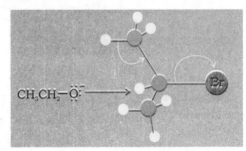

Elimination   *vs*   Substitution

3. Reaction with metals

Most organic chlorides, bromides and iodides react with certain metals to give compounds containing carbon-metal bonds. Such compounds are known as **organo-metallic compounds**. An important class of organo-metallic compounds discovered by Victor Grignard in 1900 is alkyl magnesium halide, RMgX, referred as **Grignard Reagents**. These reagents are obtained by the reaction of haloalkanes with magnesium metal in dry ether.

$$CH_3CH_2Br \ + Mg \xrightarrow{\ dry\ ether\ } CH_3CH_2MgBr$$

Grignard reagent

Victor Grignard had a strange start in academic life for a chemist - he took a maths degree. When he eventually switched to chemistry, it was not to the mathematical province of physical chemistry but to organic chemistry. While attempting to find an efficient catalyst for the process of methylation, he noted that Zn in diethyl ether had been used for this purpose and wondered whether the Mg/ether combination might be successful. Grignard reagents were first reported in 1900 and Grignard used this work for his doctoral thesis in 1901. In 1910, Grignard obtained a professorship at the University of Nancy and in 1912, he was awarded the Nobel prize for Chemistry which he shared with Paul Sabatier who had made advances in nickel catalysed hydrogenation.

In the Grignard reagent, the carbon-magnesium bond is covalent but highly polar, with carbon pulling electrons from electropositive magnesium; the magnesium halogen bond is essentially ionic.

$$\overset{\delta-}{R}-\overset{\delta+}{Mg}\ \overset{\delta-}{X}$$

Grignard reagents are highly reactive and react with any source of proton to give hydrocarbons. Even water, alcohols, amines are sufficiently acidic to convert them to corresponding hydrocarbons.

$$RMgX + H_2O \longrightarrow RH + Mg(OH)X$$

It is therefore necessary to avoid even traces of moisture from a Grignard reagent. On the other hand, this could be considered as one of the methods for converting halides to hydrocarbons.

Wurtz reaction

Alkyl halides react with sodium in dry ether to give hydrocarbons containing double the number of carbon atoms present in the halide. This reaction is known as Wurtz reaction. (Unit 13, Class XI).

$$2RX + 2Na \longrightarrow RR + 2NaX$$

10.6.2 Reactions of Haloarenes

1. Nucleophilic substitution

Aryl halides are extremely less reactive towards nucleophilic substitution reactions due to the following reasons:

(i) *Resonance effect :* In haloarenes, the electron pairs on halogen atom are in conjugation with π-electrons of the ring and the following resonating structures are possible.

C—Cl bond acquires a partial double bond character due to resonance. As a result, the bond cleavage in haloarene is difficult than haloalkane and therefore, they are less reactive towards nucleophilic substitution reaction.

(ii) *Difference in hybridisation of carbon atom in C—X bond:* In haloalkane, the carbon atom attached to halogen is sp^3 hybridised while in case of haloarene, the carbon atom attached to halogen is sp^2-hybridised.

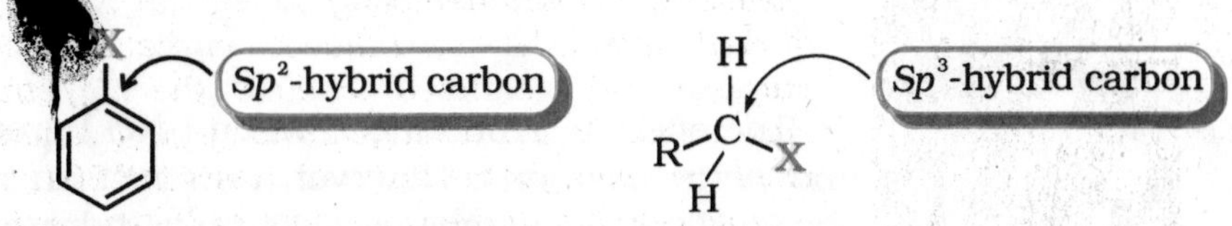

The sp^2 hybridised carbon with a greater s-character is more electronegative and can hold the electron pair of C—X bond more tightly than sp^3-hybridised carbon in haloalkane with less s-charatcer. Thus, C—Cl bond length in haloalkane is 177pm while in haloarene is 169 pm. Since it is difficult to break a shorter bond than a longer bond, therefore, haloarenes are less reactive than haloalkanes towards nucleophilic substitution reaction.

(iii) *Instability of phenyl cation:* In case of haloarenes, the phenyl cation formed as a result of self-ionisation will not be stabilised by resonance and therefore, S_N1 mechanism is ruled out.

(iv) Because of the possible repulsion, it is less likely for the electron rich nucleophile to approach electron rich arenes.

Replacement by hydroxyl group

Chlorobenzene can be converted into phenol by heating in aqueous sodium hydroxide solution at a temperature of 623K and a pressure of 300 atmospheres.

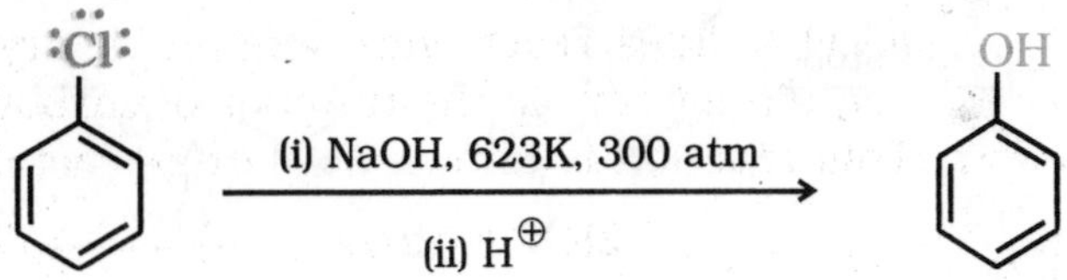

The presence of an electron withdrawing group (-NO$_2$) at *ortho-* and *para*-positions increases the reactivity of haloarenes.

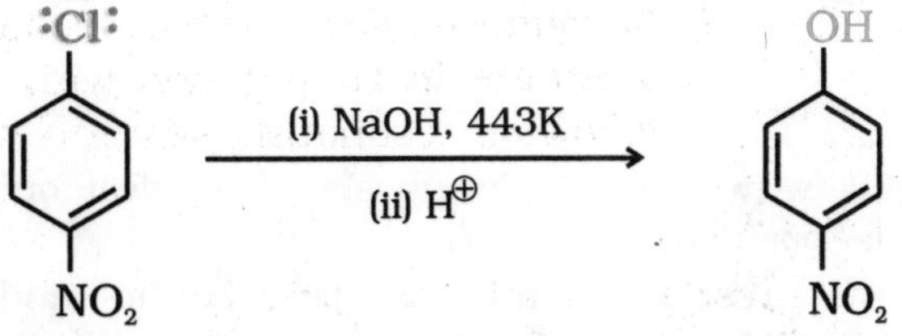

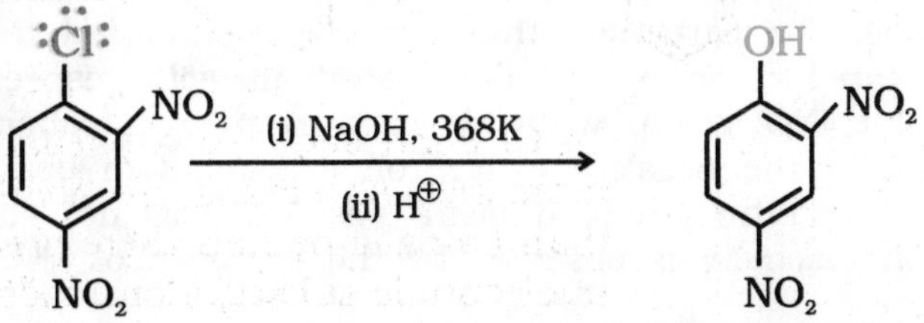

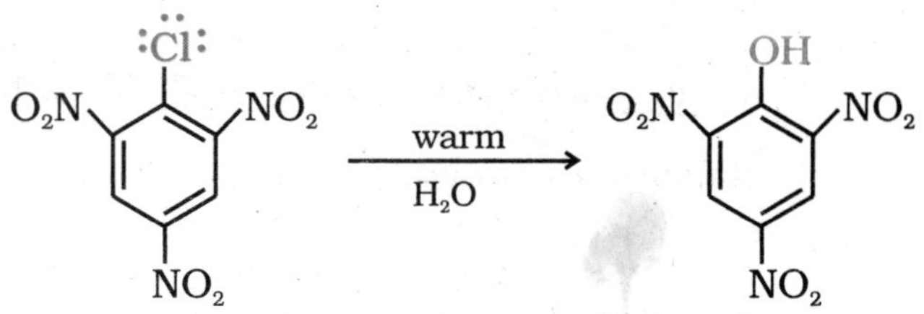

The effect is pronounced when ($-NO_2$) group is introduced at *ortho-* and *para-* positions. However, no effect on reactivity of haloarenes is observed by the presence of electron withdrawing group at *meta-*position. Mechanism of the reaction is as depicted:

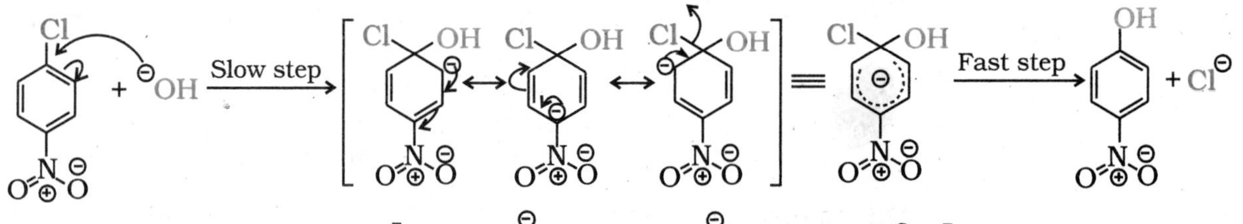

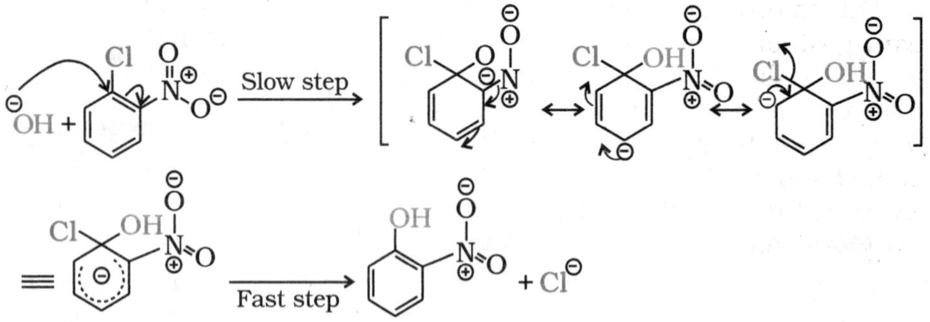

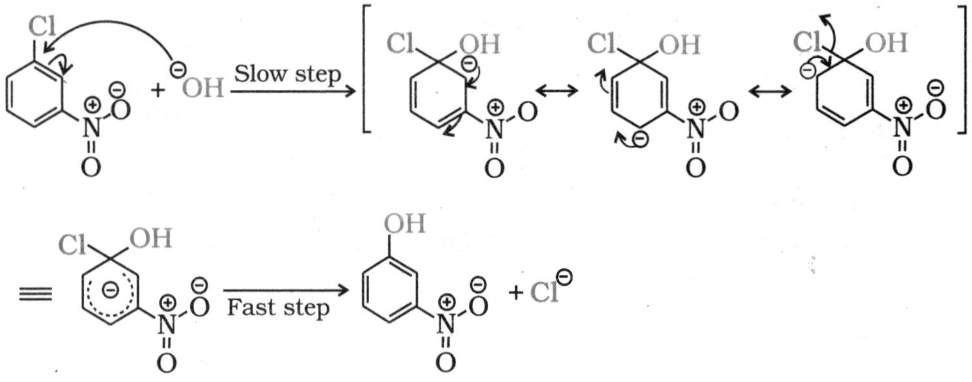

Can you think why does NO_2 group show its effect only at *ortho-* and *para-* positions and not at *meta-* position?

As shown, the presence of nitro group at *ortho-* and *para-*positions withdraws the electron density from the benzene ring and thus facilitates the attack of the nucleophile on haloarene. The carbanion thus formed is stabilised through resonance. The negative charge appeared at *ortho-* and *para-* positions with respect to the halogen substituent is stabilised by $-NO_2$ group while in case of *meta-*nitrobenzene, none of the resonating structures bear the negative charge on carbon atom bearing the $-NO_2$ group. Therefore, the presence of nitro group at *meta-* position does not stabilise the negative charge and no effect on reactivity is observed by the presence of $-NO_2$ group at *meta-*position.

2. Electrophilic substitution reactions

Haloarenes undergo the usual electrophilic reactions of the benzene ring such as halogenation, nitration, sulphonation and Friedel-Crafts reactions. Halogen atom besides being slightly deactivating is o, p-directing; therefore, further substitution occurs at ortho- and para-positions with respect to the halogen atom. The o, p-directing influence of halogen atom can be easily understood if we consider the resonating structures of halobenzene as shown:

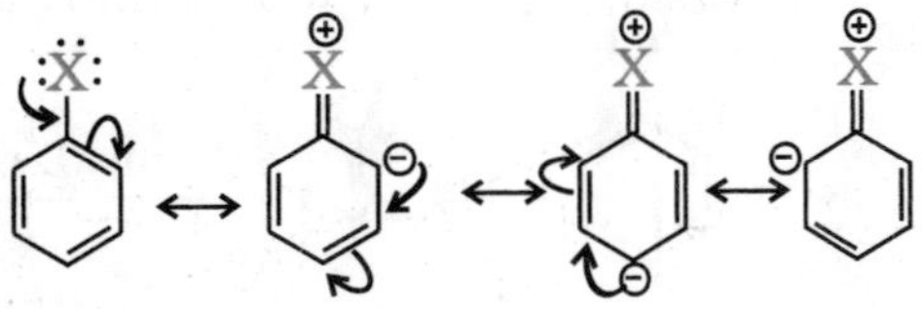

I   II   III   IV

Due to resonance, the electron density increases more at ortho- and para-positions than at meta-positions. Further, the halogen atom because of its –I effect has some tendency to withdraw electrons from the benzene ring. As a result, the ring gets somewhat deactivated as compared to benzene and hence the electrophilic substitution reactions in haloarenes occur slowly and require more drastic conditions as compared to those in benzene.

(i) Halogenation

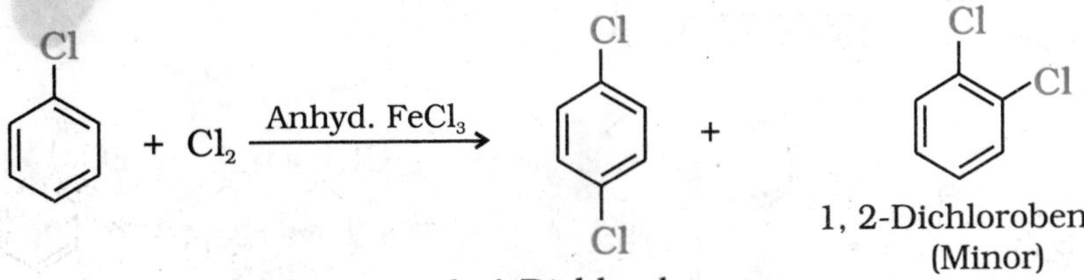

1, 4-Dichlorobenzene
(Major)

1, 2-Dichlorobenzene
(Minor)

(ii) Nitration

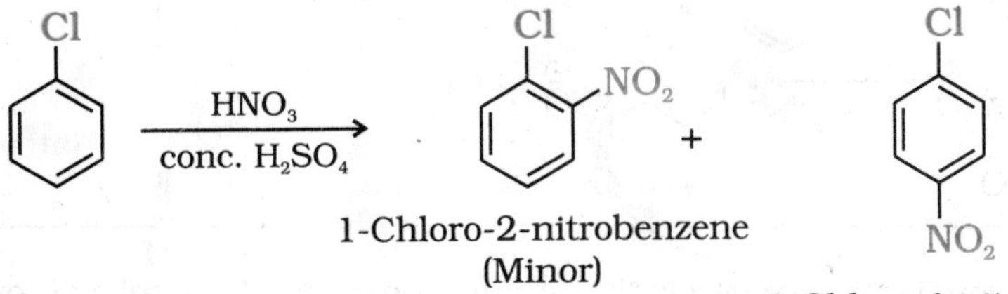

1-Chloro-2-nitrobenzene
(Minor)

1-Chloro-4-nitrobenzene
(Major)

(iii) Sulphonation

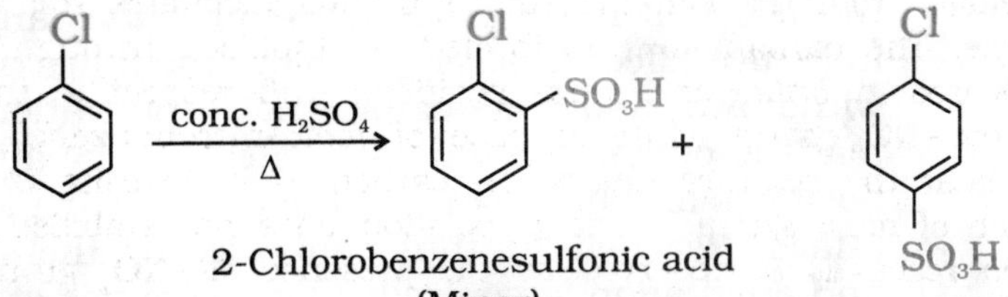

2-Chlorobenzenesulfonic acid
(Minor)

4-Chlorobenzenesulfonic acid
(Major)

305 Haloalkanes and Haloarenes

(iv) Friedel-Crafts reaction

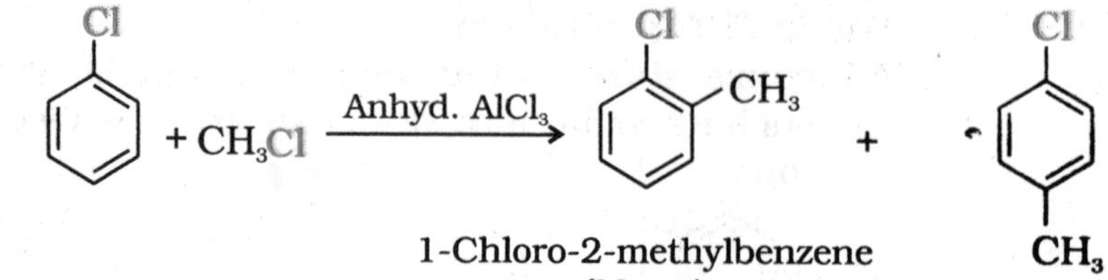

1-Chloro-2-methylbenzene
(Minor)

1-Chloro-4-methylbenzene
(Major)

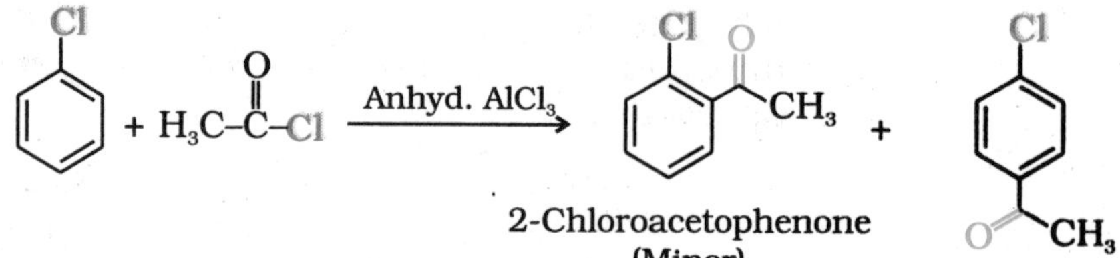

2-Chloroacetophenone
(Minor)

4-Chloroacetophenone
(Major)

Example 10.9 Although chlorine is an electron withdrawing group, yet it is *ortho-*, *para-* directing in electrophilic aromatic substitution reactions. Why?

Solution Chlorine withdraws electrons through inductive effect and releases electrons through resonance. Through inductive effect, chlorine destabilises the intermediate carbocation ⬤ed during the electrophilic substitution.

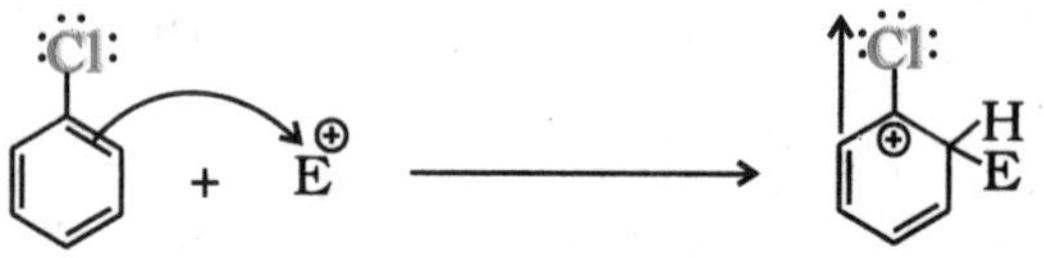

Inductive effect destabilises the
intermediate carbocation

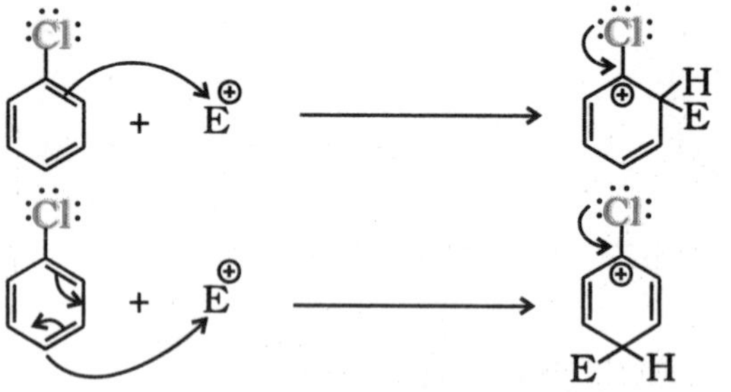

(attack at *ortho*-position)

(attack at para-position)

Resonance effect stabilises the
intermediate carbocation

Through resonance, halogen tends to stabilise the **carbocation and** the effect is more pronounced at *ortho-* and *para-* positions. The inductive effect is stronger than resonance and causes net electron withdrawal and thus causes net deactivation. The resonance effect tends to oppose the inductive effect for the attack at *ortho-* and *para-* positions and hence makes the deactivation less for *ortho-* and *para-* attack. Reactivity is thus controlled by the stronger inductive effect and orientation is controlled by resonance effect.

3. Reaction with metals

Wurtz-Fittig reaction

A mixture of an alkyl halide and aryl halide gives an alkylarene when treated with sodium in dry ether and is called Wurtz-Fittig reaction.

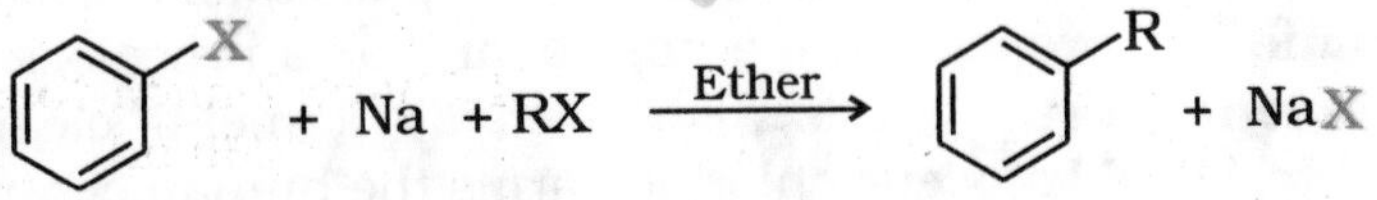

$$\text{C}_6\text{H}_5\text{X} + \text{Na} + \text{RX} \xrightarrow{\text{Ether}} \text{C}_6\text{H}_5\text{R} + \text{NaX}$$

Fittig reaction

Aryl halides also give analogous compounds when treated with sodium in dry ether, in which two aryl groups are joined together. It is called Fittig reaction.

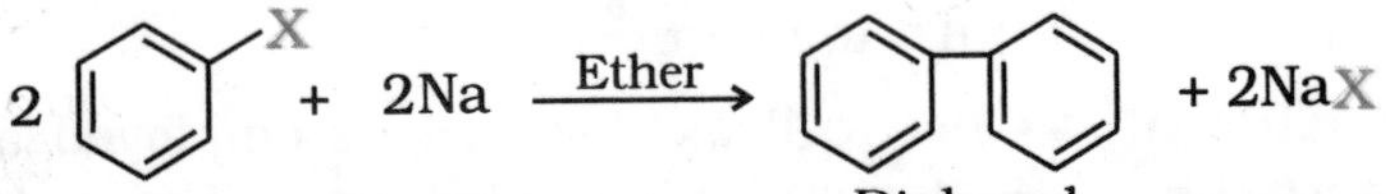

$$2\,\text{C}_6\text{H}_5\text{X} + 2\text{Na} \xrightarrow{\text{Ether}} \text{C}_6\text{H}_5\text{-C}_6\text{H}_5 + 2\text{NaX}$$

Diphenyl

Intext Questions

10.7 Which alkyl halide from the following pairs would you expect to react more rapidly by an S_N2 mechanism? Explain your answer.

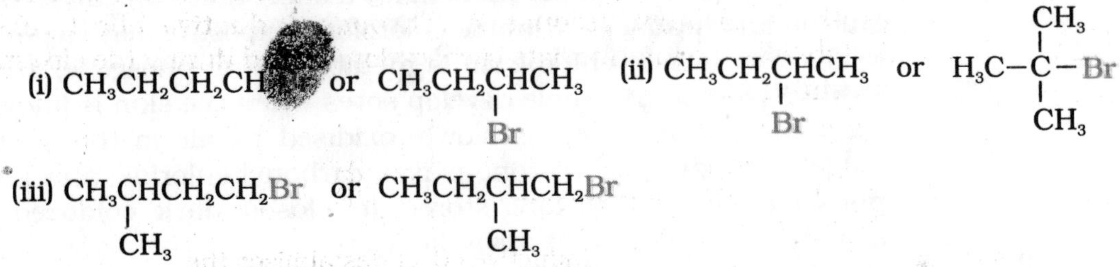

(i) $CH_3CH_2CH_2CH_2Br$ or $CH_3CH_2CHCH_3$
$\qquad\qquad\qquad\qquad\qquad\qquad\qquad |$
$\qquad\qquad\qquad\qquad\qquad\qquad\quad Br$

(ii) $CH_3CH_2CHCH_3$ or $H_3C-\underset{\underset{CH_3}{|}}{\overset{\overset{CH_3}{|}}{C}}-Br$
$\qquad\qquad\quad |$
$\qquad\qquad Br$

(iii) $CH_3CHCH_2CH_2Br$ or $CH_3CH_2CHCH_2Br$
$\qquad\quad |\qquad\qquad\qquad\qquad\qquad |$
$\qquad\quad CH_3\qquad\qquad\qquad\qquad CH_3$

10.8 In the following pairs of halogen compounds, which compound undergoes faster S_N1 reaction?

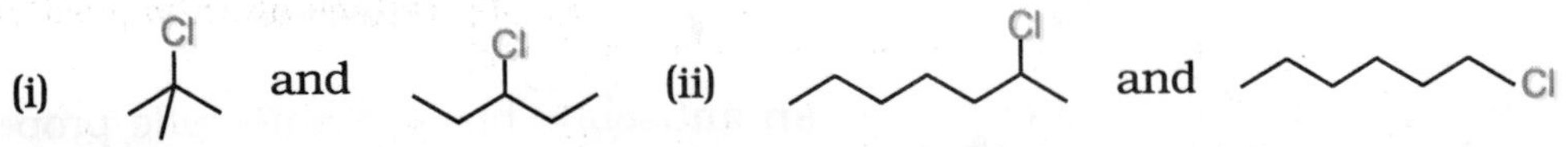

(i)

and

(ii)

and

10.9 Identify A, B, C, D, E, R and R^1 in the following:

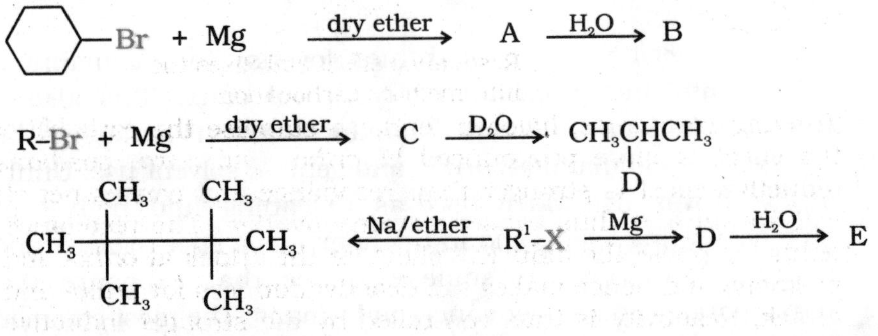

$-Br + Mg \xrightarrow{\text{dry ether}}$ A $\xrightarrow{\text{H}_2\text{O}}$ B

$R-Br + Mg \xrightarrow{\text{dry ether}}$ C $\xrightarrow{\text{D}_2\text{O}}$ CH_3CHCH_3
$\qquad\qquad\qquad\qquad\qquad\qquad\qquad\qquad\qquad\qquad |$
$\qquad\qquad\qquad\qquad\qquad\qquad\qquad\qquad\qquad\quad D$

$CH_3-\overset{\overset{CH_3}{|}}{\underset{\underset{CH_3}{|}}{C}}-\overset{\overset{CH_3}{|}}{\underset{\underset{CH_3}{|}}{C}}-CH_3 \xleftarrow{\text{Na/ether}} R^1-X \xrightarrow{\text{Mg}}$ D $\xrightarrow{\text{H}_2\text{O}}$ E

10.7 Polyhalogen Compounds

Carbon compounds containing more than one halogen atom are usually referred to as polyhalogen compounds. Many of these compounds are useful in industry and agriculture. Some polyhalogen compounds are described in this section.

10.7.1 Dichloromethane (Methylene chloride)

Dichloromethane is widely used as a solvent as a paint remover, as a propellant in aerosols, and as a process solvent in the manufacture of drugs. It is also used as a metal cleaning and finishing solvent. Methylene chloride harms the human central nervous system. Exposure to lower levels of methylene chloride in air can lead to slightly impaired hearing and vision. Higher levels of methylene chloride in air cause dizziness, nausea, tingling and numbness in the fingers and toes. In humans, direct skin contact with methylene chloride causes intense burning and mild redness of the skin. Direct contact with the eyes can burn the cornea.

10.7.2 Trichloromethane (Chloroform)

Chemically, chloroform is employed as a solvent for fats, alkaloids, iodine and other substances. The major use of chloroform today is in the production of the freon refrigerant R-22. It was once used as a general anaesthetic in surgery but has been replaced by less toxic, safer anaesthetics, such as ether. As might be expected from its use as an anaesthetic, inhaling chloroform vapours depresses the central nervous system. Breathing about 900 parts of chloroform per million parts of air (900 parts per million) for a short time can cause dizziness, fatigue, and headache. Chronic chloroform exposure may cause damage to the liver (where chloroform is metabolised to phosgene) and to the kidneys, and some people develop sores when the skin is immersed in chloroform. Chloroform is slowly oxidised by air in the presence of light to an extremely poisonous gas, carbonyl chloride, also known as phosgene. It is therefore stored in closed dark coloured bottles completely filled so that air is kept out.

$$2CHCl_3 + O_2 \xrightarrow{\text{light}} 2COCl_2 + 2HCl$$

Phosgene

10.7.3 Triiodomethane (Iodoform)

It was used earlier as an antiseptic but the antiseptic properties are due to the liberation of free iodine and not due to iodoform itself. Due to its objectionable smell, it has been replaced by other formulations containing iodine.

10.7.4 Tetrachloromethane (Carbon tetrachloride)

It is produced in large quantities for use in the manufacture of refrigerants and propellants for aerosol cans. It is also used as feedstock in the synthesis of chlorofluorocarbons and other chemicals, pharmaceutical manufacturing, and general solvent use. Until the mid 1960s, it was also widely used as a cleaning fluid, both in industry, as a degreasing agent, and in the home, as a spot remover and as fire extinguisher. There is some evidence that exposure to carbon tetrachloride causes liver cancer in humans. The most common effects are dizziness, light headedness, nausea and vomiting, which can cause permanent damage to nerve cells. In severe cases, these effects can lead rapidly to stupor, coma, unconsciousness or death. Exposure to CCl_4 can make the heart beat irregularly or stop. The chemical may irritate the eyes on contact. When carbon tetrachloride is released into the air, it rises to the atmosphere and depletes the ozone layer. Depletion of the ozone layer is believed to increase human exposure to ultraviolet rays, leading to increased skin cancer, eye diseases and disorders, and possible disruption of the immune system.

10.7.5 Freons

The chlorofluorocarbon compounds of methane and ethane are collectively known as freons. They are extremely stable, unreactive, non-toxic, non-corrosive and easily liquefiable gases. Freon 12 (CCl_2F_2) is one of the most common freons in industrial use. It is manufactured from tetrachloromethane by Swarts reaction. These are usually produced for aerosol propellants, refrigeration and air conditioning purposes. By 1974, total freon production in the world was about 2 billion pounds annually. Most freon, even that used in refrigeration, eventually makes its way into the atmosphere where it diffuses unchanged into the stratosphere. In stratosphere, freon is able to initiate radical chain reactions that can upset the natural ozone balance (Unit 14, Class XI).

10.7.6 p,p'-Dichlorodiphenyltrichloroethane(DDT)

DDT, the first chlorinated organic insecticides, was originally prepared in 1873, but it was not until 1939 that Paul Muller of Geigy Pharmaceuticals in Switzerland discovered the effectiveness of DDT as an insecticide. Paul Muller was awarded the Nobel Prize in Medicine and Physiology in 1948 for this discovery. The use of DDT increased enormously on a worldwide basis after World War II, primarily because of its effectiveness against the mosquito that spreads malaria and lice that carry typhus. However, problems related to extensive use of DDT began to appear in the late 1940s. Many species of insects developed resistance to DDT, and it was also discovered to have a high toxicity towards fish. The chemical stability of DDT and its fat solubility compounded the problem. DDT is not metabolised very rapidly by animals; instead, it is deposited and stored in the fatty tissues. If ingestion continues at a steady rate, DDT builds up within the animal over time. The use of DDT was banned in the United States in 1973, although it is still in use in some other parts of the world.

DDT

Summary

Alkyl/ Aryl halides may be classified as mono, di, or polyhalogen (tri-, tetra-, etc.) compounds depending on whether they contain one, two or more halogen atoms in their structures. Since halogen atoms are more electronegative than carbon, the carbon-halogen bond of alkyl halide is polarised; the carbon atom bears a partial positive charge, and the halogen atom bears a partial negative charge.

Alkyl halides are prepared by the **free radical halogenation** of alkanes, addition of halogen acids to alkenes, replacement of –OH group of alcohols with halogens using phosphorus halides, thionyl chloride or halogen acids. Aryl halides are prepared by **electrophilic substitution** to arenes. Fluorides and iodides are best prepared by halogen exchange method.

The boiling points of organohalogen compounds are comparatively higher than the corresponding hydrocarbons because of strong dipole-dipole and van der Waals forces of attraction. These are slightly soluble in water but completely soluble in organic solvents.

The polarity of carbon-halogen bond of alkyl halides is responsible for their **nucleophilic substitution, elimination** and their reaction with metal atoms to form **organometallic compounds**. Nucleophilic substitution reactions are categorised into S_N1 and S_N2 on the basis of their kinetic properties. **Chirality** has a profound role in understanding the reaction mechanisms of S_N1 and S_N2 reactions. S_N2 reactions of chiral alkyl halides are characterised by the inversion of configuration while S_N1 reactions are characterised by racemisation.

A number of polyhalogen compounds e.g., **dichloromethane, chloroform, iodoform, carbon tetrachloride, freon** and **DDT** have many industrial applications. However, some of these compounds cannot be easily decomposed and even cause depletion of ozone layer and are proving **environmental hazards**.

Exercises

10.1 Name the following halides according to IUPAC system and classify them as alkyl, allyl, benzyl (primary, secondary, tertiary), vinyl or aryl halides:

(i) $(CH_3)_2CHCH(Cl)CH_3$ (ii) $CH_3CH_2CH(CH_3)CH(C_2H_5)Cl$

(iii) $CH_3CH_2C(CH_3)_2CH_2I$ (iv) $(CH_3)_3CCH_2CH(Br)C_6H_5$

(v) $CH_3CH(CH_3)CH(Br)CH_3$ (vi) $CH_3C(C_2H_5)_2CH_2Br$

(vii) $CH_3C(Cl)(C_2H_5)CH_2CH_3$ (viii) $CH_3CH=C(Cl)CH_2CH(CH_3)_2$

(ix) $CH_3CH=CHC(Br)(CH_3)_2$ (x) $p\text{-}ClC_6H_4CH_2CH(CH_3)_2$

(xi) $m\text{-}ClCH_2C_6H_4CH_2C(CH_3)_3$ (xii) $o\text{-}Br\text{-}C_6H_4CH(CH_3)CH_2CH_3$

10.2 Give the IUPAC names of the following compounds:

(i) $CH_3CH(Cl)CH(Br)CH_3$ (ii) $CHF_2CBrClF$ (iii) $ClCH_2C{\equiv}CCH_2Br$

(iv) $(CCl_3)_3CCl$ (v) $CH_3C(p\text{-}ClC_6H_4)_2CH(Br)CH_3$ (vi) $(CH_3)_3CCH=ClC_6H_4I\text{-}p$

10.3 Write the structures of the following organic halogen compounds.

(i) 2-Chloro-3-methylpentane   (ii) *p*-Bromochlorobenzene

(iii) 1-Chloro-4-ethylcyclohexane   (iv) 2-(2-Chlorophenyl)-1-iodooctane

(v) 2-Bromobutane   (vi) 4-tert-Butyl-3-iodoheptane

(vii) 1-Bromo-4-sec-butyl-2-methylbenzene   (viii) 1,4-Dibromobut-2-ene

10.4 Which one of the following has the highest dipole moment?

   (i) CH_2Cl_2 (ii) $CHCl_3$ (iii) CCl_4

10.5 A hydrocarbon C_5H_{10} does not react with chlorine in dark but gives a single monochloro compound C_5H_9Cl in bright sunlight. Identify the hydrocarbon.

10.6 Write the isomers of the compound having formula C_4H_9Br.

10.7 Write the equations for the preparation of 1-iodobutane from

   (i) 1-butanol (ii) 1-chlorobutane (iii) but-1-ene.

10.8 What are ambident nucleophiles? Explain with an example.

10.9 Which compound in each of the following pairs will react faster in S_N2 reaction with ^-OH?

   (i) CH_3Br or CH_3I (ii) $(CH_3)_3CCl$ or CH_3Cl

10.10 Predict all the alkenes that would be formed by dehydrohalogenation of the following halides with sodium ethoxide in ethanol and identify the major alkene:

   (i) 1-Bromo-1-methylcyclohexane (ii) 2-Chloro-2-methylbutane

   (iii) 2,2,3-Trimethyl-3-bromopentane.

10.11 How will you bring about the following conversions?

   (i) Ethanol to but-1-yne (ii) Ethane to bromoethene (iii) Propene to 1-nitropropane (iv) Toluene to benzyl alcohol (v) Propene to propyne (vi) Ethanol to ethyl fluoride (vii) Bromomethane to propanone (viii) But-1-ene to but-2-ene (ix) 1-Chlorobutane to n-octane (x) Benzene to biphenyl.

10.12 Explain why

   (i) the dipole moment of chlorobenzene is lower than that of cyclohexyl chloride?

   (ii) alkyl halides, though polar, are immiscible with water?

   (iii) Grignard reagents should be prepared under anhydrous conditions?

10.13 Give the uses of freon 12, DDT, carbon tetrachloride and iodoform.

10.14 Write the structure of the major organic product in each of the following reactions:

   (i) $CH_3CH_2CH_2Cl + NaI \xrightarrow{\text{acetone}}_{\text{heat}}$

   (ii) $(CH_3)_3CBr + KOH \xrightarrow{\text{ethanol}}_{\text{heat}}$

   (iii) $CH_3CH(Br)CH_2CH_3 + NaOH \xrightarrow{\text{water}}$

   (iv) $CH_3CH_2Br + KCN \xrightarrow{\text{aq. ethanol}}$

   (v) $C_6H_5ONa + C_2H_5Cl \longrightarrow$

   (vi) $CH_3CH_2CH_2OH + SOCl_2 \longrightarrow$

   (vii) $CH_3CH_2CH = CH_2 + HBr \xrightarrow{\text{peroxide}}$

   (viii) $CH_3CH = C(CH_3)_2 + HBr \longrightarrow$

10.15 Write the mechanism of the following reaction:

   $nBuBr + KCN \xrightarrow{\text{EtOH-H}_2\text{O}} nBuCN$

10.16 Arrange the compounds of each set in order of reactivity towards S_N2 displacement:

   (i) 2-Bromo-2-methylbutane, 1-Bromopentane, 2-Bromopentane

   (ii) 1-Bromo-3-methylbutane, 2-Bromo-2-methylbutane, 2-Bromo-3-methylbutane

(iii) 1-Bromobutane, 1-Bromo-2,2-dimethylpropane, 1-Bromo-2-methylbutane, 1-Bromo-3-methylbutane.

10.17 Out of $C_6H_5CH_2Cl$ and $C_6H_5CHClC_6H_5$, which is more easily hydrolysed by aqueous KOH?

10.18 *p*-Dichlorobenzene has higher m.p. and solubility than those of *o*- and *m*-isomers. Discuss.

10.19 How the following conversions can be carried out?

 (i) Propene to propan-1-ol
 (ii) Ethanol to but-1-yne
 (iii) 1-Bromopropane to 2-bromopropane
 (iv) Toluene to benzyl alcohol
 (v) Benzene to 4-bromonitrobenzene
 (vi) Benzyl alcohol to 2-phenylethanoic acid
 (vii) Ethanol to propanenitrile
 (viii) Aniline to chlorobenzene
 (ix) 2-Chlorobutane to 3, 4-dimethylhexane
 (x) 2-Methyl-1-propene to 2-chloro-2-methylpropane
 (xi) Ethyl chloride to propanoic acid
 (xii) But-1-ene to n-butyliodide
 (xiii) 2-Chloropropane to 1-propanol
 (xiv) Isopropyl alcohol to iodoform
 (xv) Chlorobenzene to *p*-nitrophenol
 (xvi) 2-Bromopropane to 1-bromopropane
 (xvii) Chloroethane to butane
 (xviii) Benzene to diphenyl
 (xix) *tert*-Butyl bromide to isobutyl bromide
 (xx) Aniline to phenylisocyanide

10.20 The treatment of alkyl chlorides with aqueous KOH leads to the formation of alcohols but in the presence of alcoholic KOH, alkenes are major products. Explain.

10.21 Primary alkyl halide C_4H_9Br (a) reacted with alcoholic KOH to give compound (b). Compound (b) is reacted with HBr to give (c) which is an isomer of (a). When (a) is reacted with sodium metal it gives compound (d), C_8H_{18} which is different from the compound formed when n-butyl bromide is reacted with sodium. Give the structural formula of (a) and write the equations for all the reactions.

10.22 What happens when

 (i) n-butyl chloride is treated with alcoholic KOH,
 (ii) bromobenzene is treated with Mg in the presence of dry ether,
 (iii) chlorobenzene is subjected to hydrolysis,
 (iv) ethyl chloride is treated with aqueous KOH,
 (v) methyl bromide is treated with sodium in the presence of dry ether,
 (vi) methyl chloride is treated with KCN?

Answers to Some Intext Questions

10.1 (i) $CH_3CH_2CH(CH_3)CHClCH_3$

(ii) 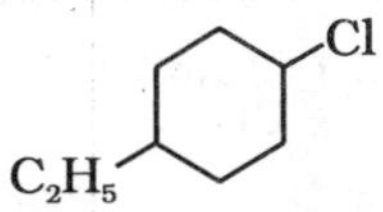 C_2H_5 (cyclohexane with Cl)

(iii) $CH_3CH_2CH_2\underset{\underset{\displaystyle CH_3}{\overset{\displaystyle |}{\underset{|}{C}}}{CH}\,CH(I)CH_2CH_3$

$$H_3C-\underset{\underset{\displaystyle CH_3}{|}}{\overset{\overset{\displaystyle CH_3}{|}}{C}}-CH_3$$

(iv) $BrCH_2CH = CHCH_2Br$

(v)

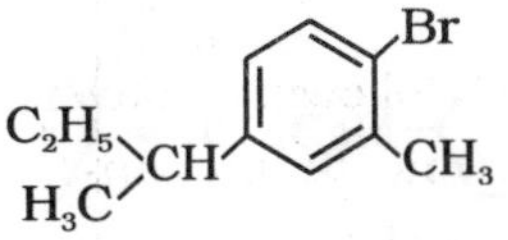

10.2 (i) H_2SO_4 cannot be used along with KI in the conversion of an alcohol to an alkyl iodide as it converts KI to corresponding acid, HI which is then oxidised by it to I_2.

10.3 (i) $ClCH_2CH_2CH_2Cl$ (ii) $ClCH_2CHClCH_3$ (iii) $Cl_2CHCH_2CH_3$ (iv) $CH_3CCl_2CH_3$

10.4 (i) $$H_3C-\underset{\underset{\displaystyle CH_3}{|}}{\overset{\overset{\displaystyle CH_3}{|}}{C}}-CH_3$$ All the hydrogen atoms are equivalent and replacement of any hydrogen will give the same product.

(ii) $C^aH_3C^bH_2C^cH_2C^bH_2C^aH_3$ The equivalent hydrogens are grouped as a, b and c. The replacement of equivalent hydrogens will give the same product.

(iii) $C^aH_3C^bHC^cH_2C^dH_3$ below is $\underset{|}{C^bH}$ with CH_3^a

Similarly the equivalent hydrogens are grouped as a, b, c and d. Thus, four isomeric products are possible.

10.5 (i) 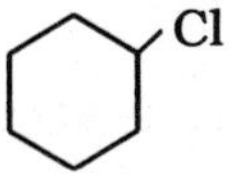 (cyclohexane with Cl)

(ii) 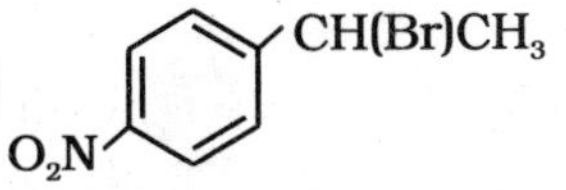 $CH(Br)CH_3$ with O_2N

(iii) 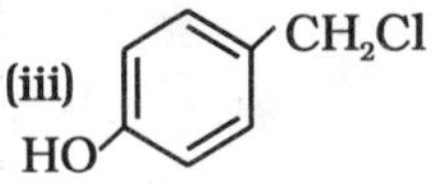 CH_2Cl with HO

(iv) 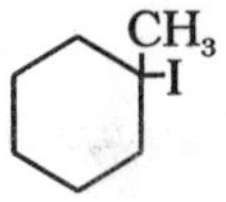 (cyclohexane with CH_3 and I)

(v) CH_3CH_2I

(vi) 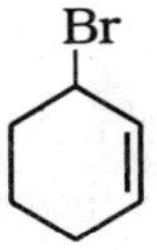 (cyclohexene with Br)

10.6 (i) Chloromethane, Bromomethane, Dibromomethane, Bromoform. Boiling point increases with increase in molecular mass.

(ii) Isopropylchloride, 1-Chloropropane, 1-Chlorobutane. Isopropylchloride being branched has lower b.p. than 1-Chloropropane.

10.7 (i) $CH_3CH_2CH_2CH_2Br$ Being primary halide, there won't be any steric hindrance.

(ii) $CH_3CH_2\underset{\underset{\displaystyle Br}{|}}{CH}CH_3$ Secondary halide reacts faster than tertiary halide.

(iii) $CH_3\underset{\underset{\displaystyle CH_3}{|}}{CH}CH_2CH_2Br$ The presence of methyl group closer to the halide group will increase the steric hindrance and decrease the rate.

10.8 (i)

Cl
|
(structure: tert-butyl chloride — carbon bearing Cl with three methyl groups)

Tertiary halide reacts faster than secondary halide because of the greater stability of tert-carbocation.

(ii)

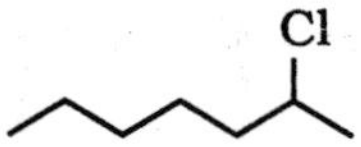

Cl
|
(structure: carbon chain with Cl on secondary carbon)

Because of greater stability of secondary carbocation than primary.

10.9 A = (cyclohexyl)—MgBr   B = (cyclohexane)

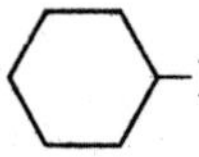

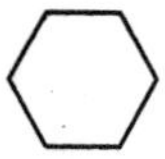

C = RMgBr   R = CH$_3$CHCH$_3$
|

        CH$_3$ CH$_3$ CH$_3$
         | | |
R¹ = H$_3$C–C   D = H$_3$C–C–MgX   E = H$_3$C–C–H
         | | |
        CH$_3$ CH$_3$ CH$_3$

Alcohols, Phenols and Ethers

Alcohols, phenols and ethers are the basic compounds for the formation of detergents, antiseptics and fragrances, respectively.

Objectives

After studying this Unit, you will be able to

- name alcohols, phenols and ethers according to the IUPAC system of nomenclature;

- discuss the reactions involved in the preparation of alcohols from (i) alkenes (ii) aldehydes, ketones and carboxylic acids;

- discuss the reactions involved in the preparation of phenols from (i) haloarenes (ii) benzene sulphonic acids (iii) diazonium salts and (iv) cumene;

- discuss the reactions for preparation of ethers from (i) alcohols and (ii) alkyl halides and sodium alkoxides/aryloxides;

- correlate physical properties of alcohols, phenols and ethers with their structures;

- discuss chemical reactions of the three classes of compounds on the basis of their functional groups.

You have learnt that substitution of one or more hydrogen atom(s) from a hydrocarbon by another atom or a group of atoms result in the formation of an entirely new compound having altogether different properties and applications. **Alcohols** and **phenols** are formed when a hydrogen atom in a hydrocarbon, aliphatic and aromatic respectively, is replaced by –OH group. These classes of compounds find wide applications in industry as well as in day-to-day life. For instance, have you ever noticed that ordinary spirit used for polishing wooden furniture is chiefly a compound containing hydroxyl group, ethanol. The sugar we eat, the cotton used for fabrics, the paper we use for writing, are all made up of compounds containing –OH groups. Just think of life without paper; no note-books, books, news-papers, currency notes, cheques, certificates, etc. The magazines carrying beautiful photographs and interesting stories would disappear from our life. It would have been really a different world.

An alcohol contains one or more hydroxyl (OH) group(s) directly attached to carbon atom(s), of an aliphatic system (CH_3OH) while a phenol contains –OH group(s) directly attached to carbon atom(s) of an aromatic system (C_6H_5OH).

The subsitution of a hydrogen atom in a hydrocarbon by an alkoxy or aryloxy group (R–O/Ar–O) yields another class of compounds known as 'ethers', for example, CH_3OCH_3 (dimethyl ether). You may also visualise ethers as compounds formed by substituting the hydrogen atom of hydroxyl group of an alcohol or phenol by an alkyl or aryl group.

In this unit, we shall discuss the chemistry of three classes of compounds, namely — alcohols, phenols and ethers.

The classification of compounds makes their study systematic and hence simpler. Therefore, let us first learn how are alcohols, phenols and ethers classified?

11.1.1 Mono, Di, Tri or Polyhydric Compounds

Alcohols and phenols may be classified as mono–, di–, tri- or polyhydric compounds depending on whether they contain one, two, three or many hydroxyl groups respectively in their structures as given below:

C_2H_5OH

$$\begin{array}{c} CH_2OH \\ | \\ CH_2OH \end{array}$$

$$\begin{array}{c} CH_2OH \\ | \\ CHOH \\ | \\ CH_2OH \end{array}$$

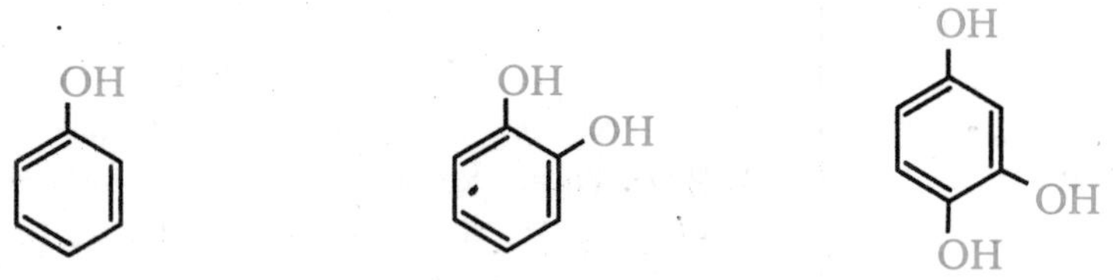

| Monohydric | Dihydric | Trihydric |

Monohydric alcohols may be further classified according to the hybridisation of the carbon atom to which the hydroxyl group is attached.

(i) *Compounds containing* $C_{sp^3}-OH$ *bond:* In this class of alcohols, the –OH group is attached to an sp^3 hybridised carbon atom of an alkyl group. They are further classified as follows:

Primary, secondary and tertiary alcohols: In these three types of alcohols, the –OH group is attached to primary, secondary and tertiary carbon atom, respectively as depicted below:

$-CH_2-OH$ $>CH-OH$ $>C-OH$

Primary (1°)   Secondary (2°)   Tertiary (3°)

Allylic alcohols: In these alcohols, the —OH group is attached to a sp^3 hybridised carbon next to the carbon-carbon double bond, that is to an allylic carbon. For example

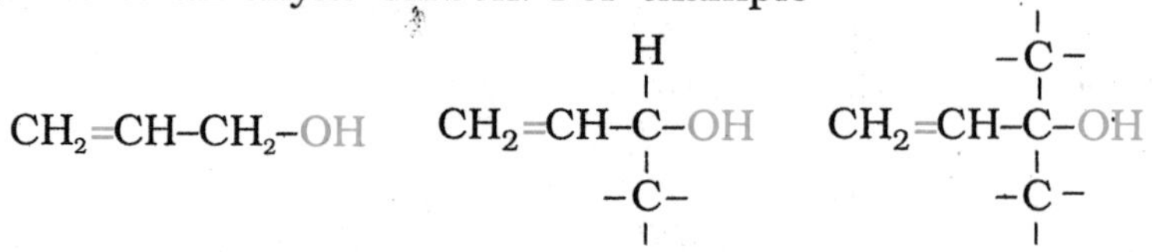

$CH_2=CH-CH_2-OH$

$$CH_2=CH-\overset{\displaystyle H}{\underset{\displaystyle -C-}{C}}-OH$$

$$CH_2=CH-\overset{\displaystyle -C-}{\underset{\displaystyle -C-}{C}}-OH$$

Primary   Secondary   Tertiary

Benzylic alcohols: In these alcohols, the —OH group is attached to a sp^3—hybridised carbon atom next to an aromatic ring. For example

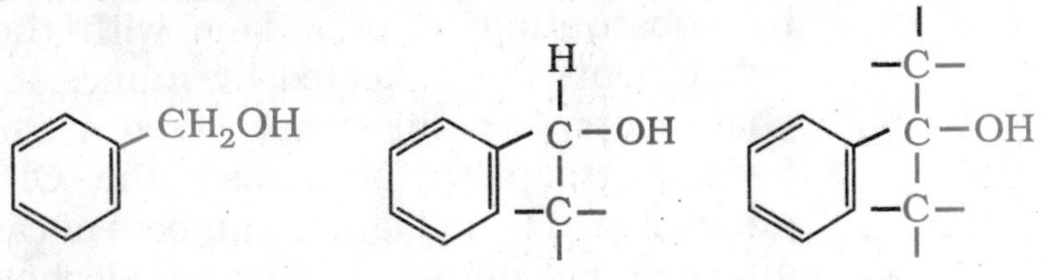

Primary   Secondary   Tertiary

Allylic and benzylic alcohols may be primary, secondary or tertiary.

(ii) *Compounds containing* C_{sp^2}–OH *bond:* These alcohols contain —OH group bonded to a carbon-carbon double bond i.e., to a vinylic carbon or to an aryl carbon. These alcohols are also known as vinylic alcohols.

Vinylic alcohol: $CH_2 = CH - OH$

Phenols:

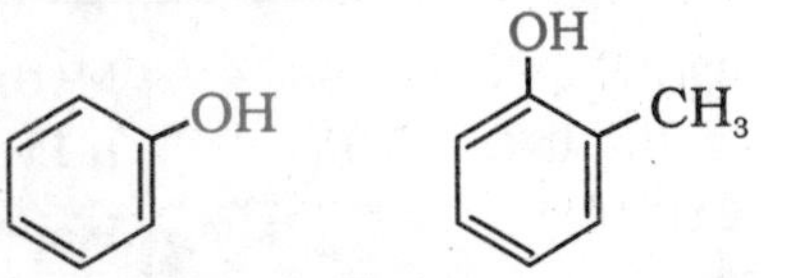

11.1.2 Ethers

Ethers are classified as **simple** or **symmetrical**, if the alkyl or aryl groups attached to the oxygen atom are the same, and **mixed** or **unsymmetrical**, if the two groups are different. Diethyl ether, $C_2H_5OC_2H_5$, is a symmetrical ether whereas $C_2H_5OCH_3$ and $C_2H_5OC_6H_5$ are unsymmetrical ethers.

Intext Questions

11.1 Classify the following as primary, secondary and tertiary alcohols:

(i)
$$CH_3 - \underset{\underset{CH_3}{|}}{\overset{\overset{CH_3}{|}}{C}} - CH_2OH$$

(ii) $H_2C = CH - CH_2OH$

(iii) $CH_3 - CH_2 - CH_2 - OH$

(iv)

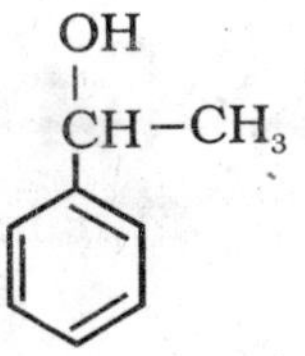

(v)

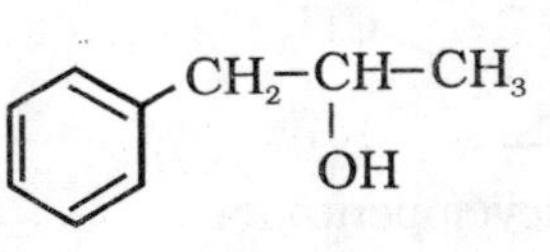

(vi)

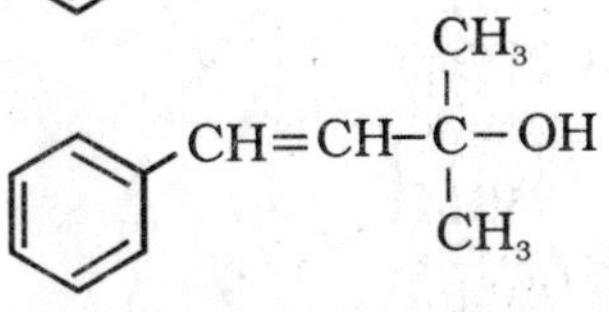

11.2 Identify allylic alcohols in the above examples.

11.2 Nomenclature

(a) Alcohols: The common name of an alcohol is derived from the common name of the alkyl group and adding the word alcohol to it. For example, CH_3OH is methyl alcohol.

According to IUPAC system (Unit 12, Class XI), the name of an alcohol is derived from the name of the alkane from which the alcohol is derived, by substituting 'e' of alkane with the suffix 'ol'. The position of substituents are indicated by numerals. For this, the longest carbon chain (parent chain) is numbered starting at the end nearest to the hydroxyl group. The positions of the –OH group and other substituents are indicated by using the numbers of carbon atoms to which these are attached. For naming polyhydric alcohols, the 'e' of alkane is retained and the ending 'ol' is added. The number of –OH groups is indicated by adding the multiplicative prefix, di, tri, etc., before 'ol'. The positions of –OH groups are indicated by appropriate locants e.g., $HO-CH_2-CH_2-OH$ is named as ethane–1, 2-diol. Table 11.1 gives common and IUPAC names of a few alcohols as examples.

Table 11.1: Common and IUPAC Names of Some Alcohols

Compound	Common name	IUPAC name
$CH_3 - OH$	Methyl alcohol	Methanol
$CH_3 - CH_2 - CH_2 - OH$	n-Propyl alcohol	Propan-1-ol
$CH_3 - CH - CH_3$ $\quad\quad\ \|$ $\quad\quad OH$	Isopropyl alcohol	Propan-2-ol
$CH_3 - CH_2 - CH_2 - CH_2 - OH$	n-Butyl alcohol	Butan-1-ol
$CH_3 - CH - CH_2 - CH_3$ $\quad\quad\ \|$ $\quad\quad OH$	sec-Butyl alcohol	Butan-2-ol
$CH_3 - CH - CH_2 - OH$ $\quad\quad\ \|$ $\quad\quad CH_3$	Isobutyl alcohol	2-Methylpropan-1-ol
$\quad\quad CH_3$ $\quad\quad\ \|$ $CH_3 - C - OH$ $\quad\quad\ \|$ $\quad\quad CH_3$	tert-Butyl alcohol	2-Methylpropan-2-ol
$CH_2 - CH - CH_2$ $\ \|\quad\ \ \|\quad\ \ \|$ $OH\ \ \ OH\ \ OH$	Glycerol	Propane -1, 2, 3-triol

Cyclic alcohols are named using the prefix cyclo and considering the —OH group attached to C–1.

Cyclohexanol   2-Methylcyclopentanol

(b) Phenols: The simplest hydroxy derivative of benzene is phenol. It is its common name and also an accepted IUPAC name. As structure of phenol involves a benzene ring, in its substituted compounds the terms ortho (1,2- disubstituted), meta (1,3-disubstituted) and para (1,4-disubstituted) are often used in the common names.

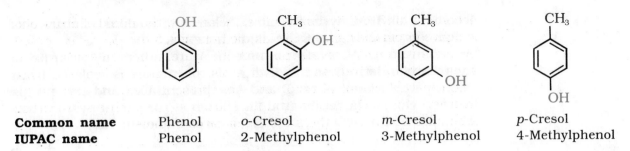

Common name	Phenol	*o*-Cresol	*m*-Cresol	*p*-Cresol
IUPAC name	Phenol	2-Methylphenol	3-Methylphenol	4-Methylphenol

Dihydroxy derivatives of benzene are known as 1, 2-, 1, 3- and 1, 4-benzenediol.

Common name	Catechol	Resorcinol	Hydroquinone or quinol
IUPAC name	Benzene-1,2-diol	Benzene-1,3-diol	Benzene-1,4-diol

(c) Ethers: Common names of ethers are derived from the names of alkyl/aryl groups written as separate words in alphabetical order and adding the word 'ether' at the end. For example, $CH_3OC_2H_5$ is ethylmethyl ether.

Table 11.2: Common and IUPAC Names of Some Ethers

Compound	Common name	IUPAC name
CH_3OCH_3	Dimethyl ether	Methoxymethane
$C_2H_5OC_2H_5$	Diethyl ether	Ethoxyethane
$CH_3OCH_2CH_2CH_3$	Methyl n-propyl ether	1-Methoxypropane
$C_6H_5OCH_3$	Methyl phenyl ether (Anisole)	Methoxybenzene (Anisole)
$C_6H_5OCH_2CH_3$	Ethyl phenyl ether (Phenetole)	Ethoxybenzene
$C_6H_5O(CH_2)_6 - CH_3$	Heptyl phenyl ether	1-Phenoxyheptane
$CH_3O-CH-CH_3$ $\quad\quad\mid$ $\quad\quad CH_3$	Methyl isopropyl ether	2-Methoxypropane
$C_6H_5-O-CH_2- CH_2 - CH-CH_3$ $\quad\quad\quad\quad\quad\quad\quad\quad\mid$ $\quad\quad\quad\quad\quad\quad\quad\quad CH_3$	Phenyl isopentyl ether	3- Methylbutoxybenzene
$CH_3- O - CH_2 - CH_2 - OCH_3$	—	1,2-Dimethoxyethane
(structure) H_3C CH_3 OC_2H_5 cyclohexane	—	2-Ethoxy--1,1-dimethylcyclohexane

If both the alkyl groups are the same, the prefix 'di' is added before the alkyl group. For example, $C_2H_5OC_2H_5$ is diethyl ether.

According to IUPAC system of nomenclature, ethers are regarded as hydrocarbon derivatives in which a hydrogen atom is replaced by an –OR or –OAr group, where R and Ar represent alkyl and aryl groups, respectively. The larger (R) group is chosen as the parent hydrocarbon. The names of a few ethers are given as examples in Table 11.2.

Example 11.1   Give IUPAC names of the following compounds:

(i) $CH_3-CH-CH-CH-CH_2OH$
    $\quad\quad\;\; |\quad\;\; |\quad\; |$
    $\quad\quad\;\; Cl\quad CH_3\; CH_3$

(ii) $CH_3-CH-O-CH_2CH_3$
     $\quad\quad\;\;\; |$
     $\quad\quad\;\; CH_3$

(iii)

(iv)

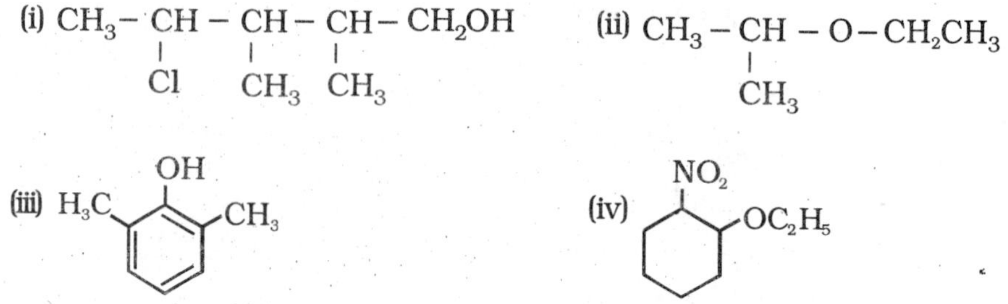

Solution   (i) 4-Chloro-2,3-dimethylpentan-1-ol   (ii) 2-Ethoxypropane

(iii) 2,6-Dimethylphenol   (iv) 1-Ethoxy-2-nitrocyclohexane

Intext Question

11.3 Name the following compounds according to IUPAC system.

(i)
$\quad\quad\quad\quad\quad CH_2OH$
$\quad\quad\quad\quad\quad |$
$CH_3-CH_2-CH-CH-CH-CH_3$
$\quad\quad\quad\quad |\quad\quad\; |$
$\quad\quad\quad CH_2Cl\quad CH_3$

(ii)
$\quad\quad\quad\quad\quad\quad\quad\quad CH_2OH$
$\quad\quad\quad\quad\quad\quad\quad\quad |$
$CH_3-CH-CH_2-CH-CH-CH_3$
$\quad\quad\;\; |\quad\quad\quad\;\; |$
$\quad\quad\; CH_3\quad\quad\; OH$

(iii)

(iv) $H_2C=CH-CH-CH_2-CH_2-CH_3$
     $\quad\quad\quad\quad |$
     $\quad\quad\quad\; OH$

(v) $CH_3-C=C-CH_2OH$
    $\quad\quad\;\; |\quad |$
    $\quad\quad\; CH_3\; Br$

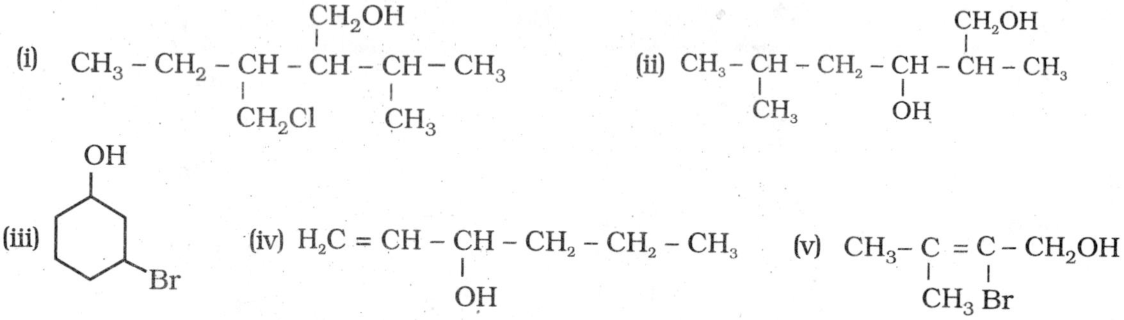

11.3 Structures of Functional Groups

In alcohols, the oxygen of the –OH group is attached to carbon by a sigma (σ) bond formed by the overlap of a sp^3 hybridised orbital of carbon with a sp^3 hybridised orbital of oxygen. Fig. 11.1 depicts structural aspects of methanol, phenol and methoxymethane.

Methanol   Phenol   Methoxymethane

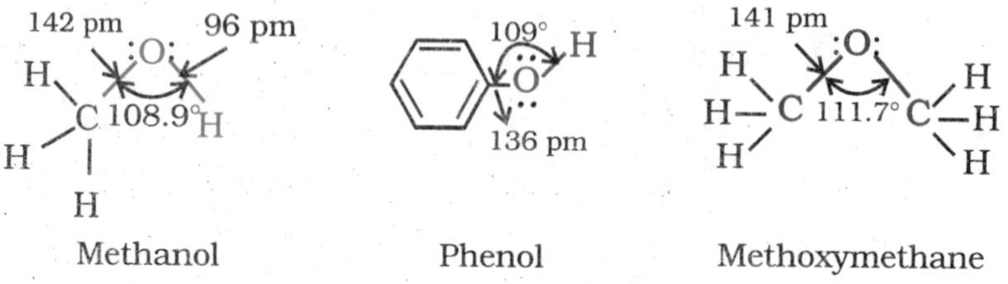

Fig. 11.1: *Structures of methanol, phenol and methoxymethane*

The bond angle $\overset{\ddot{\,}O\ddot{\,}}{\underset{C\quad H}{\diagdown}}$ in alcohols is slightly less than the tetrahedral angle (109°-28′). It is due to the repulsion between the unshared electron pairs of oxygen. In phenols, the –OH group is attached to sp^2 hybridised carbon of an aromatic ring. The carbon– oxygen bond length (136 pm) in phenol is slightly less than that in methanol. This is due to (i) partial double bond character on account of the conjugation of unshared electron pair of oxygen with the aromatic ring (Section 11.4.4) and (ii) sp^2 hybridised state of carbon to which oxygen is attached.

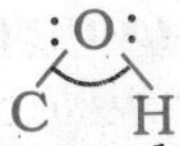

In ethers, the four electron pairs, i.e., the two bond pairs and two lone pairs of electrons on oxygen are arranged approximately in a tetrahedral arrangement. The bond angle is slightly greater than the tetrahedral angle due to the repulsive interaction between the two bulky (–R) groups. The C–O bond length (141 pm) is almost the same as in alcohols.

11.4 Alcohols and Phenols

11.4.1 Preparation of Alcohols

Alcohols are prepared by the following methods:

1. From alkenes

(i) *By acid catalysed hydration:* Alkenes react with water in the presence of acid as catalyst to form alcohols. In case of unsymmetrical alkenes, the addition reaction takes place in accordance with Markovnikov's rule (Unit 13, Class XI).

$$\overset{}{\underset{}{>}}C=C\overset{}{\underset{}{<}} + H_2O \xrightleftharpoons{H^+} \overset{}{\underset{H}{>}}C-\overset{}{\underset{OH}{}}C\overset{}{\underset{}{<}}$$

$$CH_3CH=CH_2 + H_2O \xrightleftharpoons{H^+} CH_3-\underset{OH}{CH}-CH_3$$

Mechanism

The mechanism of the reaction involves the following three steps:

Step 1: Protonation of alkene to form carbocation by electrophilic attack of H_3O^+.

$$H_2O + H^+ \rightarrow H_3O^+$$

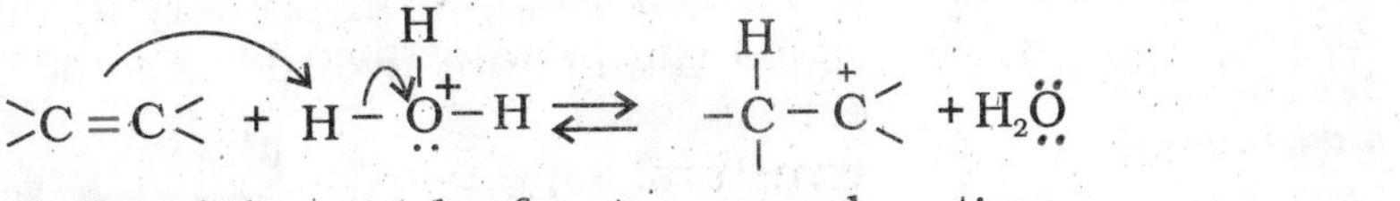

$$>C=C< + H-\overset{H}{\underset{}{\overset{+}{O}}}-H \rightleftharpoons -\overset{}{\underset{}{C}}-\overset{}{\underset{}{C}}< + H_2\ddot{O}$$

Step 2: Nucleophilic attack of water on carbocation.

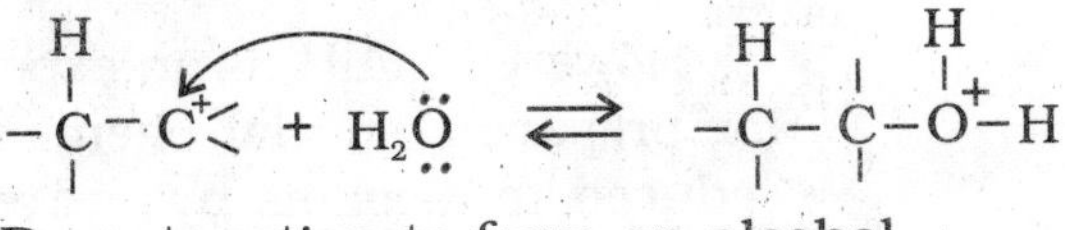

$$-\overset{H}{\underset{}{C}}-\overset{+}{\underset{}{C}}< + H_2\ddot{O} \rightleftharpoons -\overset{H}{\underset{}{C}}-\overset{H}{\underset{}{C}}-\overset{+}{O}-H$$

Step 3: Deprotonation to form an alcohol.

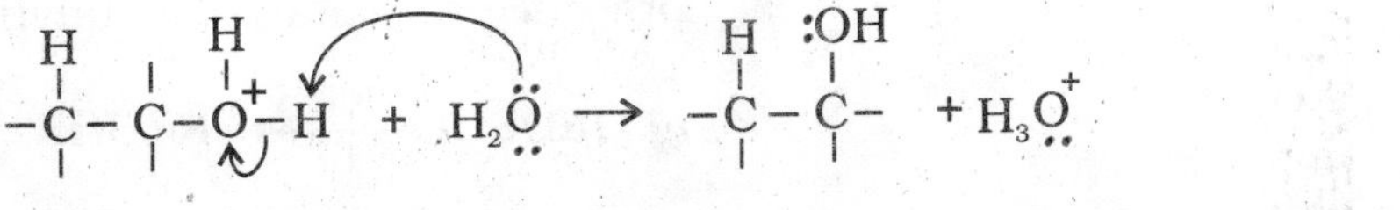

$$-\overset{H}{\underset{}{C}}-\overset{H}{\underset{}{C}}-\overset{+}{O}-H + H_2\ddot{O} \rightarrow -\overset{H}{\underset{}{C}}-\overset{\ddot{O}H}{\underset{}{C}}- + H_3\overset{+}{O}$$

(ii) *By hydroboration–oxidation:* Diborane $(BH_3)_2$ reacts with alkenes to give trialkyl boranes as addition product. This is oxidised to alcohol by hydrogen peroxide in the presence of aqueous sodium hydroxide.

$$CH_3-CH=CH_2 \ + \ (H-BH_2)_2 \longrightarrow CH_3-\underset{\underset{H}{|}}{C}H-\underset{\underset{BH_2}{|}}{C}H_2$$

$$\downarrow CH_3-CH=CH_2$$

$$(CH_3-CH_2-CH_2)_3B \xleftarrow{\ CH_3-CH=CH_2\ } (CH_3-CH_2-CH_2)_2BH$$

$$H_2O \downarrow 3H_2O_2, \ \bar{O}H$$

$$3CH_3-CH_2-CH_2-OH \ + \ B(OH)_3$$
$$\text{Propan-1-ol}$$

The addition of borane to the double bond takes place in such a manner that the boron atom gets attached to the sp^2 carbon carrying greater number of hydrogen atoms. The alcohol so formed looks as if it has been formed by the addition of water to the alkene in a way opposite to the Markovnikov's rule. In this reaction, alcohol is obtained in excellent yield.

2. From carbonyl compounds

(i) *By reduction of aldehydes and ketones:* Aldehydes and ketones are reduced to the corresponding alcohols by addition of hydrogen in the presence of catalysts (catalytic hydrogenation). The usual catalyst is a finely divided metal such as platinum, palladium or nickel. It is also prepared by treating aldehydes and ketones with sodium borohydride ($NaBH_4$) or lithium aluminium hydride ($LiAlH_4$). Aldehydes yield primary alcohols whereas ketones give secondary alcohols.

$$RCHO + H_2 \xrightarrow{\text{Pd}} RCH_2OH$$

$$RCOR' \xrightarrow{\text{NaBH}_4} R-\underset{\underset{OH}{|}}{C}H-R'$$

(ii) *By reduction of carboxylic acids and esters:* Carboxylic acids are reduced to primary alcohols in excellent yields by lithium aluminium hydride, a strong reducing agent.

$$RCOOH \xrightarrow[\text{(ii) } H_2O]{\text{(i) LiAlH}_4} RCH_2OH$$

However, $LiAlH_4$ is an expensive reagent, and therefore, used for preparing special chemicals only. Commercially, acids are reduced to alcohols by converting them to the esters (Section 11.4.4), followed by their reduction using hydrogen in the presence of catalyst (catalytic hydrogenation).

$$RCOOH \xrightarrow[H^+]{R'OH} RCOOR' \xrightarrow[\text{Catalyst}]{H_2} RCH_2OH + R'OH$$

3. From Grignard reagents

Alcohols are produced by the reaction of Grignard reagents (Unit 10, Class XII) with aldehydes and ketones.

The first step of the reaction is the nucleophilic addition of Grignard reagent to the carbonyl group to form an adduct. Hydrolysis of the adduct yields an alcohol.

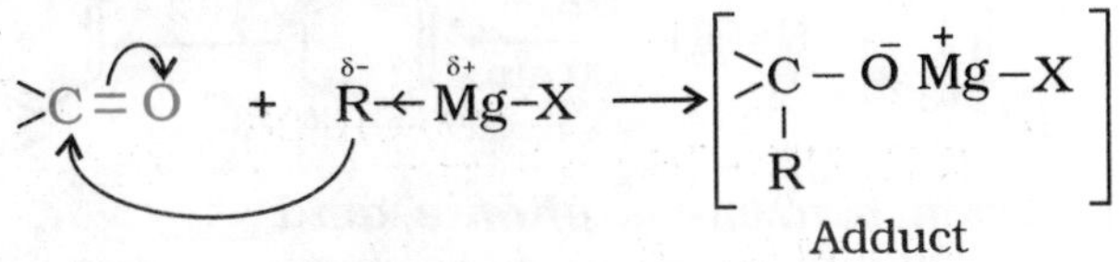

$$\underset{}{>}C=\overset{}{O} \; + \; \overset{\delta-}{R}\!\!\leftarrow\!\!\overset{\delta+}{Mg}-X \longrightarrow \left[>\!\!\underset{\underset{R}{|}}{C}-\bar{O}\;\overset{+}{Mg}-X \right] \qquad \dots (i)$$

$$\qquad\qquad\qquad\qquad \text{Adduct}$$

$$\xrightarrow{H_2O} \; >\!\!\underset{\underset{R}{|}}{C}-OH \; + \; Mg(OH)X \qquad \dots (ii)$$

The reaction of Grignard reagents with methanal produces a primary alcohol, with other aldehydes, secondary alcohols and with ketones, tertiary alcohols.

The overall reactions using different aldehydes and ketones are as follows:

$$HCHO + RMgX \rightarrow RCH_2OMgX \xrightarrow{H_2O} RCH_2OH + Mg(OH)X$$

$$RCHO + R'MgX \xrightarrow{H_2O} R-\underset{\underset{R'}{|}}{C}H-OMgX \xrightarrow{H_2O} R-\underset{\underset{R'}{|}}{C}H-OH + Mg(OH)X$$

$$RCOR + R'MgX \longrightarrow R-\underset{\underset{R}{|}}{\overset{\overset{R'}{|}}{C}}-OMgX \xrightarrow{H_2O} R-\underset{\underset{R}{|}}{\overset{\overset{R'}{|}}{C}}-OH + Mg(OH)X$$

You will notice that the reaction produces a primary alcohol with methanal, a secondary alcohol with other aldehydes and tertiary alcohol with ketones.

Give the structures and IUPAC names of the products expected from the following reactions:

(a) Catalytic reduction of butanal.

(b) Hydration of propene in the presence of dilute sulphuric acid.

(c) Reaction of propanone with methylmagnesium bromide followed by hydrolysis.

Example 11.2

Solution

(a) CH_3–CH_2–CH_2–CH_2–OH
Butan-1-ol

(b) CH_3–CH–CH_3
       |
       OH
Propan-2-ol

(c) CH_3–$\underset{\underset{CH_3}{|}}{\overset{\overset{CH_3}{|}}{C}}$–OH
2-Methylpropan-2-ol

11.4.2 Preparation of Phenols

Phenol, also known as carbolic acid, was first isolated in the early nineteenth century from coal tar. Nowadays, phenol is commercially produced synthetically. In the laboratory, phenols are prepared from benzene derivatives by any of the following methods:

1. From haloarenes

Chlorobenzene is fused with NaOH at 623K and 320 atmospheric pressure. Phenol is obtained by acidification of sodium phenoxide so produced (Unit 10, Class XII).

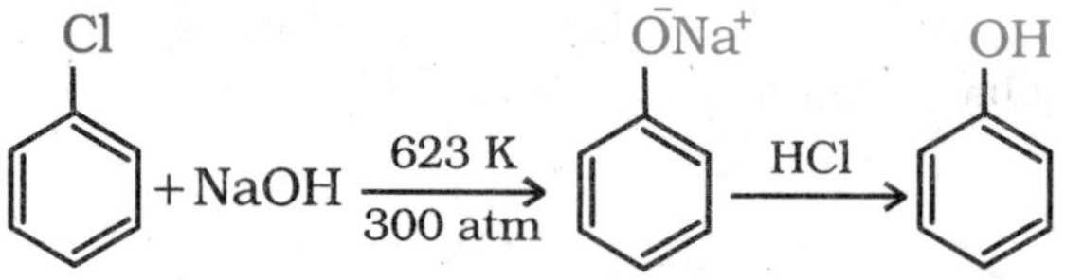

2. From benzenesulphonic acid

Benzene is sulphonated with oleum and benzene sulphonic acid so formed is converted to sodium phenoxide on heating with molten sodium hydroxide. Acidification of the sodium salt gives phenol.

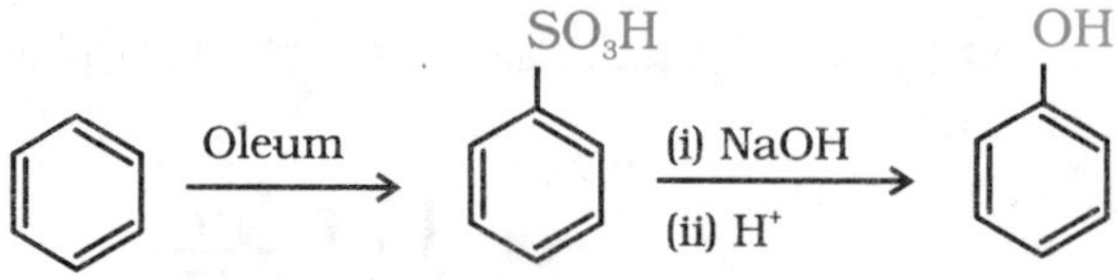

3. From diazonium salts

A diazonium salt is formed by treating an aromatic primary amine with nitrous acid ($NaNO_2$ + HCl) at 273-278 K. Diazonium salts are hydrolysed to phenols by warming with water or by treating with dilute acids (Unit 13, Class XII).

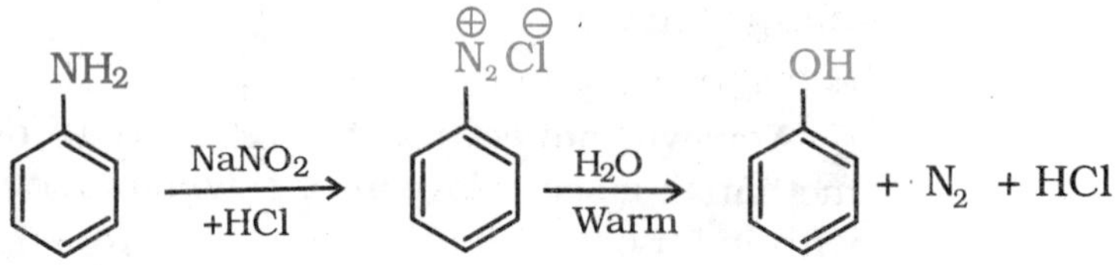

Aniline   Benzene diazonium chloride

Most of the worldwide production of phenol is from cumene.

4. From cumene

Phenol is manufactured from the hydrocarbon, cumene. Cumene (isopropylbenzene) is oxidised in the presence of air to cumene hydroperoxide. It is converted to phenol and acetone by treating it with dilute acid. Acetone, a by-product of this reaction, is also obtained in large quantities by this method.

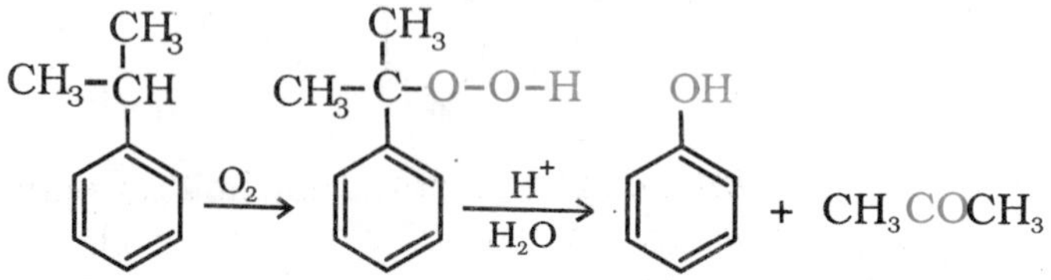

Cumene   Cumene hydroperoxide

11.4 Show how are the following alcohols prepared by the reaction of a suitable Grignard reagent on methanal ?

(i) $CH_3-CH-CH_2OH$
　　　　|
　　　CH_3

(ii)

CH_2OH

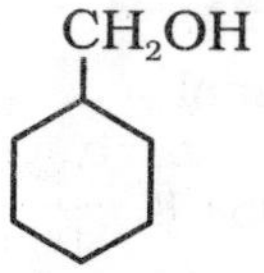

11.5 Write structures of the products of the following reactions:

(i) $CH_3 - CH = CH_2 \xrightarrow{H_2O/H^+}$

(ii)

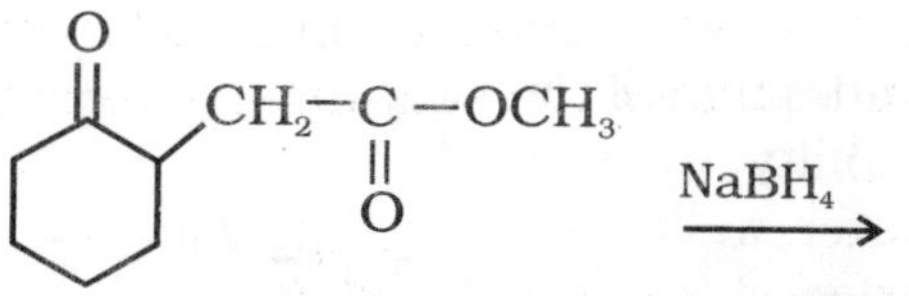

$CH_2-C-OCH_3$
　　　　||
　　　　O

$\xrightarrow{NaBH_4}$

(iii) $CH_3-CH_2-CH-CHO \xrightarrow{NaBH_4}$
　　　　　　　　　|
　　　　　　　　CH_3

11.4.3 Physical Properties

Alcohols and phenols consist of two parts, an alkyl/aryl group and a hydroxyl group. The properties of alcohols and phenols are chiefly due to the hydroxyl group. The nature of alkyl and aryl groups simply modify these properties.

Boiling Points

The boiling points of alcohols and phenols increase with increase in the number of carbon atoms (increase in van der Waals forces). In alcohols, the boiling points decrease with increase of branching in carbon chain (because of decrease in van der Waals forces with decrease in surface area).

The –OH group in alcohols and phenols is involved in intermolecular hydrogen bonding as shown below:

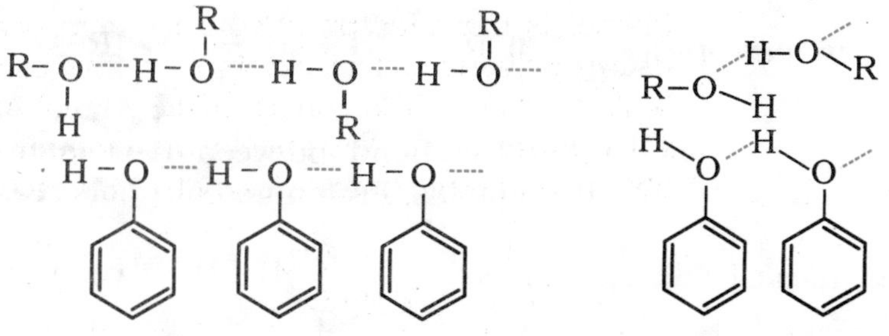

It is interesting to note that boiling points of alcohols and phenols are higher in comparison to other classes of compounds, namely hydrocarbons, ethers, haloalkanes and haloarenes of comparable molecular masses. For example, ethanol and propane have comparable molecular masses but their boiling points differ widely. The boiling point of methoxymethane is intermediate of the two boiling points.

CH₃CH₂ H
Ethanol
Molecular mass/b.p.
46/ 351 K

H₃C   CH₃
Methoxymethane
Molecular mass/b.p.
46/248 K

H   H
 \ /
  C
 / \
H₃C   CH₃
Propane
Molecular mass/b.p.
44/231 K

The high boiling points of alcohols are mainly due to the presence of intermolecular hydrogen bonding in them which is lacking in ethers and hydrocarbons.

Solubility

Solubility of alcohols and phenols in water is due to their ability to form hydrogen bonds with water molecules as shown. The solubility decreases with increase in size of alkyl/aryl (hydro-phobic) groups. Several of the lower molecular mass alcohols are miscible with water in all proportions.

$CH_3-CH_2-CH_2-\ddot{O}:$

Example 11.3   Arrange the following sets of compounds in order of their increasing boiling points:

(a) Pentan-1-ol, butan-1-ol, butan-2-ol, ethanol, propan-1-ol, methanol.

(b) Pentan-1-ol, n-butane, pentanal, ethoxyethane.

Solution   (a) Methanol, ethanol, propan-1-ol, butan-2-ol, butan-1-ol, pentan-1-ol.

(b) n-Butane, ethoxyethane, pentanal and pentan-1-ol.

11.4.4 Chemical Reactions

Alcohols are versatile compounds. They react both as nucleophiles and electrophiles. The bond between O–H is broken when alcohols react as nucleophiles.

Alcohols as nucleophiles

(i) $R-\ddot{O}-H + {}^{+}\overset{|}{C}- \longrightarrow R-\overset{+}{\underset{..}{O}}\overset{H}{-}\overset{|}{C}- \longrightarrow R-O-\overset{|}{\underset{|}{C}}- + H^{+}$

(ii) The bond between C–O is broken when they react as electrophiles. Protonated alcohols react in this manner.

Protonated alcohols as electrophiles

$$R-CH_2-OH + \overset{+}{H} \rightarrow R-CH_2-\overset{+}{O}H_2$$

$$Br^{-} + \overset{+}{C}H_2-\overset{+}{O}H_2 \longrightarrow Br-CH_2 + H_2O$$
$$\qquad\qquad\quad |\qquad\qquad\qquad\quad |$$
$$\qquad\qquad\quad R\qquad\qquad\qquad\quad R$$

Based on the cleavage of O–H and C–O bonds, the reactions of alcohols and phenols may be divided into two groups:

(a) Reactions involving cleavage of O–H bond

1. Acidity of alcohols and phenols

(i) *Reaction with metals*: Alcohols and phenols react with active metals such as sodium, potassium and aluminium to yield corresponding alkoxides/phenoxides and hydrogen.

$$2R\text{–}O\text{–}H + 2Na \longrightarrow 2R\text{–}O\text{–}Na + H_2$$

Sodium alkoxide

$$6\,CH_3\text{–}\underset{\underset{CH_3}{|}}{\overset{\overset{CH_3}{|}}{C}}\text{–}OH + 2\,Al \longrightarrow 2\left(CH_3\text{–}\underset{\underset{CH_3}{|}}{\overset{\overset{CH_3}{|}}{C}}\text{–}O\right)_3 Al + 3H_2$$

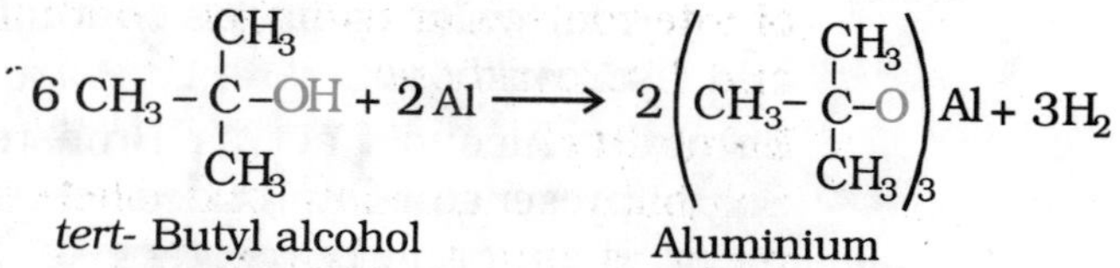

tert- Butyl alcohol   Aluminium *tert-* butoxide

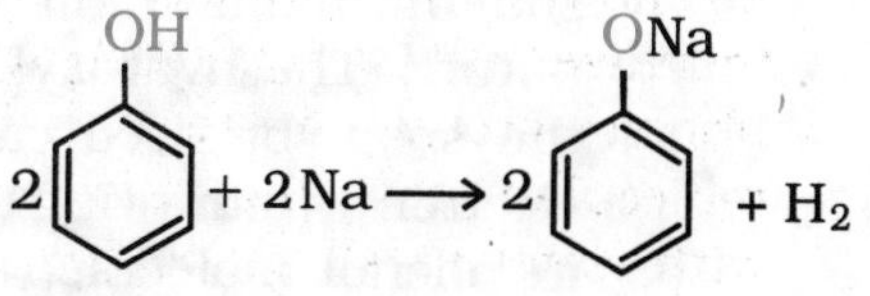

Phenol   Sodium phenoxide

In addition to this, phenols react with aqueous sodium hydroxide to form sodium phenoxides.

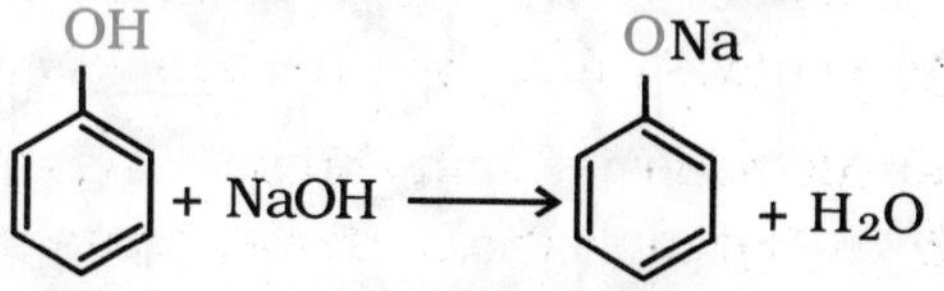

Sodium phenoxide

The above reactions show that alcohols and phenols are acidic in nature. In fact, alcohols and phenols are Brönsted acids i.e., they can donate a proton to a stronger base (B:).

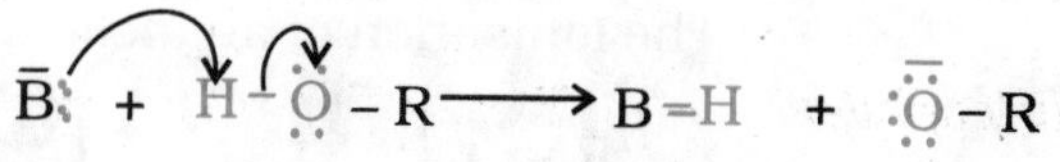

$$\bar{B}: + H\text{–}\ddot{O}\text{–}R \longrightarrow B\text{=}H + :\ddot{O}\text{–}R$$

Base   Acid   Conjugate acid   Conjugate base

(ii) *Acidity of alcohols*: The acidic character of alcohols is due to the polar nature of O–H bond. An electron-releasing group (–CH$_3$, –C$_2$H$_5$) increases electron density on oxygen tending to decrease the polarity of O-H bond. This decreases the acid strength. For this reason, the acid strength of alcohols decreases in the following order:

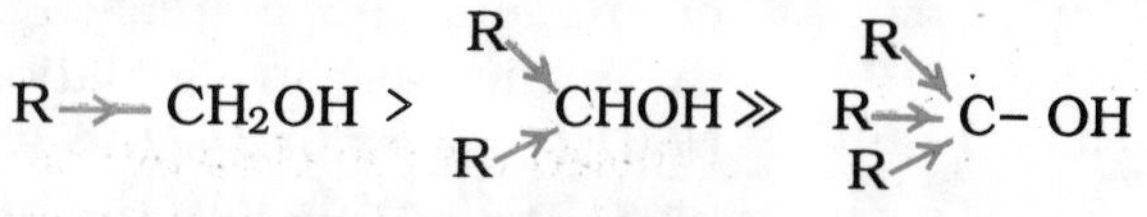

$$R\longrightarrow CH_2OH > \underset{R\nearrow}{\overset{R\searrow}{}}CHOH \gg \underset{R\nearrow}{\overset{R\searrow}{}}C\text{–}OH$$

Primary   Secondary   Tertiary

Alcohols are, however, weaker acids than water. This can be illustrated by the reaction of water with an alkoxide.

$$R-\overset{..}{\underset{..}{O}}: \;+\; H-\overset{..}{\underset{..}{O}}-H \longrightarrow R-O-H \;+\; :\overset{..}{\underset{..}{O}}H$$

Base   Acid Conjugate Conjugate
         acid   base

This reaction shows that water is a better proton donor (i.e., stronger acid) than alcohol. Also, in the above reaction, we note that an alkoxide ion is a better proton acceptor than hydroxide ion, which suggests that alkoxides are stronger bases (sodium ethoxide is a stronger base than sodium hydroxide).

Alcohols act as Bronsted bases as well. It is due to the presence of unshared electron pairs on oxygen, which makes them proton acceptors.

(iii) *Acidity of phenols:* The reactions of phenol with metals (e.g., sodium, aluminium) and sodium hydroxide indicate its acidic nature. The hydroxyl group, in phenol is directly attached to the sp^2 hybridised carbon of benzene ring which acts as an electron withdrawing group. Due to this, the charge distribution in phenol molecule, as depicted in its resonance structures, causes the oxygen of –OH group to be positive.

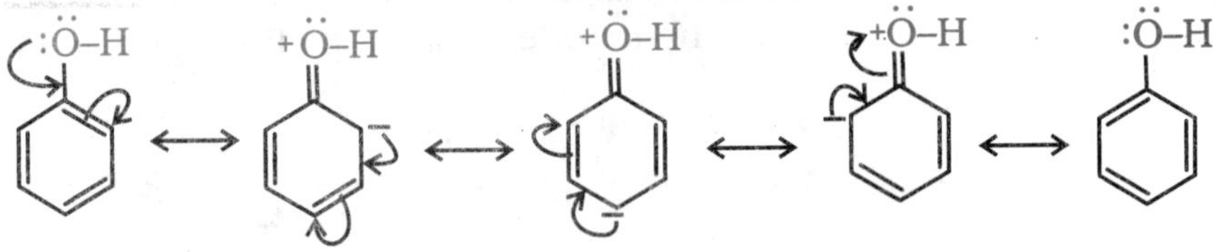

The reaction of phenol with aqueous sodium hydroxide indicates that phenols are stronger acids than alcohols and water. Let us examine how a compound in which hydroxyl group attached to an aromatic ring is more acidic than the one in which hydroxyl group is attached to an alkyl group.

The ionisation of an alcohol and a phenol takes place as follows:

$$R-\overset{..}{\underset{..}{O}}-H \rightleftharpoons R-\overset{..}{\underset{..}{O}}:^- \;+\; H^+$$

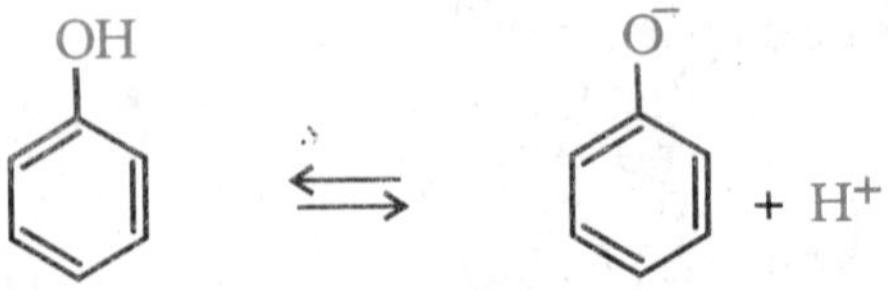

Due to the higher electronegativity of sp^2 hybridised carbon of phenol to which –OH is attached, electron density decreases on oxygen. This increases the polarity of O–H bond and results in an increase in ionisation of phenols than that of alcohols. Now let us examine the stabilities of alkoxide and phenoxide ions. In alkoxide ion, the negative charge is localised on oxygen while in phenoxide ion, the charge is delocalised. The delocalisation of negative charge (structures I-V) makes phenoxide ion more stable and favours the ionisation of phenol. Although there is also charge delocalisation in phenol, its resonance structures have charge separation due to which the phenol molecule is less stable than phenoxide ion.

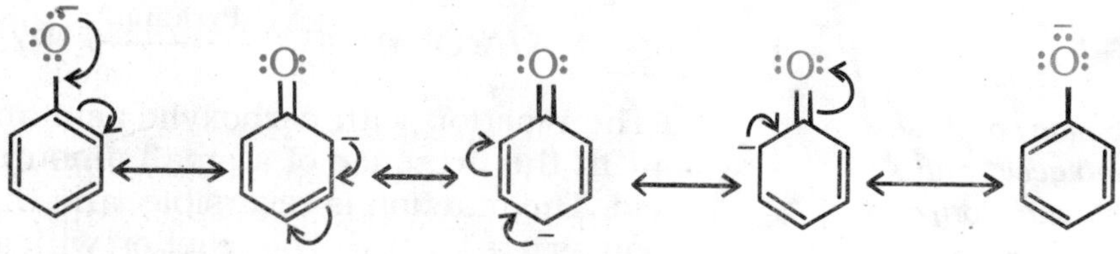

I   II   III   IV   V

In substituted phenols, the presence of electron withdrawing groups such as nitro group, enhances the acidic strength of phenol. This effect is more pronounced when such a group is present at *ortho* and *para* positions. It is due to the effective delocalisation of negative charge in phenoxide ion. On the other hand, electron releasing groups, such as alkyl groups, in general, do not favour the formation of phenoxide ion resulting in decrease in acid strength. Cresols, for example, are less acidic than phenol.

The greater the pK_a value, the weaker the acid.

Table 11.3: pK_a Values of some Phenols and Ethanol

Compound	Formula	pK_a
o-Nitrophenol	$o\text{-}O_2N\text{-}C_6H_4\text{-}OH$	7.2
m-Nitrophenol	$m\text{-}O_2N\text{-}C_6H_4\text{-}OH$	8.3
p-Nitrophenol	$p\text{-}O_2N\text{-}C_6H_4\text{-}OH$	7.1
Phenol	$C_6H_5\text{-}OH$	10.0
o-Cresol	$o\text{-}CH_3\text{-}C_6H_4\text{-}OH$	10.2
m-Cresol	$m\text{-}CH_3C_6H_4\text{-}OH$	10.1
p-Cresol	$p\text{-}CH_3\text{-}C_6H_4\text{-}OH$	10.2
Ethanol	C_2H_5OH	15.9

From the above data, you will note that phenol is million times more acidic than ethanol.

Arrange the following compounds in increasing order of their acid strength: *Example 11.4*
Propan-1-ol, 2,4,6-trinitrophenol, 3-nitrophenol, 3,5-dinitrophenol, phenol, 4-methylphenol.

Propan-1-ol, 4-methylphenol, phenol, 3-nitrophenol, 3,5-dinitrophenol, *Solution*
2,4, 6-trinitrophenol.

2. Esterification

Alcohols and phenols react with carboxylic acids, acid chlorides and acid anhydrides to form esters.

$$Ar/RO-H + R'-COOH \underset{}{\overset{H^+}{\rightleftharpoons}} Ar/ROCOR' + H_2O$$

$$Ar/R-OH + (R'CO)_2O \underset{}{\overset{H^+}{\rightleftharpoons}} Ar/ROCOR + R'COOH$$

$$R/ArOH + R'COCl \xrightarrow{Pyridine} R/ArOCOR + HCl$$

Aspirin possesses analgesic, anti-inflammatory and antipyretic properties.

The reaction with carboxylic acid and acid anhydride is carried out in the presence of a small amount of concentrated sulphuric acid. The reaction is reversible, and therefore, water is removed as soon as it is formed. The reaction with acid chloride is carried out in the presence of a base (pyridine) so as to neutralise HCl which is formed during the reaction. It shifts the equilibrium to the right hand side. The introduction of acetyl (CH_3CO) group in alcohols or phenols is known as acetylation. Acetylation of salicylic acid produces aspirin.

Salicylic acid   Acetylsalicylic acid (Aspirin)

(b) Reactions involving cleavage of carbon – oxygen (C–O) bond in alcohols

The reactions involving cleavage of C–O bond take place only in alcohols. Phenols show this type of reaction only with zinc.

1. *Reaction with hydrogen halides:* Alcohols react with hydrogen halides to form alkyl halides (Refer Unit 10, Class XII).

$$ROH + HX \rightarrow R-X + H_2O$$

The difference in reactivity of three classes of alcohols with HCl distinguishes them from one another (**Lucas test**). Alcohols are soluble in Lucas reagent (conc. HCl and $ZnCl_2$) while their halides are immiscible and produce turbidity in solution. In case of tertiary alcohols, turbidity is produced immediately as they form the halides easily. Primary alcohols do not produce turbidity at room temperature.

2. *Reaction with phosphorus trihalides:* Alcohols are converted to alkyl bromides by reaction with phosphorus tribromide (Refer Unit 10, Class XII).

3. *Dehydration:* Alcohols undergo dehydration (removal of a molecule of water) to form alkenes on treating with a protic acid e.g., concentrated H_2SO_4 or H_3PO_4, or catalysts such as anhydrous zinc chloride or alumina (Unit 13, Class XI).

$$-\overset{|}{\underset{H}{C}}-\overset{|}{\underset{OH}{C}}- \xrightarrow[\text{Heat}]{H^+} {>}C=C{<} + H_2O$$

Ethanol undergoes dehydration by heating it with concentrated H_2SO_4 at 443 K.

$$C_2H_5OH \xrightarrow[443\ K]{H_2SO_4} CH_2 = CH_2 + H_2O$$

Secondary and tertiary alcohols are dehydrated under milder conditions. For example

$$\underset{\displaystyle CH_3\overset{\displaystyle OH}{\overset{|}{C}}HCH_3}{} \xrightarrow[\text{440 K}]{\text{85\% } H_3PO_4} CH_3-CH=CH_2 +H_2O$$

$$\underset{\displaystyle CH_3-\underset{\displaystyle CH_3}{\overset{\displaystyle CH_3}{\overset{|}{\underset{|}{C}}}}-OH}{} \xrightarrow[\text{358 K}]{\text{20\% } H_3PO_4} CH_3-\overset{\displaystyle CH_2}{\overset{\|}{C}}-CH_3 +H_2O$$

Thus, the relative ease of dehydration of alcohols follows the following order:

Tertiary > Secondary > Primary

The mechanism of dehydration of ethanol involves the following steps:

Tertiary carbocations are more stable and therefore are easier to form than secondary and primary carbocations; tertiary alcohols are the easiest to dehydrate.

Mechanism

Step 1: Formation of protonated alcohol.

$$H-\overset{H}{\underset{H}{C}}-\overset{H}{\underset{H}{C}}-\overset{..}{\underset{..}{O}}-H + H^+ \underset{}{\overset{\text{Fast}}{\rightleftharpoons}} H-\overset{H}{\underset{H}{C}}-\overset{H}{\underset{H}{C}}-\overset{+}{\underset{}{O}}-H$$

Ethanol   Protonated alcohol
                              (Ethyl oxonium ion)

Step 2: Formation of carbocation: It is the slowest step and hence, the rate determining step of the reaction.

$$H-\overset{H}{\underset{H}{C}}-\overset{H}{\underset{H}{C}}-\overset{H}{\overset{+}{O}}-H \overset{\text{Slow}}{\rightleftharpoons} H-\overset{H}{\underset{H}{C}}-\overset{H}{\underset{H}{C}}{}^+ + H_2O$$

Step 3: Formation of ethene by elimination of a proton.

$$H-\overset{H}{\underset{H}{C}}-\overset{H}{\underset{H}{C}}{}^+ \rightleftharpoons \underset{H}{\overset{H}{C}}=\underset{H}{\overset{H}{C}} + H^+$$

Ethene

The acid used in step 1 is released in step 3. To drive the equilibrium to the right, ethene is removed as it is formed.

4. **Oxidation:** Oxidation of alcohols involves the formation of a carbon-oxygen double bond with cleavage of an O-H and C-H bonds.

$$H-\overset{|}{C}-O-H \longrightarrow {>}C=O$$

Bond breaking

Such a cleavage and formation of bonds occur in oxidation reactions. These are also known as **dehydrogenation** reactions as these involve loss of dihydrogen from an alcohol molecule. Depending on the oxidising agent used, a primary alcohol is oxidised to an aldehyde which in turn is oxidised to a carboxylic acid.

$$RCH_2OH \xrightarrow{\text{Oxidation}} R-\overset{\overset{\displaystyle H}{|}}{C}=O \longrightarrow R-\overset{\overset{\displaystyle OH}{|}}{C}=O$$

$$\text{Aldehyde} \qquad\qquad \text{Carboxylic acid}$$

Strong oxidising agents such as acidified potassium permanganate are used for getting carboxylic acids from alcohols directly. CrO_3 in anhydrous medium is used as the oxidising agent for the isolation of aldehydes.

$$RCH_2OH \xrightarrow{CrO_3} RCHO$$

A better reagent for oxidation of primary alcohols to aldehydes in good yield is pyridinium chlorochromate (PCC), a complex of chromium trioxide with pyridine and HCl.

$$CH_3 - CH \equiv CH - CH_2OH \xrightarrow{PCC} CH_3 - CH \equiv CH - CHO$$

Secondary alcohols are oxidised to ketones by chromic anhyride (CrO_3).

$$R-\overset{\overset{\displaystyle }{|}}{\underset{\underset{\displaystyle OH}{|}}{C}}H-R' \xrightarrow{CrO_3} R-\overset{\overset{\displaystyle }{}}{\underset{\underset{\displaystyle O}{||}}{C}}-R'$$

$$\textit{Sec-} \text{ alcohol} \qquad\qquad \text{Ketone}$$

Tertiary alcohols do not undergo oxidation reaction. Under strong reaction conditions such as strong oxidising agents ($KMnO_4$) and elevated temperatures, cleavage of various C-C bonds takes place and a mixture of carboxylic acids containing lesser number of carbon atoms is formed.

$$RCH_2OH \xrightarrow[573K]{Cu} RCHO$$

When the vapours of a primary or a secondary alcohol are passed over heated copper at 573 K, dehydrogenation takes place and an aldehyde or a ketone is formed while tertiary alcohols undergo dehydration.

$$R-\underset{\underset{\displaystyle OH}{|}}{C}H-R' \xrightarrow[573K]{Cu} R-\underset{\underset{\displaystyle O}{||}}{C}-R'$$

$$CH_3-\underset{\underset{\displaystyle CH_3}{|}}{\overset{\overset{\displaystyle CH_3}{|}}{C}}-OH \xrightarrow[573K]{Cu} CH_3-\overset{\overset{\displaystyle CH_3}{|}}{C}=CH_2$$

Biological oxidation of methanol and ethanol in the body produces the corresponding aldehyde followed by the acid. At times the alcoholics, by mistake, drink ethanol, mixed with methanol also called denatured alcohol. In the body, methanol is oxidised first to methanal and then to methanoic acid, which may cause blindness and death. A methanol poisoned patient is treated by giving intravenous infusions of diluted ethanol. The enzyme responsible for oxidation of aldehyde (HCHO) to acid is swamped allowing time for kidneys to excrete methanol.

(c) **Reactions of phenols**

Following reactions are shown by phenols only.

1. Electrophilic aromatic substitution

In phenols, the reactions that take place on the aromatic ring are electrophilic substitution reactions (Unit 13, Class XI). The –OH group attached to the benzene ring activates it towards electrophilic substitution. Also, it directs the incoming group to *ortho* and *para* positions in the ring as these positions become electron rich due to the resonance effect caused by –OH group. The resonance structures are shown under acidity of phenols.

Common electrophilic aromatic substitution reactions taking place in phenol are as follows:

(i) *Nitration:* With dilute nitric acid at low temperature (298 K), phenol yields a mixture of *ortho* and *para* nitrophenols.

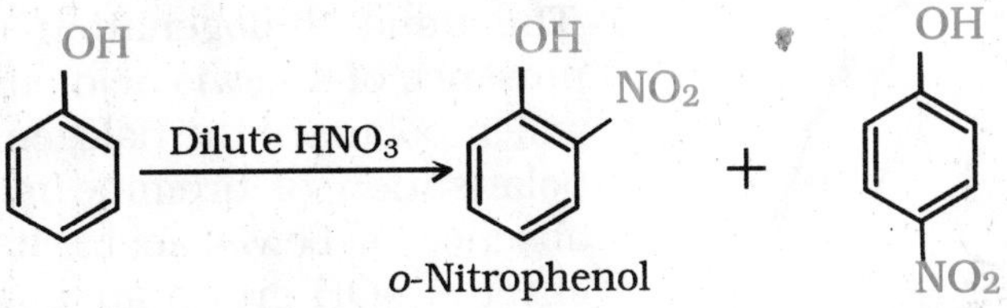

o-Nitrophenol

p-Nitrophenol

The *ortho* and *para* isomers can be separated by steam distillation. *o*-Nitrophenol is steam volatile due to intramolecular hydrogen bonding while *p*-nitrophenol is less volatile due to intermolecular hydrogen bonding which causes the association of molecules.

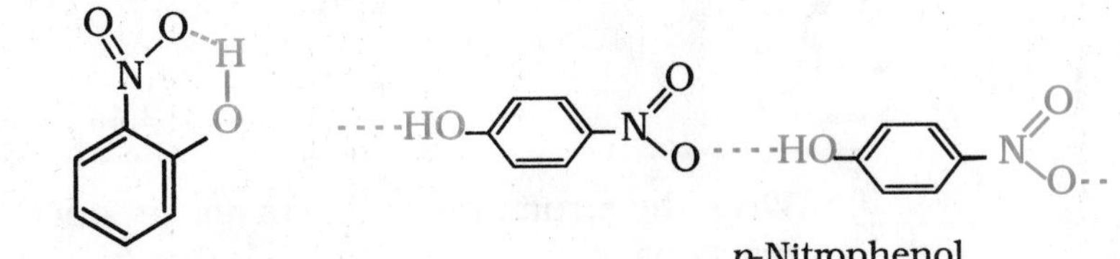

o-Nitrophenol
(Intramolecular
H-bonding)

p-Nitrophenol
(Intermolecular
H-bonding)

2, 4, 6 - Trinitrophenol is a strong acid due to the presence of three electron withdrawing –NO₂ groups which facilitate the release of hydrogen ion.

With concentrated nitric acid, phenol is converted to 2,4,6-trinitrophenol. The product is commonly known as picric acid. The yield of the reaction product is poor.

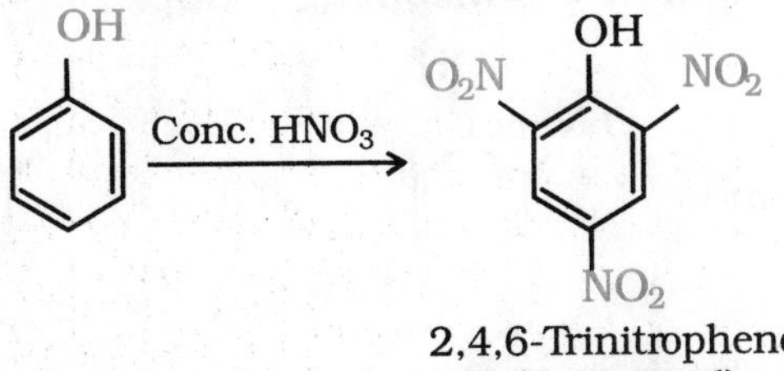

2,4,6-Trinitrophenol
(Picric acid)

Nowadays picric acid is prepared by treating phenol first with concentrated sulphuric acid which converts it to phenol-2,4-disulphonic acid, and then with concentrated nitric acid to get 2,4,6-trinitrophenol. Can you write the equations of the reactions involved?

(ii) Halogenation: On treating phenol with bromine, different reaction products are formed under different experimental conditions.

(a) When the reaction is carried out in solvents of low polarity such as $CHCl_3$ or CS_2 and at low temperature, monobromophenols are formed.

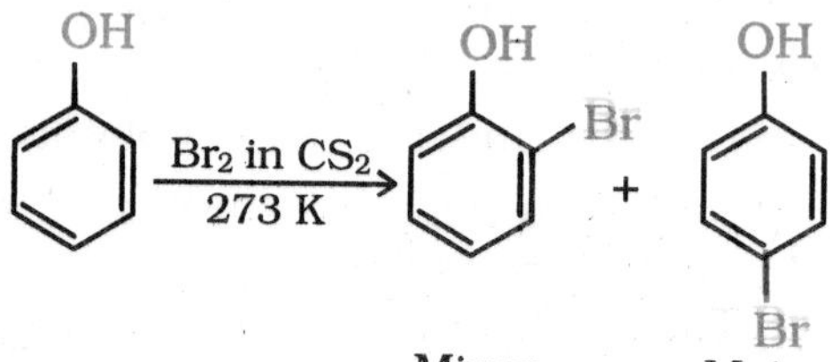

Minor   Major

The usual halogenation of benzene takes place in the presence of a Lewis acid, such as $FeBr_3$ (Unit 10, Class XII), which polarises the halogen molecule. In case of phenol, the polarisation of bromine molecule takes place even in the absence of Lewis acid. It is due to the highly activating effect of –OH group attached to the benzene ring.

(b) When phenol is treated with bromine water, 2,4,6-tribromophenol is formed as white precipitate.

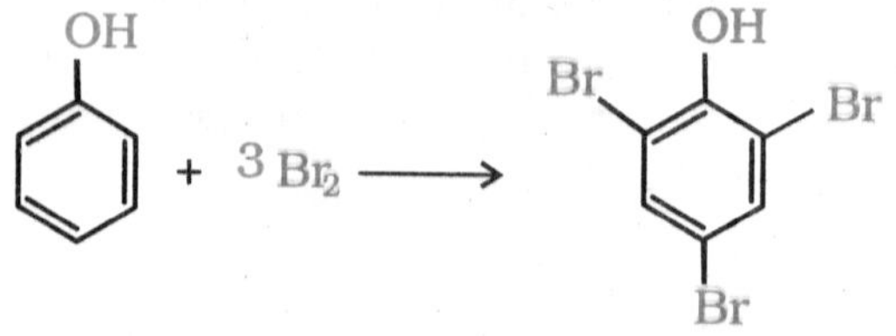

2,4,6-Tribromophenol

Example 11.5 Write the structures of the major products expected from the following reactions:

(a) Mononitration of 3-methylphenol

(b) Dinitration of 3-methylphenol

(c) Mononitration of phenyl methanoate.

Solution The combined influence of –OH and –CH_3 groups determine the position of the incoming group.

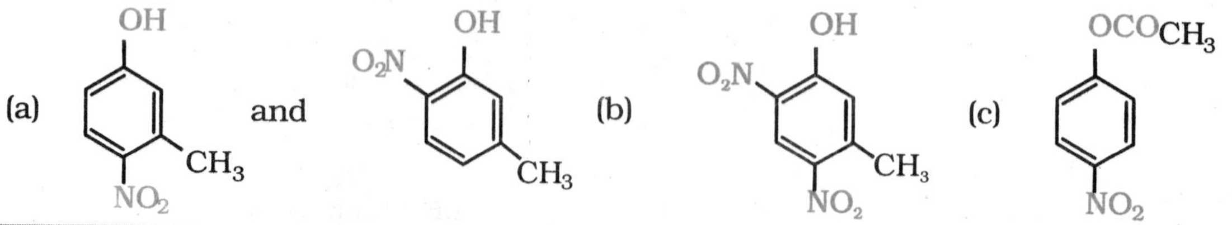

2. Kolbe's reaction

Phenoxide ion generated by treating phenol with sodium hydroxide is even more reactive than phenol towards electrophilic aromatic substitution. Hence, it undergoes electrophilic substitution with carbon dioxide, a weak electrophile. *Ortho* hydroxybenzoic acid is formed as the main reaction product.

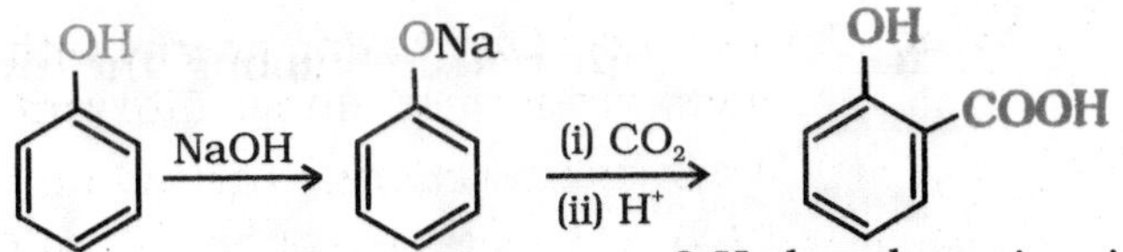

OH   ONa   OH

phenol $\xrightarrow{\text{NaOH}}$ sodium phenoxide $\xrightarrow[\text{(ii) H}^+]{\text{(i) CO}_2}$ 2-Hydroxybenzoic acid (Salicylic acid)

3. Reimer-Tiemann reaction

On treating phenol with chloroform in the presence of sodium hydroxide, a –CHO group is introduced at *ortho* position of benzene ring. This reaction is known as *Reimer - Tiemann reaction*.

The intermediate substituted benzal chloride is hydrolysed in the presence of alkali to produce salicylaldehyde.

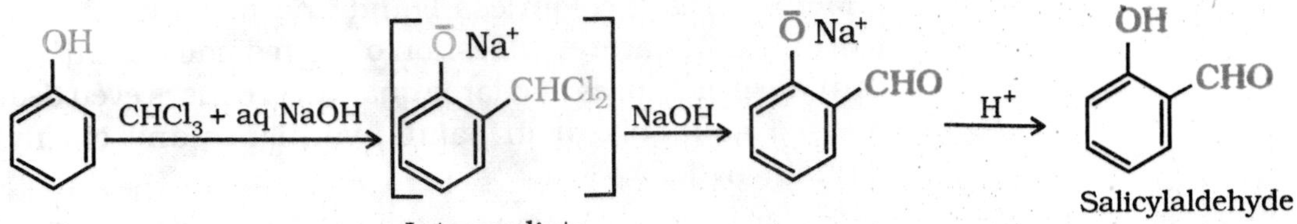

$$\text{phenol} \xrightarrow{\text{CHCl}_3 + \text{aq NaOH}} [\text{Intermediate}] \xrightarrow{\text{NaOH}} \xrightarrow{\text{H}^+} \text{Salicylaldehyde}$$

4. Reaction of phenol with zinc dust

Phenol is converted to benzene on heating with zinc dust.

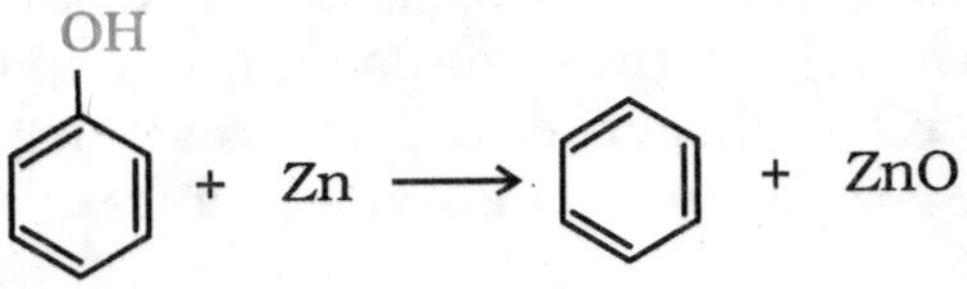

$$\text{phenol} + \text{Zn} \longrightarrow \text{benzene} + \text{ZnO}$$

5. Oxidation

Oxidation of phenol with chromic acid produces a conjugated diketone known as benzoquinone. In the presence of air, phenols are slowly oxidised to dark coloured mixtures containing quinones.

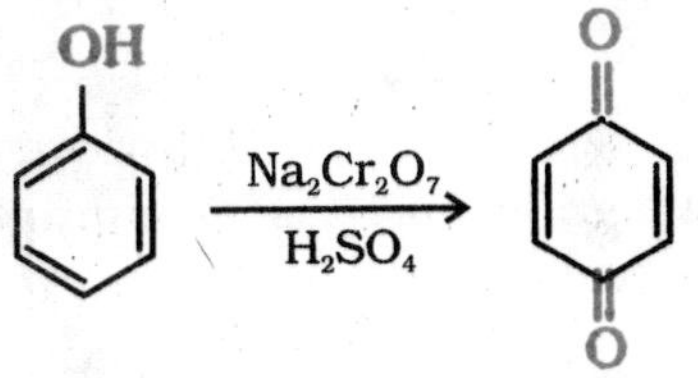

$$\text{phenol} \xrightarrow[\text{H}_2\text{SO}_4]{\text{Na}_2\text{Cr}_2\text{O}_7} \text{benzoquinone}$$

Intext Questions

11.6 Give structures of the products you would expect when each of the following alcohol reacts with (a) HCl –ZnCl$_2$ (b) HBr and (c) SOCl$_2$.

   (i) Butan-1-ol   (ii) 2-Methylbutan-2-ol

11.7 Predict the major product of acid catalysed dehydration of

   (i) 1-methylcyclohexanol and   (ii) butan-1-ol

11.8 *Ortho* and *para* nitrophenols are more acidic than phenol. Draw the resonance structures of the corresponding phenoxide ions.

11.9 Write the equations involved in the following reactions:

   (i) Reimer - Tiemann reaction   (ii) Kolbe's reaction

Methanol and ethanol are among the two commercially important alcohols.

1. Methanol

Methanol, CH_3OH, also known as 'wood spirit', was produced by destructive distillation of wood. Today, most of the methanol is produced by catalytic hydrogenation of carbon monoxide at high pressure and temperature and in the presence of $ZnO - Cr_2O_3$ catalyst.

$$CO + 2H_2 \xrightarrow[\substack{200\text{-}300 \text{ atm} \\ 573\text{-}673 \text{ K}}]{ZnO\text{-}Cr_2O_3} CH_3OH$$

Methanol is a colourless liquid and boils at 337 K. It is highly poisonous in nature. Ingestion of even small quantities of methanol can cause blindness and large quantities causes even death. Methanol is used as a solvent in paints, varnishes and chiefly for making formaldehyde.

2. Ethanol

Ethanol, C_2H_5OH, is obtained commercially by fermentation, the oldest method is from sugars. The sugar in molasses, sugarcane or fruits such as grapes is converted to glucose and fructose, (both of which have the formula $C_6H_{12}O_6$), in the presence of an enzyme, invertase. Glucose and fructose undergo fermentation in the presence of another enzyme, zymase, which is found in yeast.

$$C_{12}H_{22}O_{11} + H_2O \xrightarrow{\text{Invertase}} \underset{\text{Glucose}}{C_6H_{12}O_6} + \underset{\text{Fructose}}{C_6H_{12}O_6}$$

$$C_6H_{12}O_6 \xrightarrow{\text{Zymase}} 2C_2H_5OH + 2CO_2$$

Ingestion of ethanol acts on the central nervous system. In moderate amounts, it affects judgment and lowers inhibitions. Higher concentrations cause nausea and loss of consciousness. Even at higher concentrations, it interferes with spontaneous respiration and can be fatal.

In wine making, grapes are the source of sugars and yeast. As grapes ripen, the quantity of sugar increases and yeast grows on the outer skin. When grapes are crushed, sugar and the enzyme come in contact and fermentation starts. Fermentation takes place in anaerobic conditions i.e. in absence of air. Carbon dioxide is released during fermentation.

The action of zymase is inhibited once the percentage of alcohol formed exceeds 14 percent. If air gets into fermentation mixture, the oxygen of air oxidises ethanol to ethanoic acid which in turn destroys the taste of alcoholic drinks.

Ethanol is a colourless liquid with boiling point 351 K. It is used as a solvent in paint industry and in the preparation of a number of carbon compounds. The commercial alcohol is made unfit for drinking by mixing in it some copper sulphate (to give it a colour) and pyridine (a foul smelling liquid). It is known as **denaturation** of alcohol.

Nowadays, large quantities of ethanol are obtained by hydration of ethene (Section 11.4).

11.6 Ethers

11.6.1 Preparation of Ethers

1. By dehydration of alcohols

Alcohols undergo dehydration in the presence of protic acids (H_2SO_4, H_3PO_4). The formation of the reaction product, alkene or ether depends on the reaction conditions. For example, ethanol is dehydrated to ethene in the presence of sulphuric acid at 443 K. At 413 K, ethoxyethane is the main product.

$$CH_3CH_2OH \xrightarrow{\quad} \begin{cases} \xrightarrow[\text{443 K}]{H_2SO_4} CH_2=CH_2 \\ \\ \xrightarrow[\text{413 K}]{H_2SO_4} C_2H_5OC_2H_5 \end{cases}$$

Diethyl ether has been used widely as an inhalation anaesthetic. But due to its slow effect and an unpleasant recovery period, it has been replaced, as an anaesthetic, by other compounds.

The formation of ether is a nucleophilic bimolecular reaction (S_N2) involving the attack of alcohol molecule on a protonated alcohol, as indicated below:

(i) $CH_3–CH_2–\ddot{O}–H + H^+ \longrightarrow CH_3–CH_2–\overset{+}{\underset{|}{\overset{H}{O}}}–H$

(ii) $CH_3CH_2–\underset{H}{\ddot{O}}: + CH_3–CH_2–\overset{+}{O}\overset{H}{\underset{H}{\diagdown}} \longrightarrow CH_3CH_2–\overset{+}{\underset{H}{O}}–CH_2CH_3 + H_2O$

(iii) $CH_3CH_2–\overset{+}{\underset{H}{O}}–CH_2CH_3 \longrightarrow CH_3CH_2–O–CH_2CH_3 + \overset{+}{H}$

Acidic dehydration of alcohols, to give an alkene is also associated with substitution reaction to give an ether.

The method is suitable for the preparation of ethers having primary alkyl groups only. The alkyl group should be unhindered and the temperature be kept low. Otherwise the reaction favours the formation of alkene. The reaction follows S_N1 pathway when the alcohol is secondary or tertiary about which you will learn in higher classes. However, the dehydration of secondary and tertiary alcohols to give corresponding ethers is unsuccessful as elimination competes over substitution and as a consequence, alkenes are easily formed.

Can you explain why is bimolecular dehydration not appropriate for the preparation of ethyl methyl ether?

2. Williamson synthesis

Alexander William Williamson (1824–1904) was born in London of Scottish parents. In 1849, he became Professor of Chemistry at University College, London.

It is an important laboratory method for the preparation of symmetrical and unsymmetrical ethers. In this method, an alkyl halide is allowed to react with sodium alkoxide.

$$R–X + R'–\overset{+}{\underset{}{\overset{-}{O}}} Na \longrightarrow R–\ddot{O}–R' + Na\,X$$

Ethers containing substituted alkyl groups (secondary or tertiary) may also be prepared by this method. The reaction involves S_N2 attack of an alkoxide ion on primary alkyl halide.

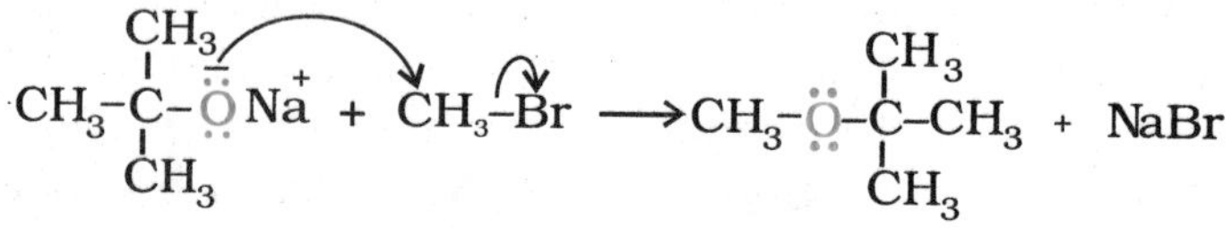

$$CH_3-\underset{\underset{CH_3}{|}}{\overset{\overset{CH_3}{|}}{C}}-\overset{+}{\ddot{O}}Na + CH_3-Br \longrightarrow CH_3-\ddot{O}-\underset{\underset{CH_3}{|}}{\overset{\overset{CH_3}{|}}{C}}-CH_3 + NaBr$$

Better results are obtained if the alkyl halide is primary. In case of secondary and tertiary alkyl halides, elimination competes over substitution. If a tertiary alkyl halide is used, an alkene is the only reaction product and no ether is formed. For example, the reaction of CH_3ONa with $(CH_3)_3C-Br$ gives exclusively 2-methylpropene.

$$CH_3-\underset{\underset{CH_3}{|}}{\overset{\overset{CH_3}{|}}{C}}-Br + \overset{+}{Na}\overset{-}{\ddot{O}}-CH_3 \longrightarrow CH_3-\underset{\underset{CH_3}{|}}{C}=CH_2 + NaBr + CH_3OH$$

2-Methylpropene

It is because alkoxides are not only nucleophiles but strong bases as well. They react with alkyl halides leading to elimination reactions.

Example 11.6   The following is not an appropriate reaction for the preparation of t-butyl ethyl ether.

$$C_2H_5ONa + CH_3-\underset{\underset{CH_3}{|}}{\overset{\overset{CH_3}{|}}{C}}-Cl \longrightarrow CH_3-\underset{\underset{CH_3}{|}}{\overset{\overset{CH_3}{|}}{C}}-OC_2H_5$$

(i) What would be the major product of this reaction ?

(ii) Write a suitable reaction for the preparation of t-butylethyl ether.

Solution   (i) The major product of the given reaction is 2-methylprop-1-ene. It is because sodium ethoxide is a strong nucleophile as well as a strong base. Thus elimination reaction predominates over substitution.

(ii) $$CH_3-\underset{\underset{CH_3}{|}}{\overset{\overset{CH_3}{|}}{C}}-\overset{+}{\ddot{O}}Na + CH_3CH_2Cl \longrightarrow CH_3-\underset{\underset{CH_3}{|}}{\overset{\overset{CH_3}{|}}{C}}-OC_2H_5$$

Phenols are also converted to ethers by this method. In this, phenol is used as the phenoxide moiety.

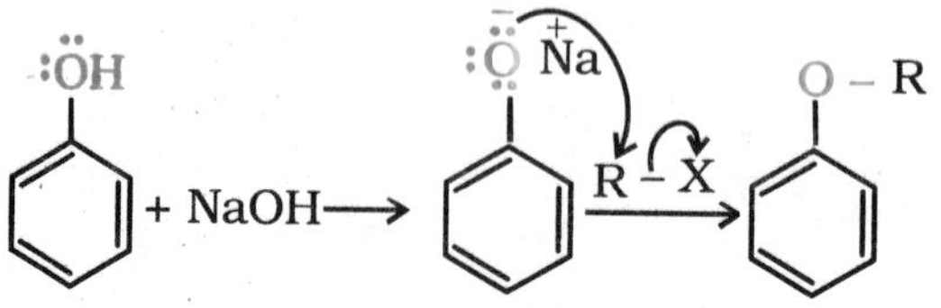

11.6.2 Physical Properties

The C-O bonds in ethers are polar and thus, ethers have a net dipole moment. The weak polarity of ethers do not appreciably affect their boiling points which are comparable to those of the alkanes of comparable molecular masses but are much lower than the boiling points of alcohols as shown in the following cases:

Formula	$CH_3(CH_2)_3CH_3$ n-Pentane	$C_2H_5-O-C_2H_5$ Ethoxyethane	$CH_3(CH_2)_3-OH$ Butan-1-ol
b.p./K	309.1	307.6	390

The large difference in boiling points of alcohols and ethers is due to the presence of hydrogen bonding in alcohols.

The miscibility of ethers with water resembles those of alcohols of the same molecular mass. Both ethoxyethane and butan-1-ol are miscible to almost the same extent i.e., 7.5 and 9 g per 100 mL water, respectively while pentane is essentially immiscible with water. Can you explain this observation ? This is due to the fact that just like alcohols, oxygen of ether can also form hydrogen bonds with water molecule as shown:

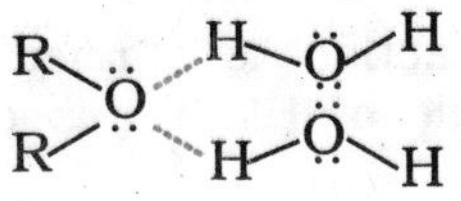

11.6.3 Chemical Reactions

1. Cleavage of C–O bond in ethers

Ethers are the least reactive of the functional groups. The cleavage of C-O bond in ethers takes place under drastic conditions with excess of hydrogen halides. The reaction of dialkyl ether gives two alkyl halide molecules.

$$R–O–R + HX \longrightarrow RX + R–OH$$

$$R–OH + HX \longrightarrow R–X + H_2O$$

Alkyl aryl ethers are cleaved at the alkyl-oxygen bond due to the more stable aryl-oxygen bond. The reaction yields phenol and alkyl halide.

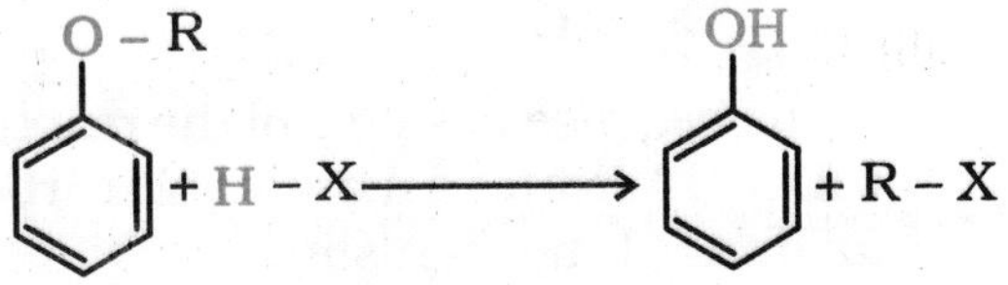

Ethers with two different alkyl groups are also cleaved in the same manner.

$$R–O–R' + HX \longrightarrow R–X + R'–OH$$

The order of reactivity of hydrogen halides is as follows: HI > HBr > HCl. The cleavage of ethers takes place with concentrated HI or HBr at high temperature.

The reaction of an ether with concentrated HI starts with protonation of ether molecule.

Step 1:

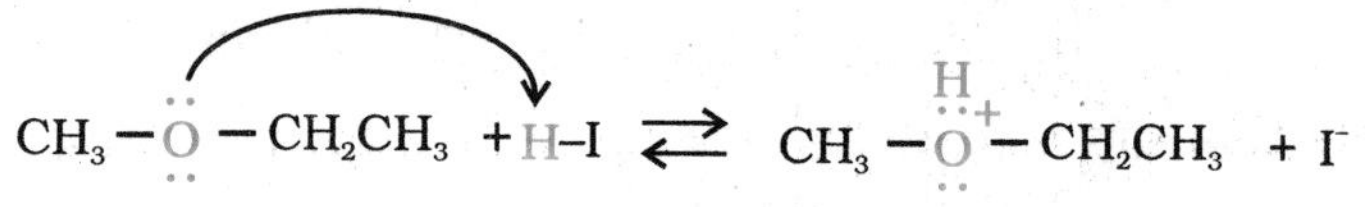

$$CH_3 - \overset{..}{\underset{..}{O}} - CH_2CH_3 + H\text{–}I \rightleftharpoons CH_3 - \overset{\overset{H}{\underset{+}{\cdot\cdot}}}{\underset{..}{O}} - CH_2CH_3 + I^-$$

The reaction takes place with HBr or HI because these reagents are sufficiently acidic.

Step 2:

Iodide is a good nucleophile. It attacks the least substituted carbon of the oxonium ion formed in step 1 and displaces an alcohol molecule by S_N2 mechanism. Thus, in the cleavage of mixed ethers with two different alkyl groups, the alcohol and alkyl iodide formed, depend on the nature of alkyl groups. When primary or secondary alkyl groups are present, it is the lower alkyl group that forms alkyl iodide (S_N2 reaction).

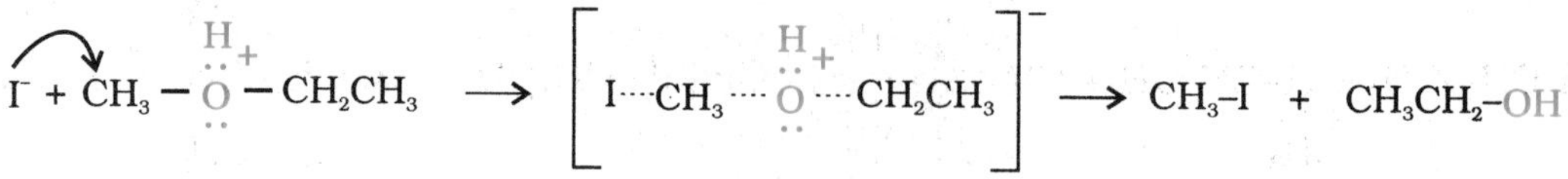

$$I^- + CH_3 - \overset{\overset{H}{\underset{+}{\cdot\cdot}}}{\underset{..}{O}} - CH_2CH_3 \longrightarrow \left[I \cdots CH_3 \cdots \overset{\overset{H}{\underset{+}{\cdot\cdot}}}{\underset{..}{O}} \cdots CH_2CH_3 \right]^- \longrightarrow CH_3\text{–}I + CH_3CH_2\text{–}OH$$

When HI is in excess and the reaction is carried out at high temperature, ethanol reacts with another molecule of HI and is converted to ethyl iodide.

Step 3:

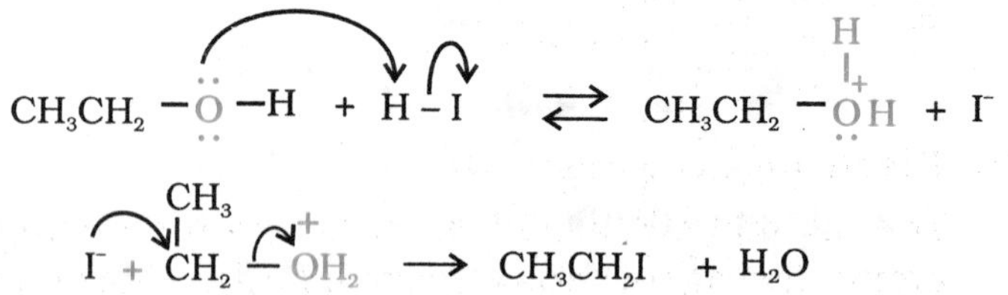

$$CH_3CH_2 - \overset{..}{\underset{..}{O}} - H + H - I \rightleftharpoons CH_3CH_2 - \overset{\overset{H}{\underset{+}{|}}}{\underset{..}{O}}H + I^-$$

$$I^- + CH_2 \overset{CH_3}{\underset{}{|}} \overset{+}{OH_2} \longrightarrow CH_3CH_2I + H_2O$$

However, when one of the alkyl group is a tertiary group, the halide formed is a tertiary halide.

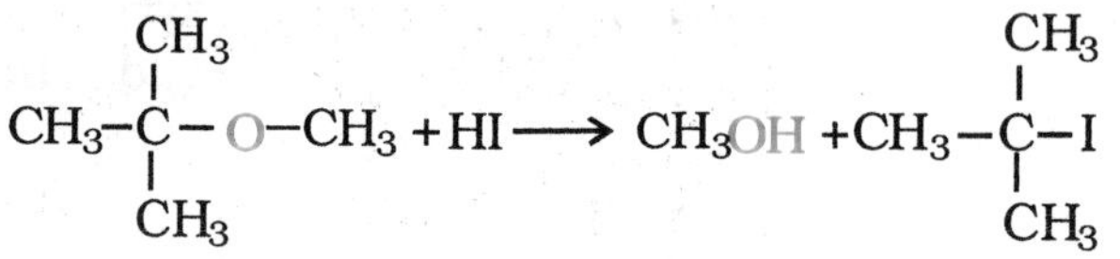

$$CH_3 - \overset{\overset{CH_3}{|}}{\underset{\underset{CH_3}{|}}{C}} - O\text{–}CH_3 + HI \longrightarrow CH_3OH + CH_3 - \overset{\overset{CH_3}{|}}{\underset{\underset{CH_3}{|}}{C}} - I$$

It is because in step 2 of the reaction, the departure of leaving group ($HO\text{–}CH_3$) creates a more stable carbocation [$(CH_3)_3C^+$], and the reaction follows S_N1 mechanism.

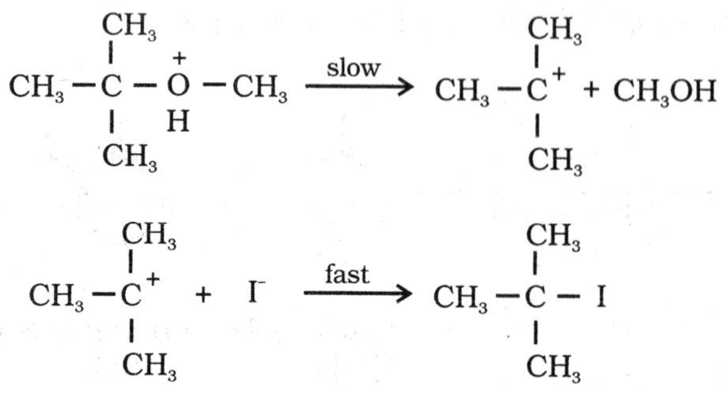

$$CH_3 - \overset{\overset{CH_3}{|}}{\underset{\underset{CH_3}{|}}{\underset{H}{C} - \overset{+}{O} - CH_3}} \xrightarrow{\text{slow}} CH_3 - \overset{\overset{CH_3}{|}}{\underset{\underset{CH_3}{|}}{C^+}} + CH_3OH$$

$$CH_3 - \overset{\overset{CH_3}{|}}{\underset{\underset{CH_3}{|}}{C^+}} + I^- \xrightarrow{\text{fast}} CH_3 - \overset{\overset{CH_3}{|}}{\underset{\underset{CH_3}{|}}{C}} - I$$

In case of anisole, methylphenyl oxonium ion, $C_6H_5 - \overset{\overset{+}{O}}{\underset{H}{|}} - CH_3$ is formed by protonation of ether. The bond between $O\text{–}CH_3$ is weaker than the bond between $O\text{–}C_6H_5$ because the carbon of phenyl group is sp^2 hybridised and there is a partial double bond character.

Therefore the attack by I^- ion breaks $O–CH_3$ bond to form CH_3I. Phenols do not react further to give halides because the sp^2 hybridised carbon of phenol cannot undergo nucleophilic substitution reaction needed for conversion to the halide.

Example 11.7

Give the major products that are formed by heating each of the following ethers with HI.

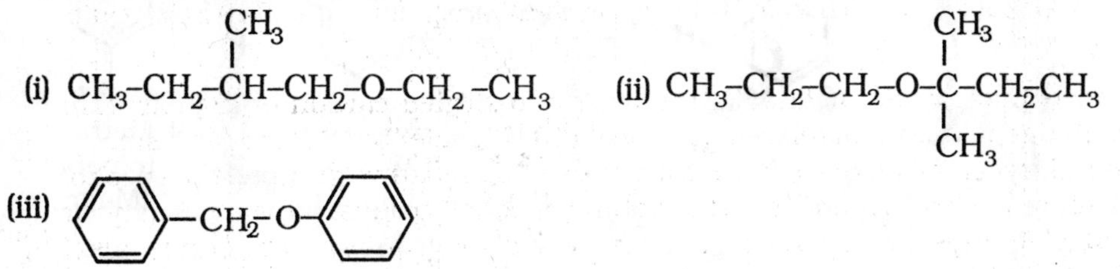

(i) $CH_3–CH_2–CH(CH_3)–CH_2–O–CH_2–CH_3$
(ii) $CH_3–CH_2–CH_2–O–C(CH_3)_2–CH_2–CH_3$
(iii) $C_6H_5–CH_2–O–C_6H_5$

Solution

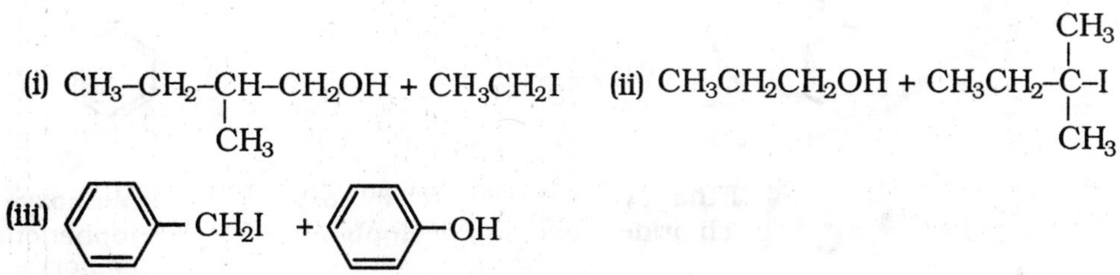

(i) $CH_3–CH_2–CH(CH_3)–CH_2OH + CH_3CH_2I$
(ii) $CH_3CH_2CH_2OH + CH_3CH_2–C(CH_3)_2–I$
(iii) $C_6H_5CH_2I + C_6H_5OH$

2. *Electrophilic substitution*

The alkoxy group (-OR) is *ortho, para* directing and activates the aromatic ring towards electrophilic substitution in the same way as in phenol.

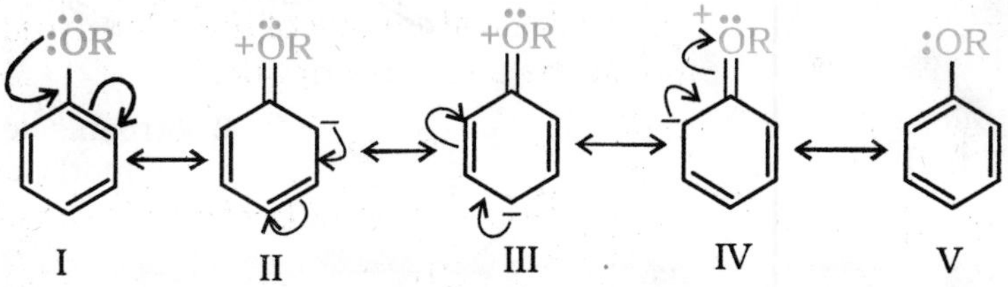

:ÖR
+ÖR
+ÖR
+ÖR
:OR
I
II
III
IV
V

(i) *Halogenation*: Phenylalkyl ethers undergo usual halogenation in the benzene ring, *e.g.*, anisole undergoes bromination with bromine in ethanoic acid even in the absence of iron (III) bromide catalyst. It is due to the activation of benzene ring by the methoxy group. *Para* isomer is obtained in 90% yield.

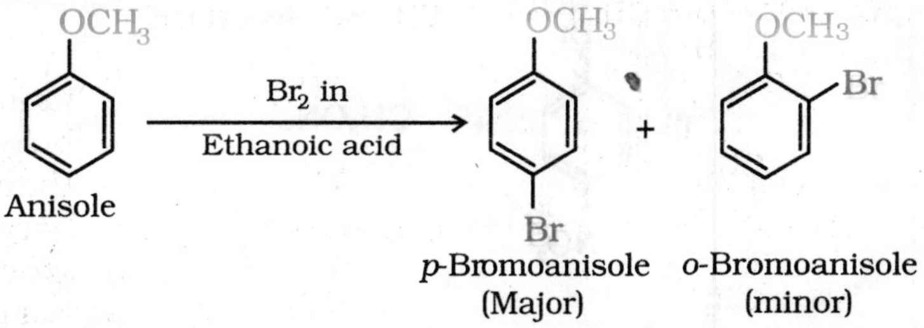

OCH_3
Br_2 in
Ethanoic acid
Anisole
OCH_3
Br
+
OCH_3
Br
p-Bromoanisole
(Major)
o-Bromoanisole
(minor)

(ii) *Friedel-Crafts reaction*: Anisole undergoes Friedel-Crafts reaction, i.e., the alkyl and acyl groups are introduced at *ortho* and *para* positions by reaction with alkyl halide and acyl halide in the presence of anhydrous aluminium chloride (a Lewis acid) as catalyst.

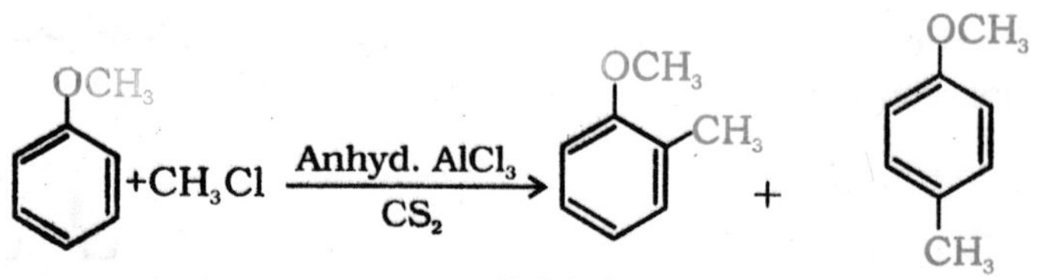

2-Methoxy-toluene (Minor)

4-Methoxy-toluene (Major)

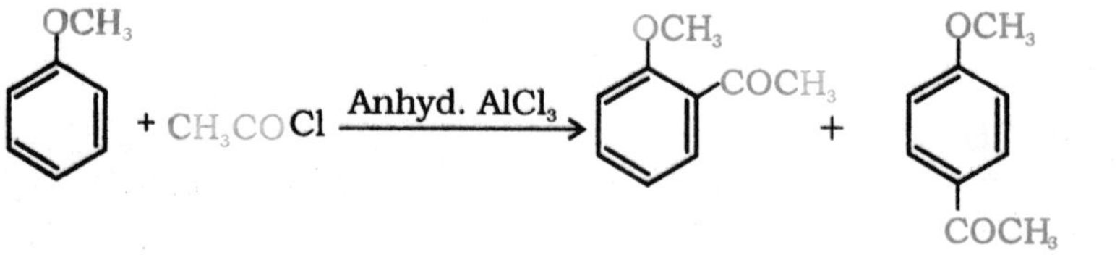

Ethanoyl chloride

2-Methoxy-acetophenone (Minor)

4-Methoxy-acetophenone (Major)

(iii) *Nitration*: Anisole reacts with a mixture of concentrated sulphuric and nitric acids to yield a mixture of *ortho* and *para* nitroanisole.

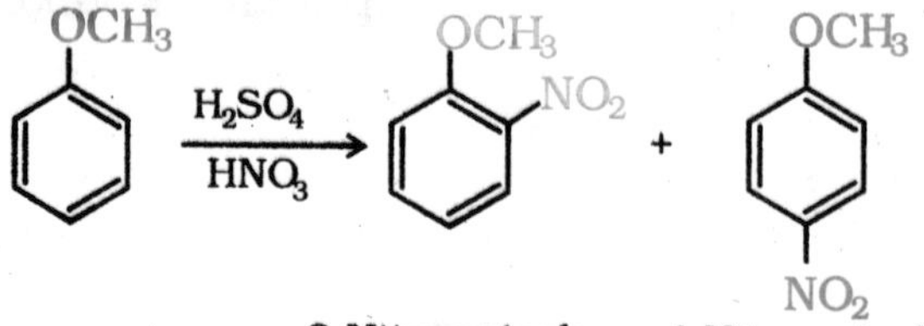

2-Nitroanisole (Minor)

4-Nitroanisole (Major)

Intext Questions

11.10 Write the reactions of Williamson synthesis of 2-ethoxy-3-methylpentane starting from ethanol and 3-methylpentan-2-ol.

11.11 Which of the following is an appropriate set of reactants for the preparation of 1-methoxy-4-nitrobenzene and why?

(i)

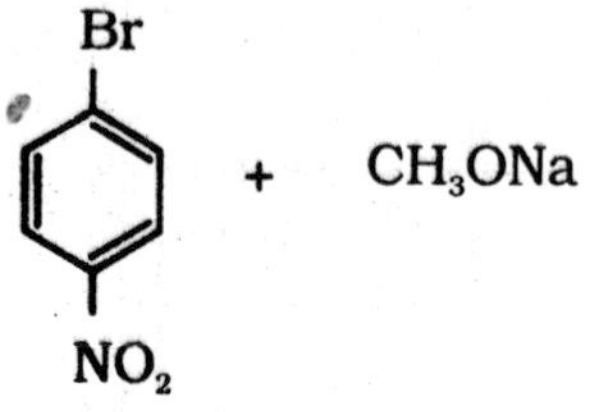

+ CH$_3$ONa

(ii)

+ CH$_3$Br

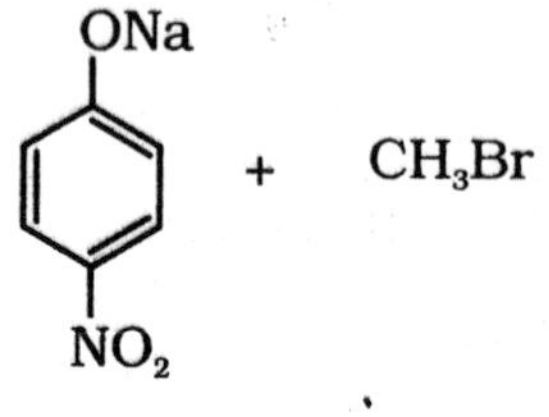

11.12 Predict the products of the following reactions:

(i) $CH_3 - CH_2 - CH_2 - O - CH_3 + HBr \rightarrow$

(ii)

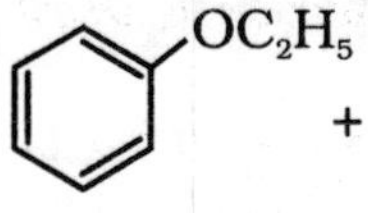

OC_2H_5 + HBr $\longrightarrow$

(iii)

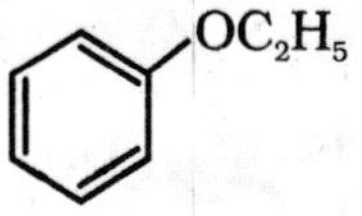

OC_2H_5 $\xrightarrow[\text{Conc. } HNO_3]{\text{Conc. } H_2SO_4}$

(iv) $(CH_3)_3 C - OC_2H_5 \xrightarrow{HI}$

Summary

Alcohols and **phenols** are classified (i) on the basis of the number of hydroxyl groups and (ii) according to the hybridisation of the carbon atom, sp^3 or sp^2 to which the –OH group is attached. **Ethers** are classified on the basis of groups attached to the oxygen atom.

Alcohols may be prepared (1) by hydration of alkenes (i) in presence of an acid and (ii) by hydroboration-oxidation reaction (2) from carbonyl compounds by (i) catalytic reduction and (ii) the action of Grignard reagents. Phenols may be prepared by (1) substitution of (i) halogen atom in haloarenes and (ii) sulphonic acid group in aryl sulphonic acids, by –OH group (2) by hydrolysis of diazonium salts and (3) industrially from cumene.

Alcohols are higher boiling than other classes of compounds, namely hydrocarbons, ethers and haloalkanes of comparable molecular masses. The ability of alcohols, phenols and ethers to form intermolecular hydrogen bonding with water makes them soluble in it.

Alcohols and phenols are acidic in nature. **Electron withdrawing groups** in phenol increase its acidic strength and **electron releasing groups** decrease it.

Alcohols undergo nucleophilic substitution with hydrogen halides to yield alkyl halides. Dehydration of alcohols gives alkenes. On oxidation, primary alcohols yield aldehydes with mild oxidising agents and carboxylic acids with strong oxidising agents while secondary alcohols yield ketones. Tertiary alcohols are resistant to oxidation.

The presence of –OH group in phenols activates the aromatic ring towards **electrophilic substitution** and directs the incoming group to *ortho* and *para* positions due to resonance effect. **Reimer-Tiemann reaction** of phenol yields salicylaldehyde. In presence of sodium hydroxide, **phe**nol generates phenoxide ion which is even more reactive than phenol. Thus, in alkaline medium, phenol undergoes **Kolbe's reaction**.

Ethers may be prepared by (i) dehydration of alcohols and (ii) **Williamson synthesis**. The boiling points of ethers resemble those of alkanes while their solubility is comparable to those of alcohols having same molecular mass. The C–O bond in ethers can be cleaved by hydrogen halides. In electrophilic substitution, the alkoxy group activates the aromatic ring and directs the incoming group to ortho and para positions.

Exercises

11.1 Write IUPAC names of the following compounds:

(i)
$$CH_3 - \overset{\displaystyle CH_3}{\underset{\displaystyle CH_3}{|}}{CH} - \underset{\displaystyle OH}{CH} - \overset{\displaystyle CH_3}{\underset{\displaystyle CH_3}{C}} - CH_3$$

(i) $CH_3-\underset{\underset{CH_3}{|}}{CH}-\underset{\underset{OH}{|}}{CH}-\underset{\overset{|}{CH_3}}{\overset{\overset{CH_3}{|}}{C}}-CH_3$

(ii) $H_3C-\underset{\underset{OH}{|}}{CH}-CH_2-\underset{\underset{OH}{|}}{CH}-\underset{\underset{C_2H_5}{|}}{CH}-CH_2-CH_3$

(iii) $CH_3-\underset{\underset{OH}{|}}{CH}-\underset{\underset{OH}{|}}{CH}-CH_3$

(iv) $HO-CH_2-\underset{\underset{OH}{|}}{CH}-CH_2-OH$

(v) (vi) (vii) (viii)

(ix) $CH_3-O-CH_2-\underset{\underset{CH_3}{|}}{CH}-CH_3$

(x) $C_6H_5-O-C_2H_5$

(xi) $C_6H_5-O-C_7H_{15}(n-)$

(xii) $CH_3-CH_2-O-\underset{\underset{CH_3}{|}}{CH}-CH_2-CH_3$

11.2 Write structures of the compounds whose IUPAC names are as follows:

(i) 2-Methylbutan-2-ol
(ii) 1-Phenylpropan-2-ol
(iii) 3,5-Dimethylhexane –1, 3, 5-triol
(iv) 2,3 – Diethylphenol
(v) 1 – Ethoxypropane
(vi) 2-Ethoxy-3-methylpentane
(vii) Cyclohexylmethanol
(viii) 3-Cyclohexylpentan-3-ol
(ix) Cyclopent-3-en-1-ol
(x) 4-Chloro-3-ethylbutan-1-ol.

11.3 (i) Draw the structures of all isomeric alcohols of molecular formula $C_5H_{12}O$ and give their IUPAC names.

(ii) Classify the isomers of alcohols in question 11.3 (i) as primary, secondary and tertiary alcohols.

11.4 Explain why propanol has higher boiling point than that of the hydrocarbon, butane?

11.5 Alcohols are comparatively more soluble in water than hydrocarbons of comparable molecular masses. Explain this fact.

11.6 What is meant by hydroboration-oxidation reaction? Illustrate it with an example.

11.7 Give the structures and IUPAC names of monohydric phenols of molecular formula, C_7H_8O.

11.8 While separating a mixture of *ortho* and *para* nitrophenols by steam distillation, name the isomer which will be steam volatile. Give reason.

11.9 Give the equations of reactions for the preparation of phenol from cumene.

11.10 Write chemical reaction for the preparation of phenol from chlorobenzene.

11.11 Write the mechanism of hydration of ethene to yield ethanol.

11.12 You are given benzene, conc. H_2SO_4 and NaOH. Write the equations for the preparation of phenol using these reagents.

11.13 Show how will you synthesise:

(i) 1-phenylethanol from a suitable alkene.

(ii) cyclohexylmethanol using an alkyl halide by an S_N2 reaction.

(iii) pentan-1-ol using a suitable alkyl halide?

11.14 Give two reactions that show the acidic nature of phenol. Compare acidity of phenol with that of ethanol.

11.15 Explain why is *ortho* nitrophenol more acidic than *ortho* methoxyphenol ?

11.16 Explain how does the –OH group attached to a carbon of benzene ring activate it towards electrophilic substitution?

11.17 Give equations of the following reactions:

(i) Oxidation of propan-1-ol with alkaline $KMnO_4$ solution.

(ii) Bromine in CS_2 with phenol.

(iii) Dilute HNO_3 with phenol.

(iv) Treating phenol wih chloroform in presence of aqueous NaOH.

11.18 Explain the following with an example.

(i) Kolbe's reaction.

(ii) Reimer-Tiemann reaction.

(iii) Williamson ether synthesis.

(iv) Unsymmetrical ether.

11.19 Write the mechanism of acid dehydration of ethanol to yield ethene.

11.20 How are the following conversions carried out?

(i) Propene $\rightarrow$ Propan-2-ol.

(ii) Benzyl chloride $\rightarrow$ Benzyl alcohol.

(iii) Ethyl magnesium chloride $\rightarrow$ Propan-1-ol.

(iv) Methyl magnesium bromide $\rightarrow$ 2-Methylpropan-2-ol.

11.21 Name the reagents used in the following reactions:

(i) Oxidation of a primary alcohol to carboxylic acid.

(ii) Oxidation of a primary alcohol to aldehyde.

(iii) Bromination of phenol to 2,4,6-tribromophenol.

(iv) Benzyl alcohol to benzoic acid.

(v) Dehydration of propan-2-ol to propene.

(vi) Butan-2-one to butan-2-ol.

11.22 Give reason for the higher boiling point of ethanol in comparison to methoxymethane.

11.23 Give IUPAC names of the following ethers:

(i) $C_2H_5OCH_2 - \underset{\underset{\displaystyle CH_3}{|}}{CH} - CH_3$ (ii) $CH_3OCH_2CH_2Cl$ (iii) $O_2N-C_6H_4-OCH_3(p)$

(iv) $CH_3CH_2CH_2OCH_3$ (v) 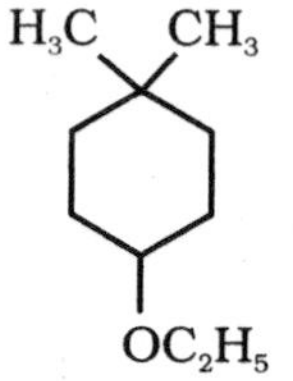   (vi)

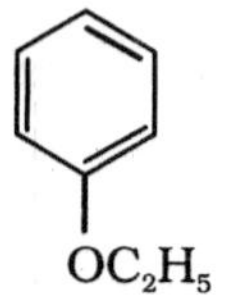

11.24 Write the names of reagents and equations for the preparation of the following ethers by Williamson's synthesis:

    (i) 1-Propoxypropane   (ii) Ethoxybenzene

    (iii) 2-Methoxy-2-methylpropane   (iv) 1-Methoxyethane

11.25 Illustrate with examples the limitations of Williamson synthesis for the preparation of certain types of ethers.

11.26 How is 1-propoxypropane synthesised from propan-1-ol? Write mechanism of this reaction.

11.27 Preparation of ethers by acid dehydration of secondary or tertiary alcohols is not a suitable method. Give reason.

11.28 Write the equation of the reaction of hydrogen iodide with:
(i) 1-propoxypropane (ii) methoxybenzene and (iii) benzyl ethyl ether.

11.29 Explain the fact that in aryl alkyl ethers (i) the alkoxy group activates the benzene ring towards electrophilic substitution and (ii) it directs the incoming substituents to ortho and para positions in benzene ring.

11.30 Write the mechanism of the reaction of HI with methoxymethane.

11.31 Write equations of the following reactions:

    (i) Friedel-Crafts reaction – alkylation of anisole.

    (ii) Nitration of anisole.

    (iii) Bromination of anisole in ethanoic acid medium.

    (iv) Friedel-Craft's acetylation of anisole.

11.32 Show how would you synthesise the following alcohols from appropriate alkenes?

(i) 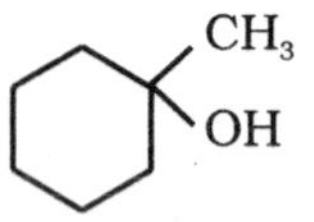   (ii)

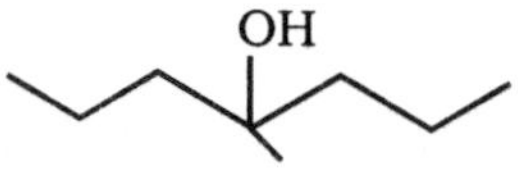

(iii) 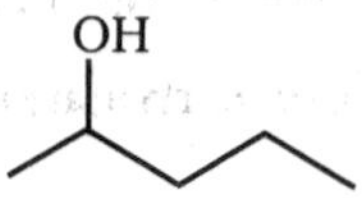   (iv)

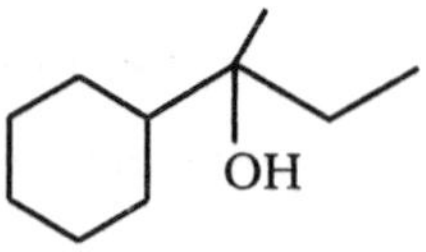

11.33 When 3-methylbutan-2-ol is treated with HBr, the following reaction takes place:

$$CH_3 - \underset{\underset{\displaystyle CH_3}{|}}{CH} - \underset{\underset{\displaystyle OH}{|}}{CH} - CH_3 \xrightarrow{\text{HBr}} CH_3 - \underset{\underset{\displaystyle CH_3}{|}}{\overset{\overset{\displaystyle Br}{|}}{C}} - CH_2 - CH_3$$

Give a mechanism for this reaction.

(Hint : The secondary carbocation formed in step II rearranges to a more stable tertiary carbocation by a hydride ion shift from 3rd carbon atom.

Answers to Some Intext Questions

11.1 Primary alcohols   (i), (ii), (iii)

     Secondary alcohols   (iv) and (v)

     Tertiary alcohols   (vi)

11.2 Allylic alcohols   (ii) and (vi)

11.3 (i) 3-Chloromethyl-2-isopropylpentan-1-ol

    (ii) 2, 5-Dimethylhexane-1,3-diol

    (iii) 3-Bromocyclohexanol

    (iv) Hex-1-en-3-ol

    (v) 2-Bromo-3-methylbut-2-en-1-ol

11.4 (i) $CH_3-CH(CH_3)-MgBr + HCHO \longrightarrow CH_3-CH(CH_3)-CH_2-OMgBr \xrightarrow{H_2O}$

$CH_3-CH(CH_3)-CH_2OH + Mg(OH)Br$

(ii) 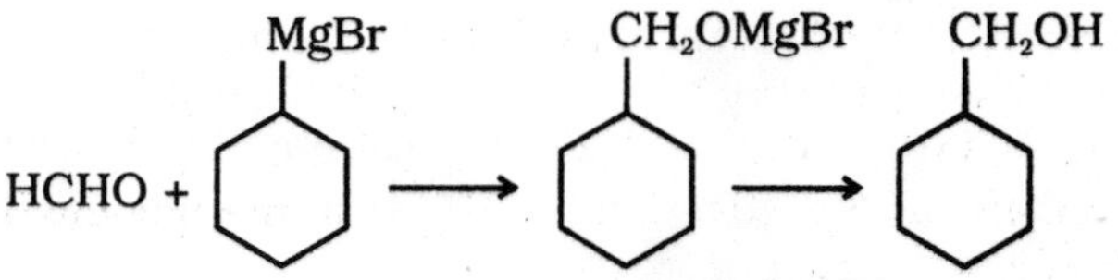 HCHO + (cyclohexyl-MgBr) $\longrightarrow$ (cyclohexyl-CH_2OMgBr) $\longrightarrow$ (cyclohexyl-CH_2OH)

11.5 (i) $CH_3-CH(OH)-CH_3$

(ii) 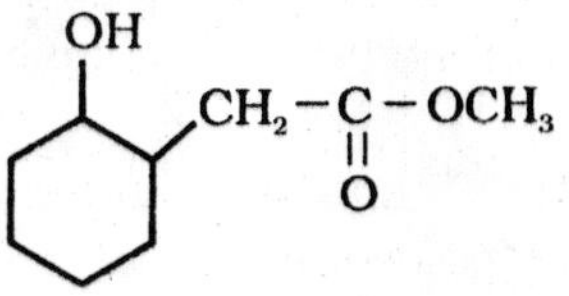 cyclohexane with OH and $CH_2-C(=O)-OCH_3$

(iii) $CH_3-CH_2-CH(CH_3)-CH_2OH$

11.7 (i) 1-Methylcyclohexene

(ii) A Mixture of but-1-ene and but-2-ene. But-1-ene is the major product formed due to rearrangement to give secondary carbocation.

11.10 $CH_3-CH_2-CH(CH_3)-CH(OH)-CH_3 \xrightarrow{Na} CH_3-CH_2-CH(CH_3)-CH(CH_3)-ONa$

$C_2H_5OH \xrightarrow{HBr} C_2H_5Br$

$CH_3-CH_2-CH(CH_3)-CH(CH_3)-ONa + C_2H_5Br \rightarrow CH_3-CH_2-CH(CH_3)-CH(CH_3)-OC_2H_5$

2-Ethoxy-3-methylpentane

347 Alcohols, Phenols and Ethers

11.11 (ii)

11.12 (i) $CH_3CH_2CH_2OH + CH_3Br$

(ii)

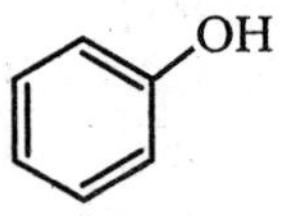

$+ \quad C_2H_5Br$

(iii)

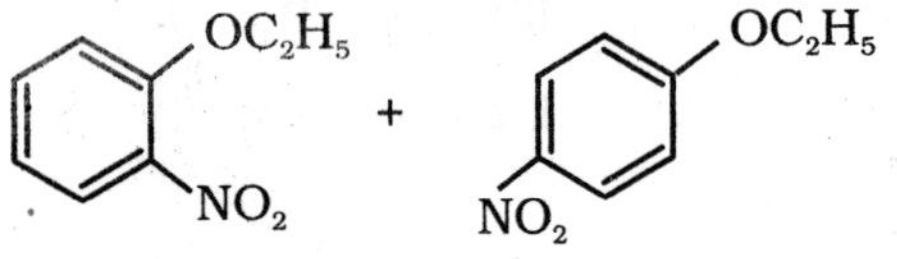

$+$

(iv) $(CH_3)_3 C - I + C_2H_5OH$

Aldehydes, Ketones and Carboxylic Acids

Carbonyl compounds are of utmost importance to organic chemistry. They are constituents of fabrics, flavourings, plastics and drugs.

Objectives

After studying this Unit, you will be able to

- write the common and IUPAC names of aldehydes, ketones and carboxylic acids;
- write the structures of the compounds containing functional groups namely carbonyl and carboxyl groups;
- describe the important methods of preparation and reactions of these classes of compounds;
- correlate physical properties and chemical reactions of aldehydes, ketones and carboxylic acids, with their structures;
- explain the mechanism of a few selected reactions of aldehydes and ketones;
- understand various factors affecting the acidity of carboxylic acids and their reactions;
- describe the uses of aldehydes, ketones and carboxylic acids.

In the previous Unit, you have studied organic compounds with functional groups containing carbon-oxygen single bond. In this Unit, we will study about the organic compounds containing carbon-oxygen double bond (>C=O) called carbonyl group, which is one of the most important functional groups in organic chemistry.

In aldehydes, the carbonyl group is bonded to a carbon and hydrogen while in the ketones, it is bonded to two carbon atoms. The carbonyl compounds in which carbonyl group is bonded to oxygen are known as carboxylic acids, and their derivatives (e.g. esters, anhydrides) while in compounds where carbon is attached to nitrogen and to halogens are called amides and acyl halides respectively. The general formulas of these classes of compounds are given below:

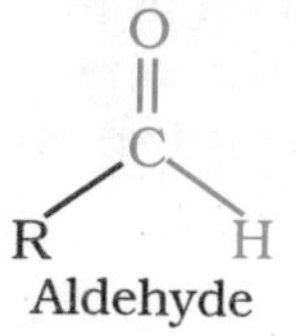

Aldehyde 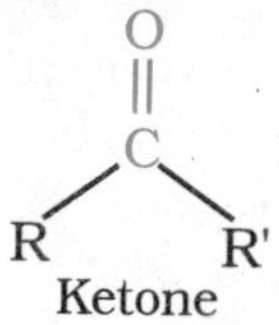   Ketone 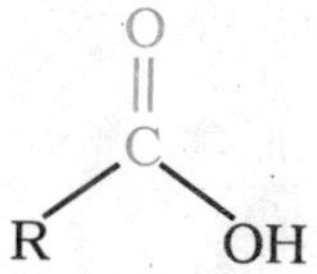   Carboxylic acid

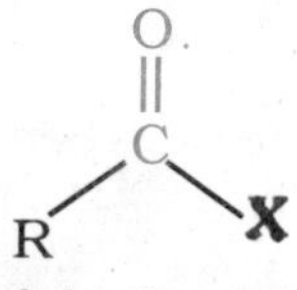

Acyl halide; X = (Halogen) 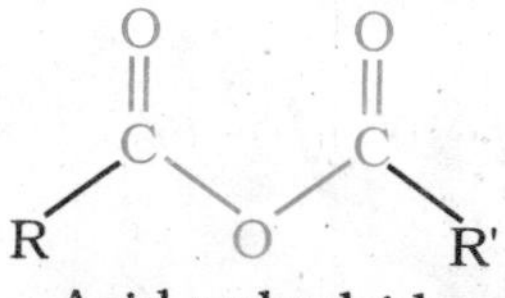   Acid anhydride

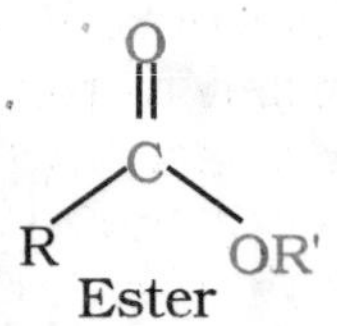

Ester

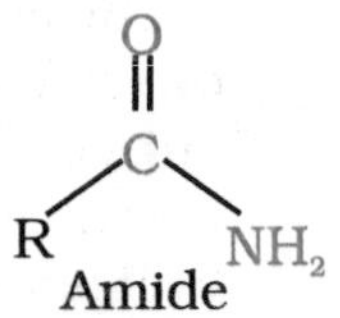

Amide

Aldehydes, ketones and carboxylic acids are widespread in plants and animal kingdom. They play an important role in biochemical processes of life. They add fragrance and flavour to nature, for example, vanillin (from vanilla beans), salicylaldehyde (from meadow sweet) and cinnamaldehyde (from cinnamon) have very pleasant fragrances.

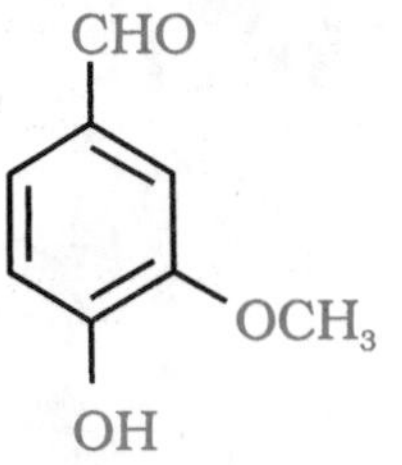

Vanillin

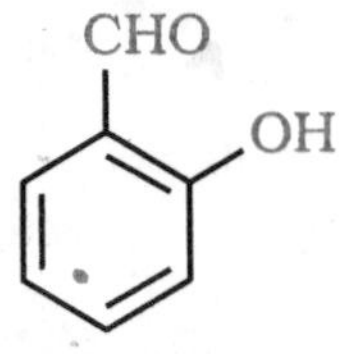

Salicylaldehyde

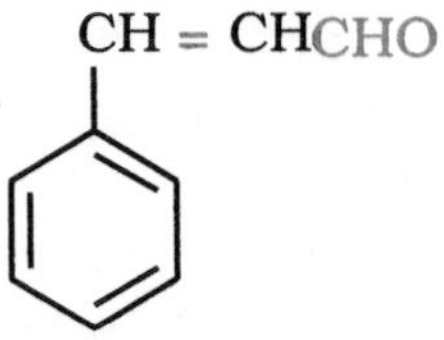

Cinnamaldehyde

They are used in many food products and pharmaceuticals to add flavours. Some of these families are manufactured for use as solvents (i.e., acetone) and for preparing materials like adhesives, paints, resins, perfumes, plastics, fabrics, etc.

12.1 Nomenclature and Structure of Carbonyl Group

12.1.1 Nomenclature

I. Aldehydes and ketones

Aldehydes and ketones are the simplest and most important carbonyl compounds.

There are two systems of nomenclature of aldehydes and ketones.

(a) Common names

Aldehydes and ketones are often called by their common names instead of IUPAC names. The common names of most aldehydes are derived from the common names of the corresponding carboxylic acids [Section 12.6.1] by replacing the ending –ic of acid with aldehyde. At the same time, the names reflect the Latin or Greek term for the original source of the acid or aldehyde. The location of the substituent in the carbon chain is indicated by Greek letters α, β, γ, δ, etc. The α-carbon being the one directly linked to the aldehyde group, β-carbon the next, and so on. For example

CH_3CHO

Acetaldehyde

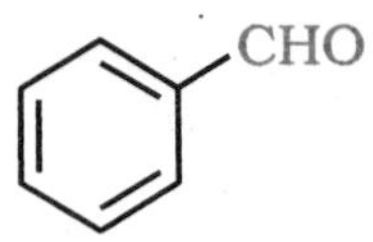

Benzaldehyde

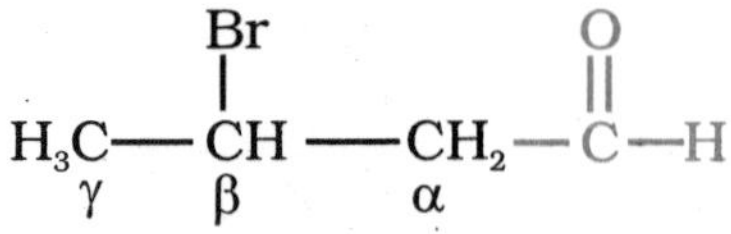

β-Bromobutyraldehyde

The common names of ketones are derived by naming two alkyl or aryl groups bonded to the carbonyl group. The locations of substituents are indicated by Greek letters, α α', β β' and so on beginning with the carbon atoms next to the carbonyl group, indicated as αα'. Some ketones have historical common names, the simplest dimethyl ketone is called acetone. Alkyl phenyl ketones are usually named by adding the acyl group as prefix to phenone. For example

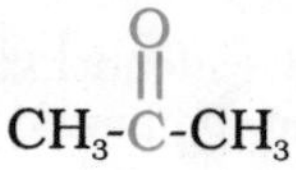

$$CH_3-\overset{\overset{\displaystyle O}{\|}}{C}-CH_3 \qquad \qquad \qquad$$

Acetone 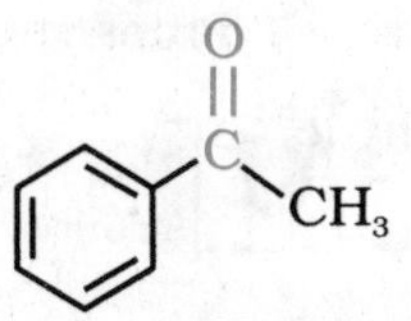   Acetophenone 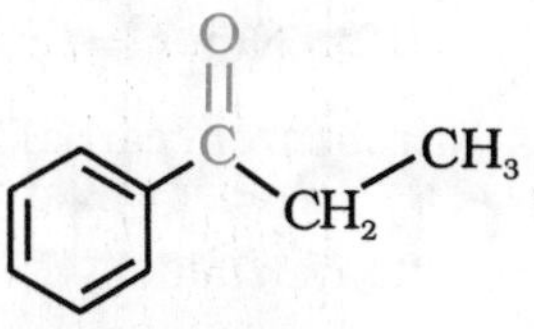   Propiophenone 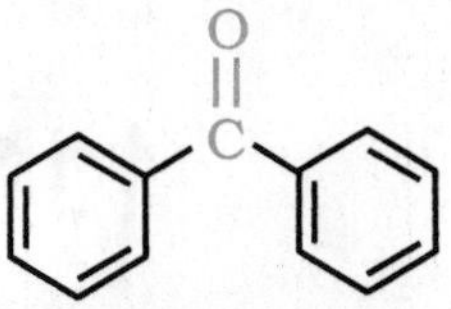   Benzophenone

(b) IUPAC names

The IUPAC names of open chain aliphatic aldehydes and ketones are derived from the names of the corresponding alkanes by replacing the ending –e with –al and –one respectively. In case of aldehydes the longest carbon chain is numbered starting from the carbon of the aldehyde group while in case of ketones the numbering begins from the end nearer to the carbonyl group. The substituents are prefixed in alphabetical order along with numerals indicating their positions in the carbon chain. The same applies to cyclic ketones, where the carbonyl carbon is numbered one. When the aldehyde group is attached to a ring, the suffix carbaldehyde is added after the full name of the cycloalkane. The numbering of the ring carbon atoms start from the carbon atom attached to the aldehyde group. The name of the simplest aromatic aldehyde carrying the aldehyde group on a benzene ring is benzenecarbaldehyde. However, the common name benzaldehyde is also accepted by IUPAC. Other aromatic aldehydes are hence named as substituted benzaldehydes.

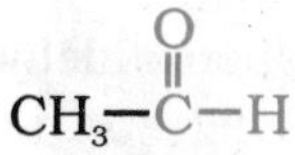

$$CH_3-\overset{\overset{\displaystyle O}{\|}}{C}-H$$

Ethanal

$$CH_3-CH_2-CH_2-\overset{\overset{\displaystyle Br}{|}}{C}H-\overset{\overset{\displaystyle CH_3}{|}}{C}H-CH_2-\overset{\overset{\displaystyle O}{\|}}{C}-H$$

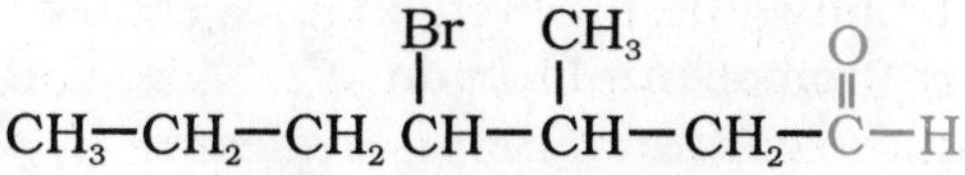

4-Bromo-3-methylheptanal

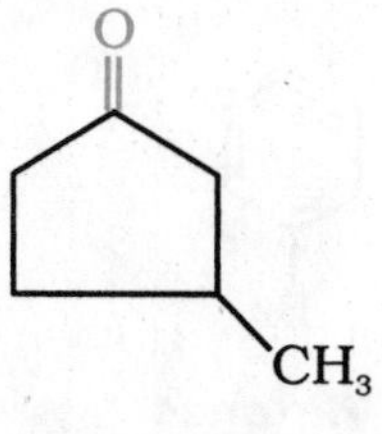

3-Methylcyclopentanone

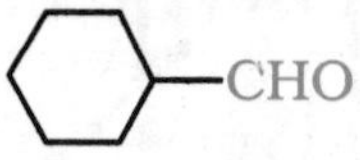

Cyclohexanecarbaldehyde

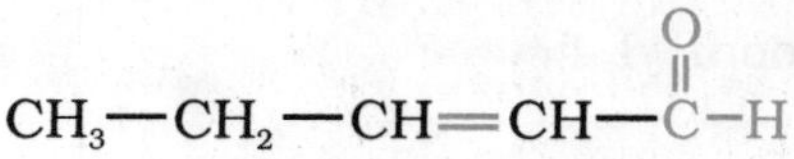

$$CH_3-CH_2-CH=CH-\overset{\overset{\displaystyle O}{\|}}{C}-H$$

Pent-2-enal

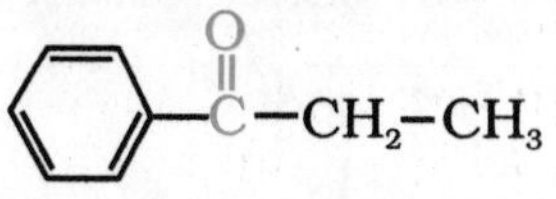

1-Phenylpropan-1-one

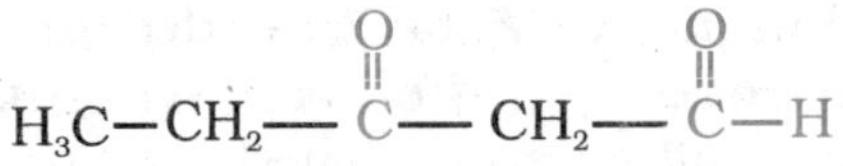

$$H_3C-CH_2-\overset{\overset{\displaystyle O}{\|}}{C}-CH_2-\overset{\overset{\displaystyle O}{\|}}{C}-H$$

3-Oxopentanal

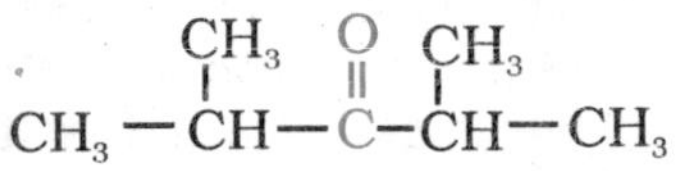

$$CH_3-\overset{\overset{\displaystyle CH_3}{|}}{CH}-\overset{\overset{\displaystyle O}{\|}}{C}-\overset{\overset{\displaystyle CH_3}{|}}{CH}-CH_3$$

2,4-Dimethylpentan-3-one

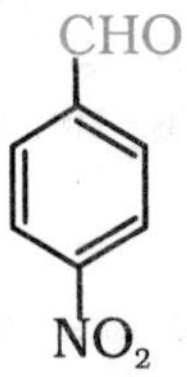

4-Nitrobenzenecarbaldehyde
or
4-Nitrobenzaldehyde

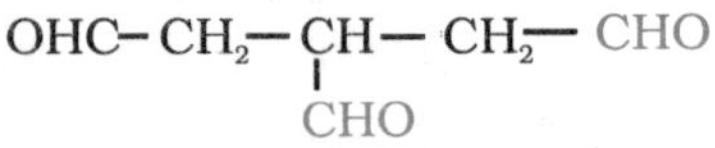

$$OHC-CH_2-\overset{\overset{\displaystyle }{|}}{\underset{\underset{\displaystyle CHO}{|}}{CH}}-CH_2-CHO$$

Propane–1,2,3-tricarbaldehyde

[Note: To give identical treatment to all aldehydic groups, the compound is named as shown above.]

The common and IUPAC names of some aldehydes and ketones are given in Table 12.1.

Table 12.1: Common and IUPAC Names of Some Aldehydes and Ketones

Structure	Common name	IUPAC name
Aldehydes		
HCHO	Formaldehyde	Methanal
CH_3CHO	Acetaldehyde	Ethanal
$(CH_3)_2CHCHO$	Isobutyraldehyde	2-Methylpropanal
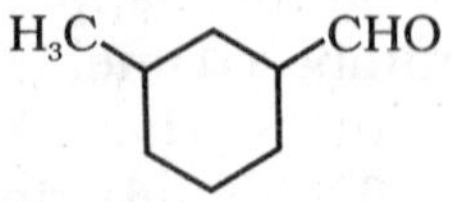	γ-Methylcyclohexanecarbaldehyde	3-Methylcyclohexanecarbaldehyde
$CH_3CH(OCH_3)CHO$	α-Methoxypropionaldehyde	2-Methoxypropanal
$CH_3CH_2CH_2CH_2CHO$	Valeraldehyde	Pentanal
$CH_2=CHCHO$	Acrolein	Prop-2-enal
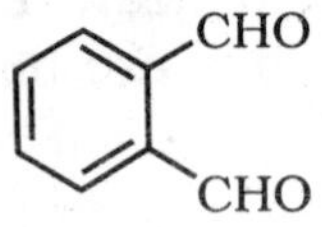	Phthaldehyde	Benzene-1,2-dicarbaldehyde
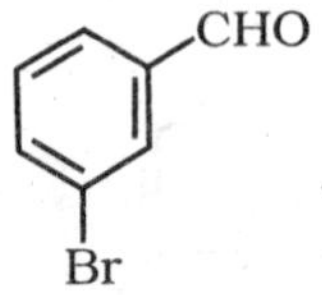	*m*-Bromobenzaldehyde	3-Bromobenzenecarbaldehyde or 3-Bromobenzaldehyde
Ketones		
$CH_3COCH_2CH_2CH_3$	Methyl *n*-propyl ketone	Pentan-2-one
$(CH_3)_2CHCOCH(CH_3)_2$	Diisopropyl ketone	2,4-Dimethylpentan-3-one
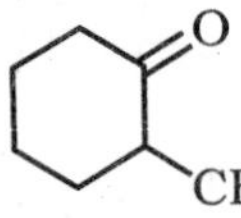	α-Methylcyclohexanone	2-Methylcyclohexanone
$(CH_3)_2C=CHCOCH_3$	Mesityl oxide	4-Methylpent-3-en-2-one

12.1.2 Structure of the Carbonyl Group

The carbonyl carbon atom is sp^2-hybridised and forms three sigma (σ) bonds. The fourth valence electron of carbon remains in its p-orbital and forms a π-bond with oxygen by overlap with p-orbital of an oxygen. In addition, the oxygen atom also has two non bonding electron pairs. Thus, the carbonyl carbon and the three atoms attached to it lie in the same plane and the π-electron cloud is above and below this plane. The bond angles are approximately 120° as expected of a trigonal coplanar structure (Figure 12.1).

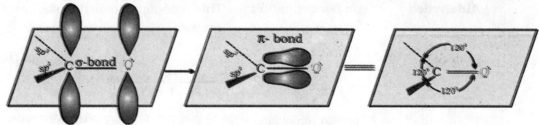

Fig.12.1 *Orbital diagram for the formation of carbonyl group*

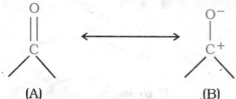

The carbon-oxygen double bond is polarised due to higher electronegativity of oxygen relative to carbon. Hence, the carbonyl carbon is an electrophilic (Lewis acid), and carbonyl oxygen, a nucleophilic (Lewis base) centre. Carbonyl compounds have substantial dipole moments and are polar than ethers. The high polarity of the carbonyl group is explained on the basis of resonance involving a neutral (A) and a dipolar (B) structures as shown.

Intext Questions

12.1 Write the structures of the following compounds.

(i) α-Methoxypropionaldehyde   (ii) 3-Hydroxybutanal

(iii) 2-Hydroxycyclopentane carbaldehyde   (iv) 4-Oxopentanal

(v) Di-sec. butyl ketone   (vi) 4-Fluoroacetophenone

12.2 Preparation of Aldehydes and Ketones

Some important methods for the preparation of aldehydes and ketones are as follows:

12.2.1 Preparation of Aldehydes and Ketones

1. By oxidation of alcohols

Aldehydes and ketones are generally prepared by oxidation of primary and secondary alcohols, respectively (Unit 11, Class XII).

2. By dehydrogenation of alcohols

This method is suitable for volatile alcohols and is of industrial application. In this method alcohol vapours are passed over heavy metal catalysts (Ag or Cu). Primary and secondary alcohols give aldehydes and ketones, respectively (Unit 11, Class XII).

3. From hydrocarbons

(i) *By ozonolysis of alkenes:* As we know, ozonolysis of alkenes followed by reaction with zinc dust and water gives aldehydes, ketones or a mixture of both depending on the substitution pattern of the alkene (Unit 13, Class XI).

(ii) *By hydration of alkynes:* Addition of water to ethyne in the presence of H_2SO_4 and $HgSO_4$ gives acetaldehyde. All other alkynes give ketones in this reaction (Unit 13, Class XI).

12.2.2 Preparation of Aldehydes

1. *From acyl chloride (acid chloride)*

Acyl chloride (acid chloride) is hydrogenated over catalyst, palladium on barium sulphate. This reaction is called **Rosenmund reduction**.

$$\underset{\text{Benzoyl chloride}}{} \xrightarrow[\text{Pd – BaSO}_4]{\text{H}_2} \underset{\text{Benzaldehyde}}{}$$

2. *From nitriles and esters*

Nitriles are reduced to corresponding imine with stannous chloride in the presence of hydrochloric acid, which on hydrolysis give corresponding aldehyde.

$$RCN + SnCl_2 + HCl \longrightarrow RCH = NH \xrightarrow{H_3\overset{+}{O}} RCHO$$

This reaction is called **Stephen** reaction.

Alternatively, nitriles are selectively reduced by diisobutylaluminium hydride, (DIBAL-H) to imines followed by hydrolysis to aldehydes:

$$RCN \xrightarrow[\text{2. H}_2\text{O}]{\text{1. AlH(i-Bu)}_2} R\text{-CHO}$$

$$CH_3 - CH{=}CH\text{-}CH_2CH_2\text{-}CN \xrightarrow[\text{2. H}_2\text{O}]{\text{1. AlH(i-Bu)}_2} CH_3 - CH{=}CH\text{-}CH_2CH_2\text{-}CHO$$

Similarly, esters are also reduced to aldehydes with DIBAL-H.

$$CH_3(CH_2)_9 - \overset{\overset{\displaystyle O}{\|}}{C} - OC_2H_5 \xrightarrow[\text{2. H}_2\text{O}]{\text{1. DIBAL-H}} CH_3(CH_2)_9 - \overset{\overset{\displaystyle O}{\|}}{C} - H$$

3. *From hydrocarbons*

Aromatic aldehydes (benzaldehyde and its derivatives) are prepared from aromatic hydrocarbons by the following methods:

(i) *By oxidation of methylbenzene*

Strong oxidising agents oxidise toluene and its derivatives to benzoic acids. However, it is possible to stop the oxidation at the aldehyde stage with suitable reagents that convert the methyl group to an intermediate that is difficult to oxidise further. The following methods are used for this purpose.

(a) Use of chromyl chloride (CrO_2Cl_2): Chromyl chloride oxidises methyl group to a chromium complex, which on hydrolysis gives corresponding benzaldehyde.

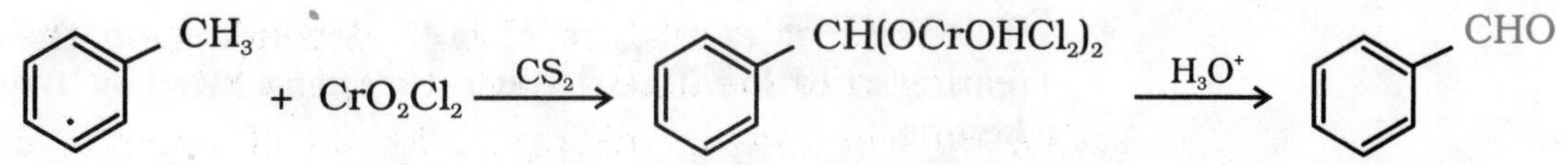

Toluene + CrO_2Cl_2 $\xrightarrow{CS_2}$ Chromium complex CH(OCrOHCl$_2$)$_2$ $\xrightarrow{H_3O^+}$ Benzaldehyde CHO

This reaction is called **Etard reaction**.

(b) Use of chromic oxide (CrO_3): Toluene or substituted toluene is converted to benzylidene diacetate on treating with chromic oxide in acetic anhydride. The benzylidene diacetate can be hydrolysed to corresponding benzaldehyde with aqueous acid.

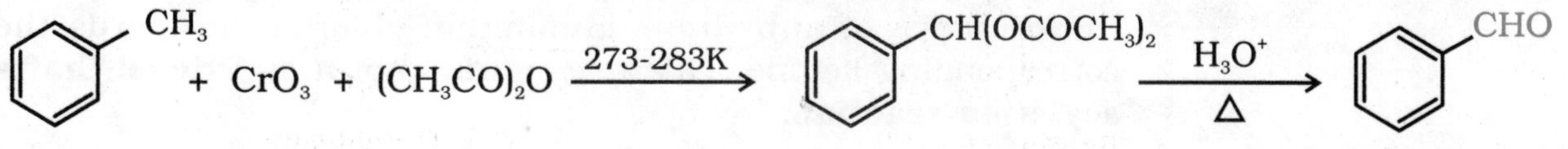

Toluene CH$_3$ + CrO_3 + $(CH_3CO)_2O$ $\xrightarrow{273-283K}$ CH(OCOCH$_3$)$_2$ $\xrightarrow[\Delta]{H_3O^+}$ Benzaldehyde CHO

(ii) *By side chain chlorination followed by hydrolysis*

Side chain chlorination of toluene gives benzal chloride, which on hydrolysis gives benzaldehyde. This is a commercial method of manufacture of benzaldehyde.

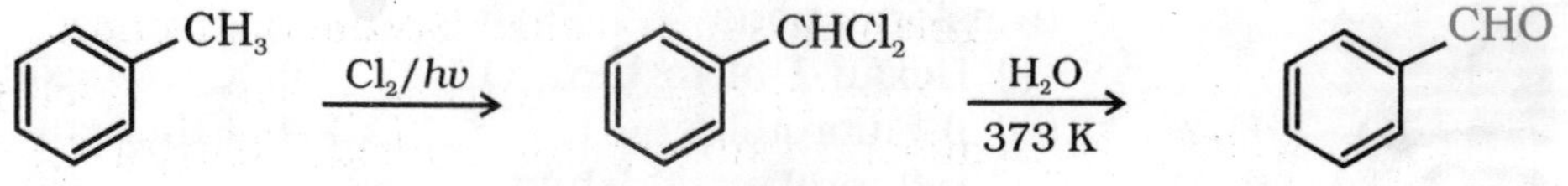

Toluene CH$_3$ $\xrightarrow{Cl_2/h\upsilon}$ Benzal chloride CHCl$_2$ $\xrightarrow[373\ K]{H_2O}$ Benzaldehyde CHO

(iii) *By Gatterman – Koch reaction*

When benzene or its derivative is treated with carbon monoxide and hydrogen chloride in the presence of anhydrous aluminium chloride or cuprous chloride, it gives benzaldehyde or substituted benzaldehyde.

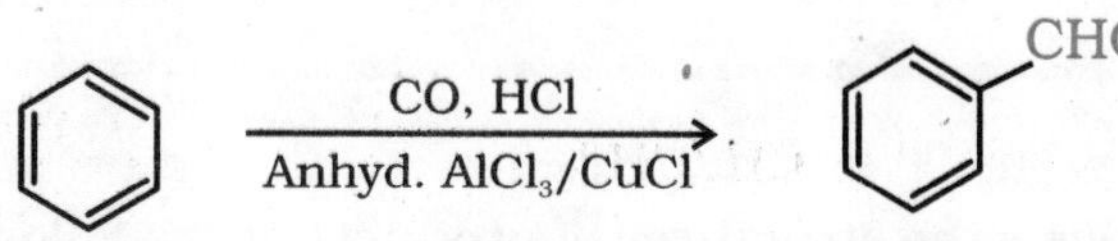

Benzene $\xrightarrow[\text{Anhyd. AlCl}_3/\text{CuCl}]{\text{CO, HCl}}$ Benzaldehyde CHO

This reaction is known as **Gatterman-Koch** reaction.

12.2.3 Preparation of Ketones

1. *From acyl chlorides*

Treatment of acyl chlorides with dialkylcadmium, prepared by the reaction of cadmium chloride with Grignard reagent, gives ketones.

$$2\ R - Mg - X\ +\ CdCl_2 \longrightarrow R_2Cd\ +\ 2Mg(X)Cl$$

$$2\ R' - \underset{\underset{O}{\|}}{C} - Cl\ +\ R_2Cd \longrightarrow 2\ R' - \underset{\underset{O}{\|}}{C} - R\ +\ CdCl_2$$

2. From nitriles

Treating a nitrile with Grignard reagent followed by hydrolysis yields a ketone.

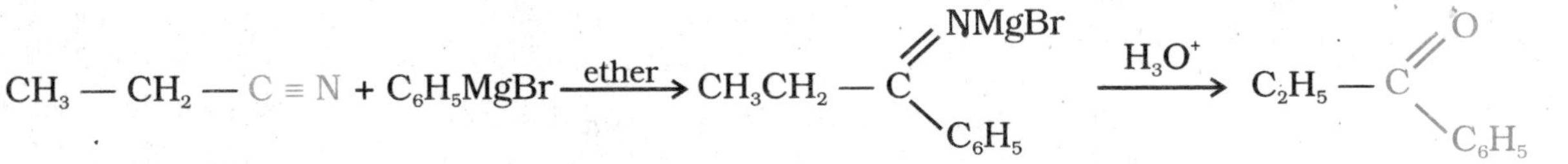

$$CH_3 - CH_2 - C \equiv N + C_6H_5MgBr \xrightarrow{\text{ether}} CH_3CH_2 - \overset{\displaystyle NMgBr}{\underset{\displaystyle C_6H_5}{C}} \xrightarrow{H_3O^+} C_2H_5 - \overset{\displaystyle O}{\underset{\displaystyle C_6H_5}{C}}$$

Propiophenone
(1-Phenylpropanone)

3. From benzene or substituted benzenes

When benzene or substituted benzene is treated with acid chloride in the presence of anhydrous aluminium chloride, it affords the corresponding ketone. This reaction is known as **Friedel-Crafts acylation reaction**.

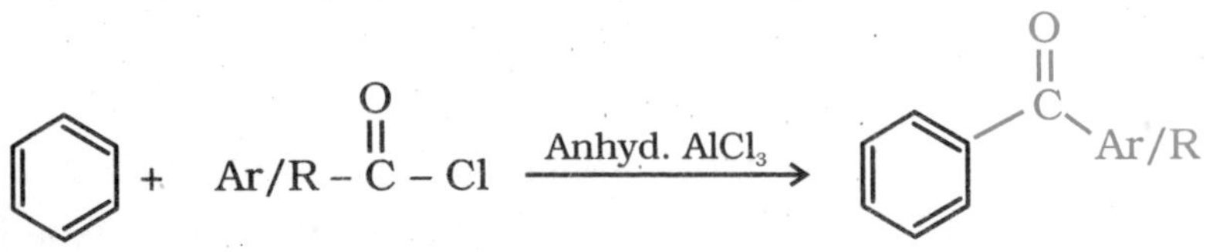

$$\text{[benzene]} + Ar/R - \overset{\displaystyle O}{\overset{\|}{C}} - Cl \xrightarrow{\text{Anhyd. AlCl}_3} \text{[benzene]} - \overset{\displaystyle O}{\overset{\|}{C}} - Ar/R$$

Example 12.1 Give names of the reagents to bring about the following transformations:

(i) Hexan-1-ol to hexanal

(ii) Cyclohexanol to cyclohexanone

(iii) *p*-Fluorotoluene to *p*-fluorobenzaldehyde

(iv) Ethanenitrile to ethanal

(v) Allyl alcohol to propenal

(vi) But-2-ene to ethanal

Solution

(i) $C_5H_5NH^+CrO_3Cl^-$(PCC)

(ii) $K_2Cr_2O_7$ in acidic medium

(iii) CrO_3 in the presence of acetic anhydride/ 1. CrO_2Cl_2 2. HOH

(iv) (Diisobutyl)aluminium hydride (DIBAL-H)

(v) PCC

(vi) O_3/H_2O-Zn dust

Intext Question

12.2 Write the structures of products of the following reactions;

(i) 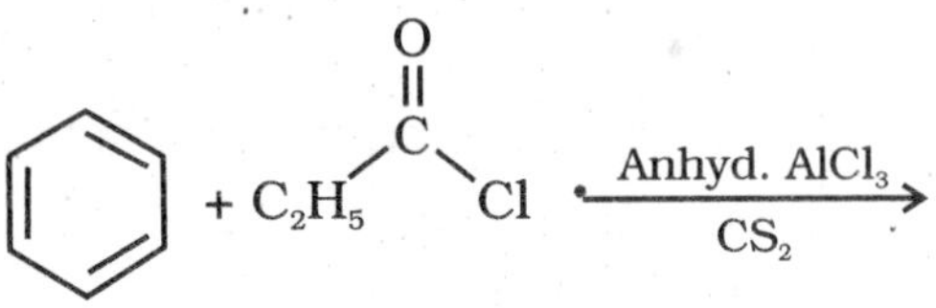 $\text{[benzene]} + C_2H_5 - \overset{\displaystyle O}{\overset{\|}{C}} - Cl \xrightarrow[\text{CS}_2]{\text{Anhyd. AlCl}_3}$

(ii) $(C_6H_5CH_2)_2 Cd + 2 CH_3 COCl \rightarrow$

(iii) $H_3C - C \equiv C - H \xrightarrow{Hg^{2+}, H_2SO_4}$

(iv) 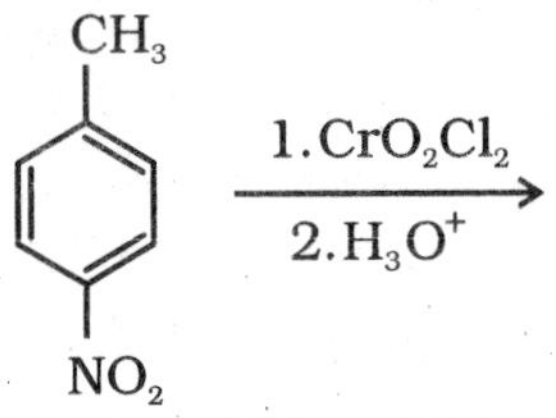 $\text{[}p\text{-nitrotoluene, CH}_3 \text{ top, NO}_2 \text{ bottom]} \xrightarrow[\text{2. H}_3O^+]{\text{1. CrO}_2Cl_2}$

12.3 Physical Properties

The physical properties of aldehydes and ketones are described as follows.

Methanal is a gas at room temperature. Ethanal is a volatile liquid. Other aldehydes and ketones are liquid or solid at room temperature. The boiling points of aldehydes and ketones are higher than hydrocarbons and ethers of comparable molecular masses. It is due to weak molecular association in aldehydes and ketones arising out of the dipole-dipole interactions. Also, their boiling points are lower than those of alcohols of similar molecular masses due to absence of intermolecular hydrogen bonding. The following compounds of molecular masses 58 and 60 are ranked in order of increasing boiling points.

	b.p.(K)	Molecular Mass
n-Butane	273	58
Methoxyethane	281	60
Propanal	322	58
Acetone	329	58
Propan-1-ol	370	60

The lower members of aldehydes and ketones such as methanal, ethanal and propanone are miscible with water in all proportions, because they form hydrogen bond with water.

However, the solubility of aldehydes and ketones decreases rapidly on increasing the length of alkyl chain. All aldehydes and ketones are fairly soluble in organic solvents like benzene, ether, methanol, chloroform, etc. The lower aldehydes have sharp pungent odours. As the size of the molecule increases, the odour becomes less pungent and more fragrant. In fact, many naturally occurring aldehydes and ketones are used in the blending of perfumes and flavouring agents.

Example 12.2

Arrange the following compounds in the increasing order of their boiling points:

$CH_3CH_2CH_2CHO$, $CH_3CH_2CH_2CH_2OH$, H_5C_2-O-C_2H_5, $CH_3CH_2CH_2CH_2CH_3$

Solution

The molecular masses of these compounds are in the range of 72 to 74. Since only butan-1-ol molecules are associated due to extensive intermolecular hydrogen bonding, therefore, the boiling point of butan-1-ol would be the highest. Butanal is more polar than ethoxyethane. Therefore, the intermolecular dipole-dipole attraction is stronger in the former. n-Pentane molecules have only weak **van der Waals forces**. Hence increasing order of boiling points of the given compounds is as follows:

$CH_3CH_2CH_2CH_2CH_3 < H_5C_2$-$O$-$C_2H_5 < CH_3CH_2CH_2CHO < CH_3CH_2CH_2CH_2OH$

Intext Question

12.3 Arrange the following compounds in increasing order of their boiling points.

CH_3CHO, CH_3CH_2OH, CH_3OCH_3, $CH_3CH_2CH_3$

12.4 Chemical Reactions

Since aldehydes and ketones both possess the carbonyl functional group, they undergo similar chemical reactions.

1. Nucleophilic addition reactions

Contrary to electrophilic addition reactions observed in alkenes (refer Unit 13, Class XI), the aldehydes and ketones undergo nucleophilic addition reactions.

(i) Mechanism of nucleophilic addition reactions

A nucleophile attacks the electrophilic carbon atom of the polar carbonyl group from a direction approximately perpendicular to the plane of sp^2 hybridised orbitals of carbonyl carbon (Fig. 12.2). The hybridisation of carbon changes from sp^2 to sp^3 in this process, and a tetrahedral alkoxide intermediate is produced. This intermediate captures a proton from the reaction medium to give the electrically neutral product. The net result is addition of Nu^- and H^+ across the carbon oxygen double bond as shown in Fig. 12.2.

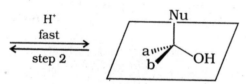

Planar

slow step 1

Nu

H⁺
fast
⇌
step 2

Tetrahedral intermediate   Addition product

Fig.12.2: *Nucleophilic attack on carbonyl carbon*

(ii) Reactivity

Aldehydes are generally more reactive than ketones in nucleophilic addition reactions due to steric and electronic reasons. Sterically, the presence of two relatively large substituents in ketones hinders the approach of nucleophile to carbonyl carbon than in aldehydes having only one such substituent. Electronically, aldehydes are more reactive than ketones because two alkyl groups reduce the electrophilicity of the carbonyl more effectively than in former.

Example 12.3 Would you expect benzaldehyde to be more reactive or less reactive in nucleophilic addition reactions than propanal? Explain your answer.

Solution The carbon atom of the carbonyl group of benzaldehyde is less electrophilic than carbon atom of the carbonyl group present in propanal. The polarity of the carbonyl group is reduced in benzaldehyde due to resonance as shown below and hence it is less reactive than propanal.

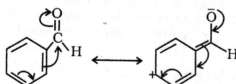

(iii) Some important examples of nucleophilic addition and nucleophilic addition-elimination reactions:

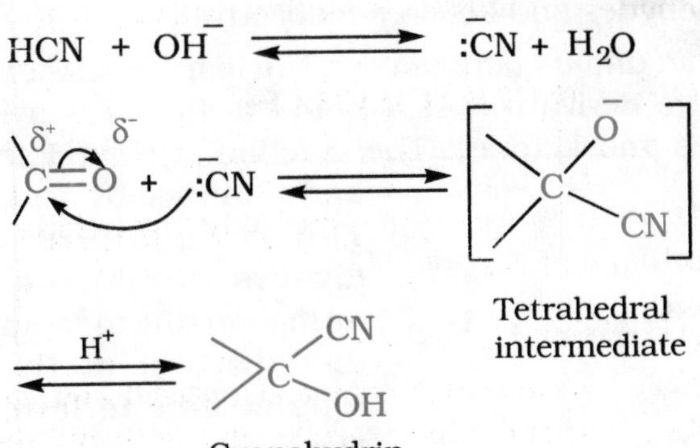

$$HCN + OH^- \rightleftharpoons :CN^- + H_2O$$

Tetrahedral intermediate

Cyanohydrin

(a) *Addition of hydrogen cyanide (HCN):* Aldehydes and ketones react with hydrogen cyanide (HCN) to yield cyanohydrins. This reaction occurs very slowly with pure HCN. Therefore, it is catalysed by a base and the generated cyanide ion (CN⁻) being a stronger nucleophile readily adds to carbonyl compounds to yield corresponding cyanohydrin.

Cyanohydrins are useful synthetic intermediates.

(b) *Addition of sodium hydrogensulphite:* Sodium hydrogensulphite adds to aldehydes and ketones to form the addition products.

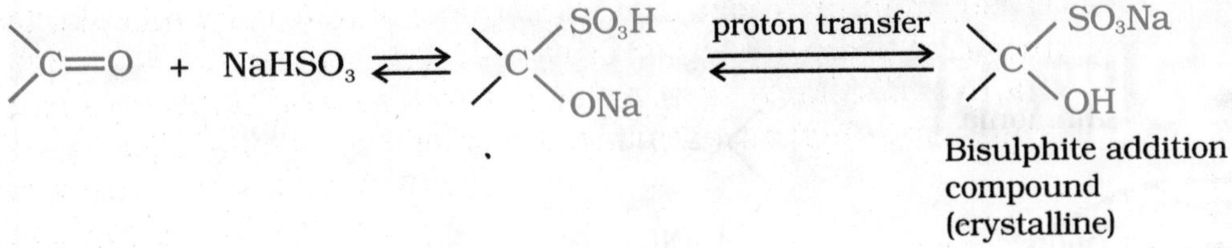

Bisulphite addition compound (crystalline)

The position of the equilibrium lies largely to the right hand side for most aldehydes and to the left for most ketones due to steric reasons. The hydrogensulphite addition compound is water soluble and can be converted back to the original carbonyl compound by treating it with dilute mineral acid or alkali. Therefore, these are useful for separation and purification of aldehydes.

(c) *Addition of Grignard reagents:* (refer Unit 11, Class XII).

(d) *Addition of alcohols:* Aldehydes react with one equivalent of monohydric alcohol in the presence of dry hydrogen chloride to yield alkoxyalcohol intermediate, known as hemiacetals, which further react with one more molecule of alcohol to give *a gem*-dialkoxy compound known as acetal as shown in the reaction.

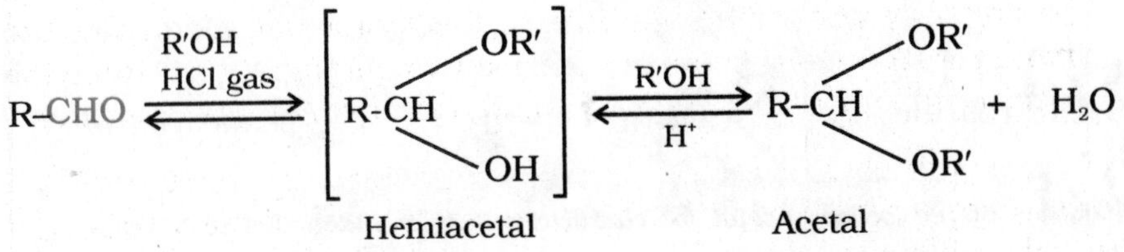

Ketones react with ethylene glycol under similar conditions to form cyclic products known as ethylene glycol ketals.

Dry hydrogen chloride protonates the oxygen of the carbonyl compounds and therefore, increases the electrophilicity of the carbonyl carbon facilitating

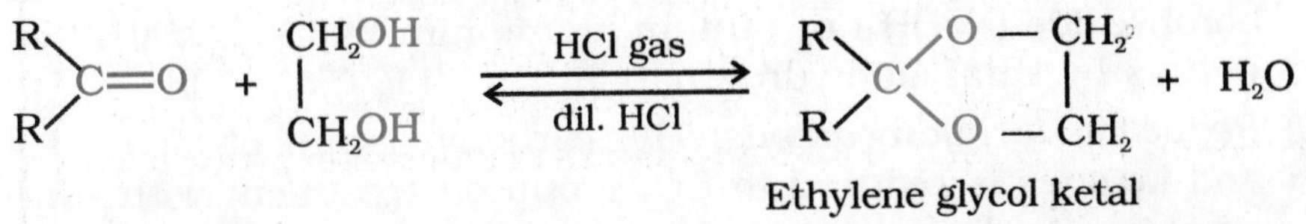

Hemiacetal   Acetal

Ethylene glycol ketal

the nucleophilic attack of ethylene glycol. Acetals and ketals are hydrolysed with aqueous mineral acids to yield corresponding aldehydes and ketones respectively.

(e) *Addition of ammonia and its derivatives*: Nucleophiles, such as ammonia and its derivatives H_2N-Z add to the carbonyl group of aldehydes and ketones. The reaction is reversible and catalysed by acid. The equilibrium favours the product formation due to rapid dehydration of the intermediate to form $>C=N$-Z.

$$>C=O \ + \ H_2N\text{-}Z \ \rightleftharpoons \ \left[>C \begin{array}{c} OH \\ NHZ \end{array} \right] \longrightarrow \ >C=N\text{-}Z \ + \ H_2O$$

Z = Alkyl, aryl, OH, NH_2, C_6H_5NH, $NHCONH_2$, etc.

Table 12.2: Some N-Substituted Derivatives of Aldehydes and Ketones ($>C=N$-Z)

Z	Reagent name	Carbonyl derivative	Product name
-H	Ammonia	$>C=NH$	Imine
-R	Amine	$>C=NR$	Substituted imine (Schiff's base)
—OH	Hydroxylamine	$>C=N$–OH	Oxime
—NH_2	Hydrazine	$>C=N$–NH_2	Hydrazone
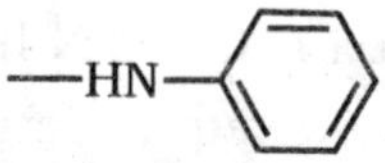 —HN—C$_6$H$_5$	Phenylhydrazine	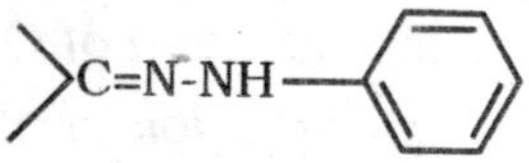 $>C=N$-NH—C$_6$H$_5$	Phenylhydrazone
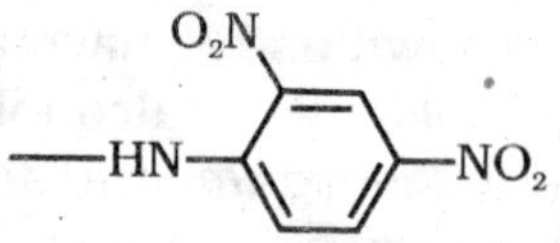 —HN—(2-O_2N, 4-NO_2 phenyl)	2,4-Dinitrophenyl-hydrazine	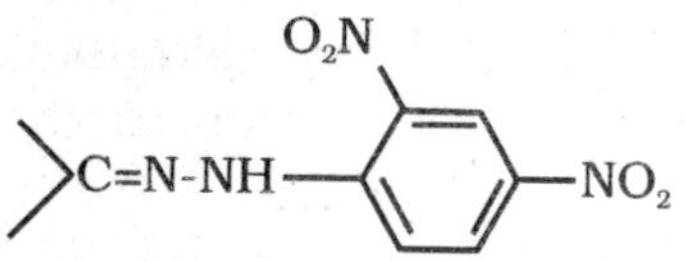 $>C=N$-NH—(2-O_2N, 4-NO_2 phenyl)	2,4 Dinitrophenyl-hydrazone
—NH—C(=O)—NH_2	Semicarbazide	$>C=N$-NH—C(=O)—NH_2	Semicarbazone

* *2,4-DNP-derivatives are yellow, orange or red solids, useful for characterisation of aldehydes and ketones.*

2. Reduction

(i) *Reduction to alcohols*: Aldehydes and ketones are reduced to primary and secondary alcohols respectively by sodium borohydride ($NaBH_4$) or lithium aluminium hydride ($LiAlH_4$) as well as by catalytic hydrogenation (Unit 11, Class XII).

(ii) *Reduction to hydrocarbons*: The carbonyl group of aldehydes and ketones is reduced to CH_2 group on treatment with zinc-amalgam and concentrated hydrochloric acid [**Clemmensen**

reduction] or with hydrazine followed by heating with sodium or potassium hydroxide in high boiling solvent such as ethylene glycol (**Wolff-Kishner reduction**).

$$\text{C=O} \xrightarrow[\text{HCl}]{\text{Zn-Hg}} \text{CH}_2 + H_2O \qquad \text{(Clemmensen reduction)}$$

$$\text{C=O} \xrightarrow[-H_2O]{NH_2NH_2} \text{C=NNH}_2 \xrightarrow[\text{heat}]{\text{KOH/ethylene glycol}} \text{CH}_2 + N_2$$

(Wolff-Kishner rduction)

3. Oxidation

Bernhard Tollens (1841-1918) was a Professor of Chemistry at the University of Gottingen, Germany.

Aldehydes differ from ketones in their oxidation reactions. Aldehydes are easily oxidised to carboxylic acids on treatment with common oxidising agents like nitric acid, potassium permanganate, potassium dichromate, etc. Even mild oxidising agents, mainly Tollens' reagent and Fehlings' reagent also oxidise aldehydes.

$$\text{R-CHO} \xrightarrow{[O]} \text{R-COOH}$$

Ketones are generally oxidised under vigorous conditions, i.e., strong oxidising agents and at elevated temperatures. Their oxidation involves carbon-carbon bond cleavage to afford a mixture of carboxylic acids having lesser number of carbon atoms than the parent ketone.

$$\overset{1}{R}-\overset{2}{CH_2}-\overset{3}{\underset{\underset{O}{\|}}{C}}-CH_2-R' \xrightarrow{[O]} \text{R-COOH} + \text{R'-CH}_2\text{COOH}$$

(By cleavage of C_1-C_2 bond)

+

$$\text{R-CH}_2\text{COOH} + \text{R'-COOH}$$

(By cleavage of C_2-C_3 bond)

The mild oxidising agents given below are used to distinguish aldehydes from ketones:

(i) *Tollens' test:* On warming an aldehyde with freshly prepared ammoniacal silver nitrate solution (Tollens' reagent), a bright silver mirror is produced due to the formation of silver metal. The aldehydes are oxidised to corresponding carboxylate anion. The reaction occurs in alkaline medium.

$$\text{RCHO} + 2[Ag(NH_3)_2]^+ + 3\,\bar{O}H \longrightarrow \text{RCOO}^- + 2Ag + 2H_2O + 4NH_3$$

(ii) *Fehling's test:* Fehling reagent comprises of two solutions, Fehling solution A and Fehling solution B. Fehling solution A is aqueous copper sulphate and Fehling solution B is alkaline sodium potassium tartarate (Rochelle salt). These two solutions are mixed in equal amounts before test. On heating an aldehyde with Fehling's reagent, a reddish brown precipitate is obtained. Aldehydes are oxidised to corresponding carboxylate anion. Aromatic aldehydes do not respond to this test.

$$\text{R-CHO} + 2Cu^{2+} + 5\,\bar{O}H \longrightarrow \text{RCOO}^- + Cu_2O + 3H_2O$$

Red-brown ppt

(iii) Oxidation of methyl ketones by haloform reaction: Aldehydes and ketones having at least one methyl group linked to the carbonyl carbon atom (methyl ketones) are oxidised by sodium hypohalite to sodium salts of corresponding carboxylic acids having one carbon atom less than that of carbonyl compound. The methyl group is converted to haloform. This oxidation does not affect a carbon-carbon double bond, if present in the molecule.

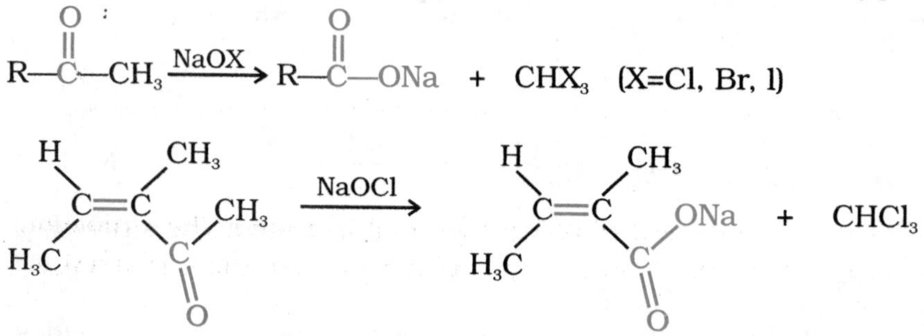

$$R-\overset{\overset{O}{\|}}{C}-CH_3 \xrightarrow{NaOX} R-\overset{\overset{O}{\|}}{C}-ONa + CHX_3 \quad (X=Cl, Br, I)$$

Iodoform reaction with sodium hypoiodite is also used for detection of CH_3CO group or $CH_3CH(OH)$ group which produces CH_3CO group on oxidation.

Example 12.4 An organic compound (A) with molecular formula C_8H_8O forms an orange-red precipitate with 2,4-DNP reagent and gives yellow precipitate on heating with iodine in the presence of sodium hydroxide. It neither reduces Tollens' or Fehlings' reagent, nor does it decolourise bromine water or Baeyer's reagent. On drastic oxidation with chromic acid, it gives a carboxylic acid (B) having molecular formula $C_7H_6O_2$. Identify the compounds (A) and (B) and explain the reactions involved.

Solution (A) forms 2,4-DNP derivative. Therefore, it is an aldehyde or a ketone. Since it does not reduce Tollens' or Fehling reagent, (A) must be a ketone. (A) responds to iodoform test. Therefore, it should be a methyl ketone. The molecular formula of (A) indicates high degree of unsaturation, yet it does not decolourise bromine water or Baeyer's reagent. This indicates the presence of unsaturation due to an aromatic ring.

Compound (B), being an oxidation product of a ketone should be a carboxylic acid. The molecular formula of (B) indicates that it should be benzoic acid and compound (A) should, therefore, be a monosubstituted aromatic methyl ketone. The molecular formula of (A) indicates that it should be phenyl methyl ketone (acetophenone). Reactions are as follows:

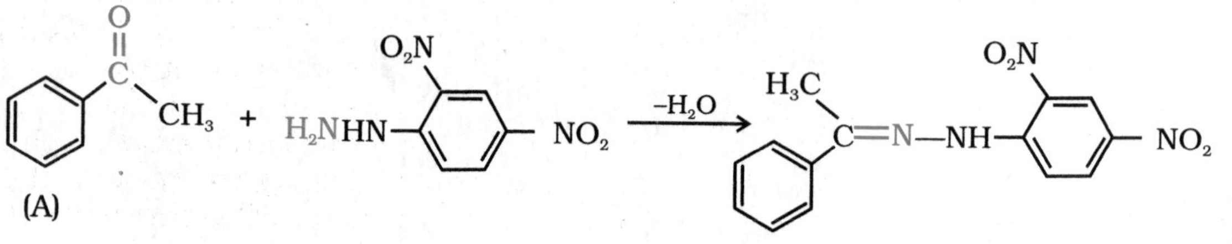

(A)

C_8H_8O 2, 4-Dinitrophenylhydrazine   2, 4-DNP derivative

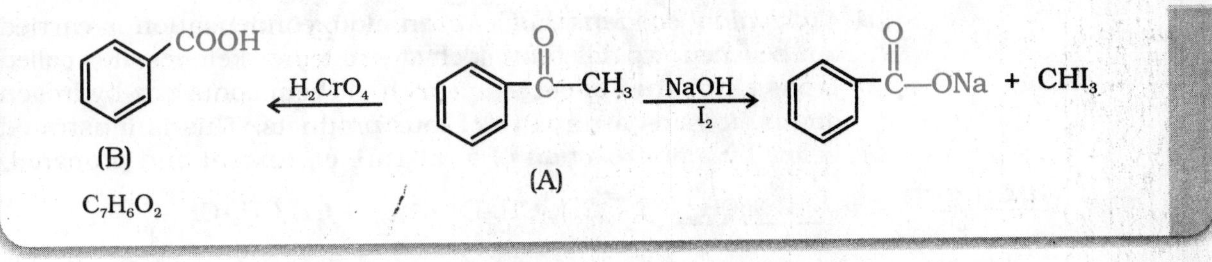

The reaction scheme at top:

C_6H_5-COOH (B), $C_7H_6O_2$ ← H_2CrO_4 ← C_6H_5-CO-CH_3 (A) $\xrightarrow[I_2]{NaOH}$ C_6H_5-CO-ONa + CHI_3

4. Reactions due to a-hydrogen

Acidity of α-hydrogens of aldehydes and ketones: The aldehydes and ketones undergo a number of reactions due to the acidic nature of α-hydrogen.

The acidity of α-hydrogen atoms of carbonyl compounds is due to the strong electron withdrawing effect of the carbonyl group and resonance stabilisation of the conjugate base.

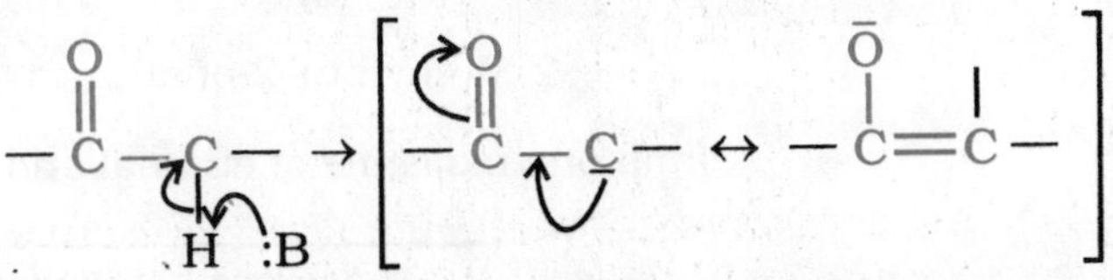

(i) *Aldol condensation:* Aldehydes and ketones having at least one α-hydrogen undergo a reaction in the presence of dilute alkali as catalyst to form β-hydroxy aldehydes (aldol) or β-hydroxy ketones (ketol), respectively. This is known as **Aldol reaction.**

$2 CH_3$-CHO $\underset{\text{dil. NaOH}}{\rightleftharpoons}$ CH_3-CH-CH_2-CHO $\xrightarrow[-H_2O]{\Delta}$ CH_3-CH=CH-CHO

Ethanal ⟶ 3-Hydroxybutanal (Aldol) [OH] ⟶ But-2-enal (Aldol condensation product)

$2CH_3$-CO-CH_3 $\underset{\text{Ba(OH)}_2}{\rightleftharpoons}$ CH_3-$\overset{CH_3}{\underset{OH}{C}}$-$CH_2$CO-$CH_3$ $\xrightarrow[-H_2O]{\Delta}$ CH_3-$\overset{CH_3}{C}$=CH-CO-CH_3

Propanone ⟶ (Ketol) 4-Hydroxy-4-methylpentan-2-one ⟶ 4-Methylpent-3-en-2-one (Aldol condensation product)

The name aldol is derived from the names of the two functional groups, aldehyde and alcohol, present in the products. The aldol and ketol readily lose water to give α,β-unsaturated carbonyl compounds which are aldol condensation products and the reaction is called **Aldol condensation.** Though ketones give ketols (compounds containing a keto and alcohol groups), the general name aldol condensation still applies to the reactions of ketones due to their similarity with aldehydes.

(*ii*) *Cross aldol condensation:* When aldol condensation is carried out between two different aldehydes and / or ketones, it is called **cross aldol condensation**. If both of them contain α-hydrogen atoms, it gives a mixture of four products. This is illustrated below by aldol reaction of a mixture of ethanal and propanal.

$$CH_3CHO + CH_3CH_2CHO \xrightarrow[2.\ \Delta]{1.\ NaOH} \underset{\text{But-2-enal}}{CH_3\text{-}CH{=}CH\text{-}CHO} + \underset{|\atop CH_3}{CH_3CH_2\text{-}CH{=}C\text{-}CHO}$$

from two molecules of ethanal — 2-Methylpent-2-enal from two molecules of propanal

simple or self aldol products

+

$$\underset{|\atop CH_3}{CH_3\text{-}CH{=}C\text{-}CHO} + CH_3CH_2\text{-}CH{=}CHCHO$$

2-Methylbut-2-enal — Pent-2-enal

from one molecule of ethanal and one molecule of propanal

cross aldol products

Ketones can also be used as one component in the cross aldol reactions.

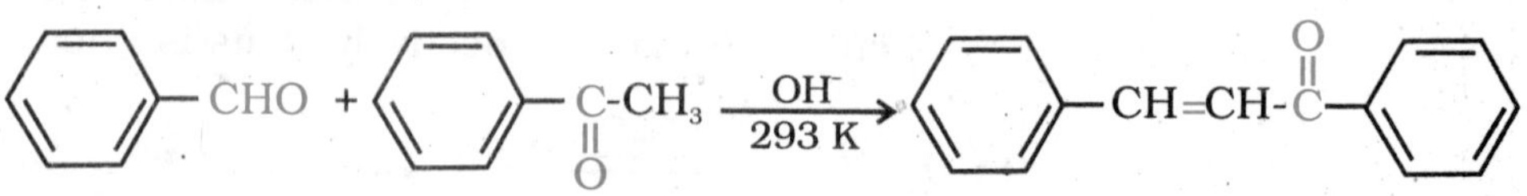

1, 3-Diphenylprop-2-en-1-one
(Benzalacetophenone)
(Major product)

5. *Other reactions*

(*i*) *Cannizzaro reaction:* Aldehydes which do not have an α-hydrogen atom, undergo self oxidation and reduction (disproportionation) reaction on heating with concentrated alkali. In this reaction, one molecule of the aldehyde is reduced to alcohol while another is oxidised to carboxylic acid salt.

$$H_2C{=}O + H_2C{=}O + \text{Conc. KOH} \xrightarrow{\Delta} H\text{-}CH_2\text{-}OH + H\text{-}C(=O)OK$$

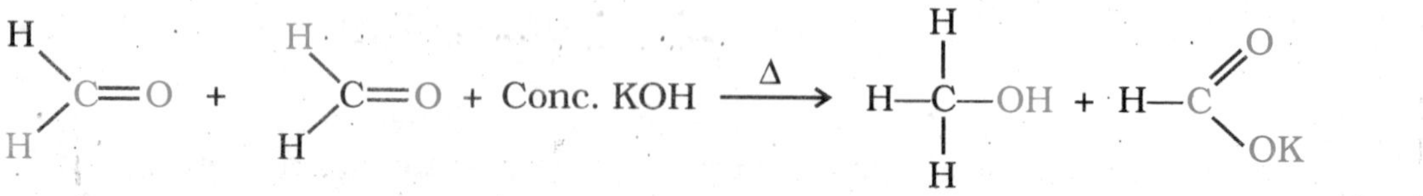

Formaldehyde — Methanol — Potassium formate

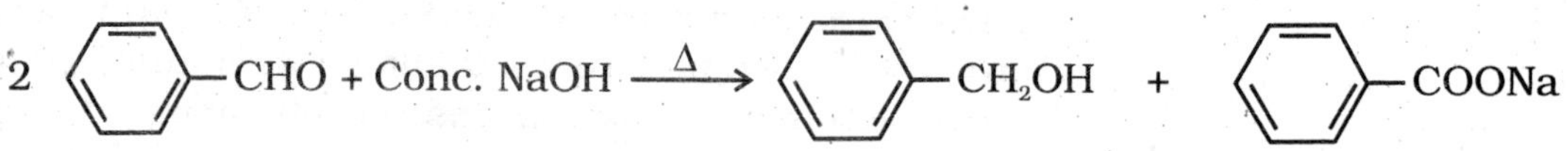

Benzaldehyde — Benzyl alcohol — Sodium benzoate

(ii) Electrophilic substitution reaction: Aromatic aldehydes and ketones undergo electrophilic substitution at the ring in which the carbonyl group acts as a deactivating and *meta*-directing group.

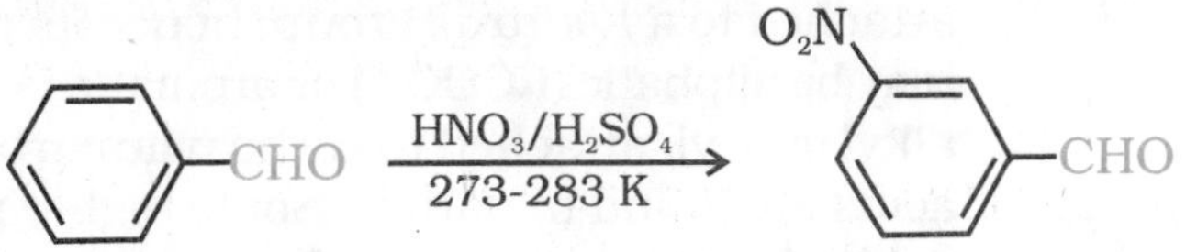

Benzaldehyde $\xrightarrow[\text{273-283 K}]{\text{HNO}_3/\text{H}_2\text{SO}_4}$ *m*-Nitrobenzaldehyde

12.4 Arrange the following compounds in increasing order of their reactivity in nucleophilic addition reactions.

(i) Ethanal, Propanal, Propanone, Butanone.

(ii) Benzaldehyde, *p*-Tolualdehyde, *p*-Nitrobenzaldehyde, Acetophenone.

Hint: Consider steric effect and electronic effect.

12.5 Predict the products of the following reactions:

(i) + HO—NH$_2$ $\xrightarrow{\text{H}^+}$

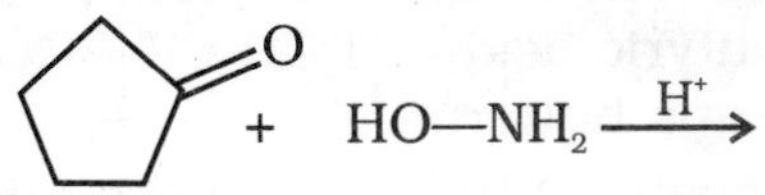

(ii) + NH$_2$—NH —NO$_2$ $\longrightarrow$

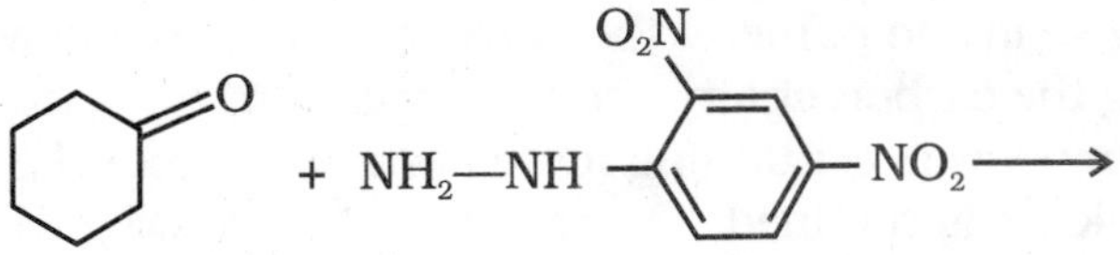

(iii) R-CH=CH-CHO + NH$_2$-C(=O)-NH-NH$_2$ $\xrightarrow{\text{H}^+}$

(iv) CH$_3$ + CH$_3$CH$_2$NH$_2$ $\xrightarrow{\text{H}^+}$

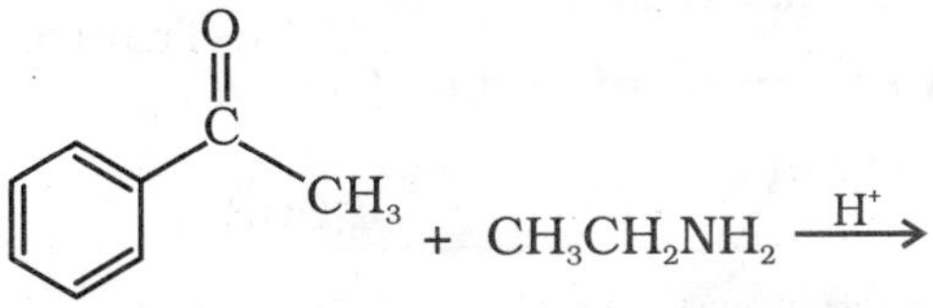

12.5 Uses of Aldehydes and Ketones

In chemical industry aldehydes and ketones are used as solvents, starting materials and reagents for the synthesis of other products. Formaldehyde is well known as formalin (40%) solution used to preserve biological specimens and to prepare bakelite (a phenol-formaldehyde resin), urea-formaldehyde glues and other polymeric products. Acetaldehyde is used primarily as a starting material in the manufacture of acetic acid, ethyl acetate, vinyl acetate, polymers and drugs. Benzaldehyde is used in perfumery and in dye industries. Acetone and ethyl methyl ketone are common industrial solvents. Many aldehydes and ketones, e.g., butyraldehyde, vanillin, acetophenone, camphor, etc. are well known for their odours and flavours.

Carboxylic Acids

Carbon compounds containing a carboxyl functional group, –COOH are called carboxylic acids. The carboxyl group, consists of a *carbonyl* group attached to a *hydroxyl* group, hence its name *carboxyl*. Carboxylic acids may be aliphatic (RCOOH) or aromatic (ArCOOH) depending on the group, alkyl or aryl, attached to carboxylic carbon. Large number of carboxylic acids are found in nature. Some higher members of aliphatic carboxylic acids (C_{12} – C_{18}) known as **fatty acids,** occur in natural fats as esters of glycerol. Carboxylic acids serve as starting material for several other important organic compounds such as anhydrides, esters, acid chlorides, amides, etc.

12.6 Nomenclature and Structure of Carboxyl Group

12.6.1 Nomenclature

Since carboxylic acids are amongst the earliest organic compounds to be isolated from nature, a large number of them are known by their common names. The common names end with the suffix –*ic* acid and have been derived from Latin or Greek names of their natural sources. For example, formic acid (HCOOH) was first obtained from red ants (Latin: *formica* means ant), acetic acid (CH_3COOH) from vinegar (Latin: *acetum*, means vinegar), butyric acid ($CH_3CH_2CH_2COOH$) from rancid butter (Latin: *butyrum*, means butter).

In the IUPAC system, aliphatic carboxylic acids are named by replacing the ending –*e* in the name of the corresponding alkane with – *oic acid*. In numbering the carbon chain, the carboxylic carbon is numbered one. For naming compounds containing more than one carboxyl group, the ending –*e* of the alkane is retained. The number of carboxyl groups are indicated by adding the multiplicative prefix, *di*, *tri*, etc. to the term **oic**. The position of –COOH groups are indicated by the arabic numeral before the multiplicative prefix. Some of the carboxylic acids along with their common and IUPAC names are listed in Table 12.3.

Table 12.3 Names and Structures of Some Carboxylic Acids

Structure	Common name	IUPAC name
HCOOH	Formic acid	Methanoic acid
CH_3COOH	Acetic acid	Ethanoic acid
CH_3CH_2COOH	Propionic acid	Propanoic acid
$CH_3CH_2CH_2COOH$	Butyric acid	Butanoic acid
$(CH_3)_2CHCOOH$	Isobutyric acid	2-Methylpropanoic acid
HOOC-COOH	Oxalic acid	Ethanedioic acid
HOOC -CH_2-COOH	Malonic acid	Propanedioic acid
HOOC -$(CH_2)_2$-COOH	Succinic acid	Butanedioic acid
HOOC -$(CH_2)_3$-COOH	Glutaric acid	Pentanedioic acid
HOOC -$(CH_2)_4$-COOH	Adipic acid	Hexanedioic acid
HOOC -CH_2-CH(COOH)-CH_2-COOH	–	Propane-1, 2, 3-tricarboxylic acid

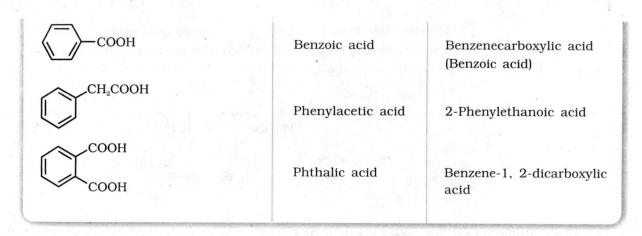

	Benzoic acid	Benzenecarboxylic acid (Benzoic acid)
	Phenylacetic acid	2-Phenylethanoic acid
	Phthalic acid	Benzene-1, 2-dicarboxylic acid

12.6.2 Structure of Carboxyl Group

In carboxylic acids, the bonds to the carboxyl carbon lie in one plane and are separated by about 120 . The carboxylic carbon is less electrophilic than carbonyl carbon because of the possible resonance structure shown below:

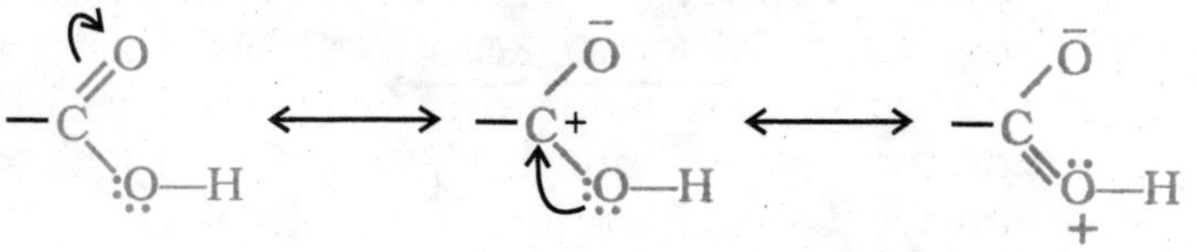

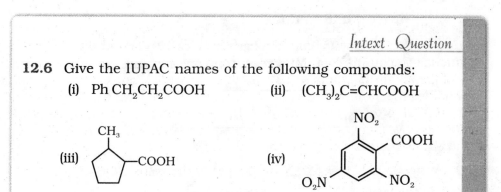

Intext Question

12.6 Give the IUPAC names of the following compounds:

    (i) $Ph\,CH_2CH_2COOH$

    (ii) $(CH_3)_2C{=}CHCOOH$

    (iii)

    (iv)

12.7 Methods of Preparation of Carboxylic Acids

Some important methods of preparation of carboxylic acids are as follows.

1. From primary alcohols and aldehydes

Primary alcohols are readily oxidised to carboxylic acids with common oxidising agents such as potassium permanganate ($KMnO_4$) in neutral, acidic or alkaline media or by potassium dichromate ($K_2Cr_2O_7$) and chromium trioxide (CrO_3) in acidic media.

$$RCH_2OH \xrightarrow[\text{2. } H_3\overset{+}{O}]{\text{1. alkaline } KMnO_4} RCOOH$$

$$CH_3(CH_2)_8CH_2OH \xrightarrow{CrO_3\text{-}H_2SO_4} CH_3(CH_2)_8COOH$$
$$\text{1-Decanol} \qquad\qquad\qquad \text{Decanoic acid}$$

Carboxylic acids are also prepared from aldehydes by the use of mild oxidising agents (Section 12.4).

2. *From alkylbenzenes*

Aromatic carboxylic acids can be prepared by vigorous oxidation of alkyl benzenes with chromic acid or acidic or alkaline potassium permanganate. The entire side chain is oxidised to the carboxyl group irrespective of length of the side chain. Primary and secondary alkyl groups are oxidised in this manner while tertiary group is not affected. Suitably substituted alkenes are also oxidised to carboxylic acids with these oxidising reagents (refer Unit 13, Class XI).

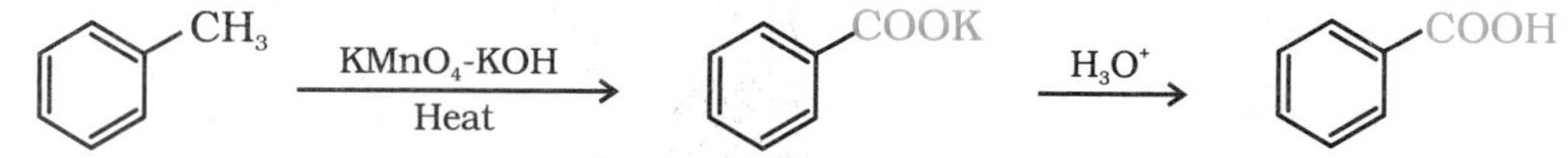

Benzoic acid

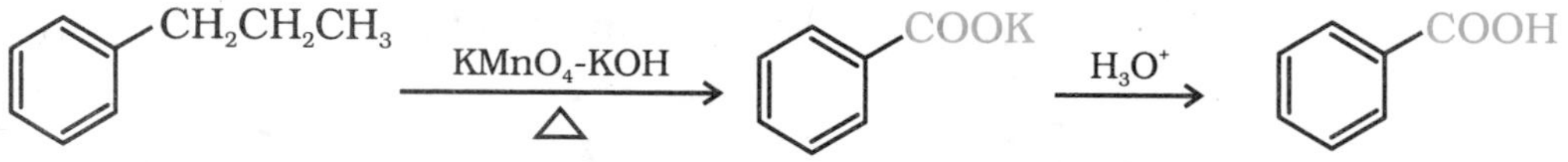

Benzoic acid

3. *From nitriles and amides*

Nitriles are hydrolysed to amides and then to acids in the presence of H^+ or $\bar{O}H$ as catalyst. Mild reaction conditions are used to stop the reaction at the amide stage.

$$\text{R-CN} \xrightarrow[\text{H}_2\text{O}]{\overset{+}{\text{H}} \text{ or } \bar{\text{O}}\text{H}} \text{R}-\overset{\overset{\displaystyle\text{O}}{\|}}{\text{C}}-\text{NH}_2 \xrightarrow[\Delta]{\overset{+}{\text{H}} \text{ or } \bar{\text{O}}\text{H}} \text{RCOOH}$$

$$\underset{\text{Ethanamide}}{\text{CH}_3\text{CONH}_2} \xrightarrow[\Delta]{\text{H}_3\overset{+}{\text{O}}} \underset{\text{Ethanoic acid}}{\text{CH}_3\text{COOH}} + \text{NH}_3$$

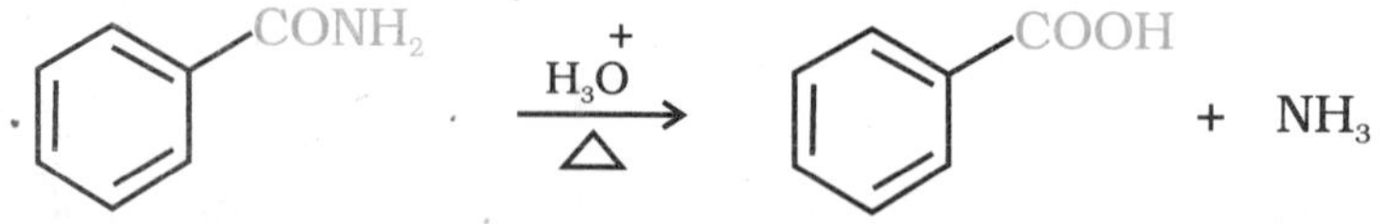

Benzamide Benzoic acid

4. *From Grignard reagents*

Grignard reagents react with carbon dioxide (dry ice) to form salts of carboxylic acids which in turn give corresponding carboxylic acids after acidification with mineral acid.

$$\text{R-Mg-X} + \text{O=C=O} \xrightarrow{\text{Dry ether}} \text{R}-\text{C}\begin{matrix}\diagup\!\!\!\!\diagup\text{O} \\ \diagdown \text{O}^-\text{MgX}^+\end{matrix} \xrightarrow{\text{H}_3\text{O}^+} \text{RCOOH}$$

As we know, the Grignard reagents and nitriles can be prepared from alkyl halides (refer Unit 10, Class XII). The above methods

(3 and 4) are useful for converting alkyl halides into corresponding carboxylic acids having one carbon atom more than that present in alkyl halides (ascending the series).

5. *From acyl halides and anhydrides*

Acid chlorides when hydrolysed with water give carboxylic acids or more readily hydrolysed with aqueous base to give carboxylate ions which on acidification provide corresponding carboxylic acids. Anhydrides on the other hand are hydrolysed to corresponding acid(s) with water.

$$RCOCl \xrightarrow{\quad H_2O \quad} RCOOH + \bar{Cl}$$

$$RCOCl \xrightarrow{\quad \bar{O}H/H_2O \quad} RCOO^- + \bar{Cl} \xrightarrow{\quad H_3O^+ \quad} RCOOH$$

$$(C_6H_5CO)_2O \xrightarrow{\quad H_2O \quad} 2\ C_6H_5COOH$$
Benzoic anhydride   Benzoic acid

$$C_6H_5COOCOCH_3 \xrightarrow{\quad H_2O \quad} C_6H_5COOH + CH_3COOH$$
Benzoic ethanoic anhydride   Benzoic acid   Ethanoic acid

6. *From esters*

Acidic hydrolysis of esters gives directly carboxylic acids while basic hydrolysis gives carboxylates, which on acidification give corresponding carboxylic acids.

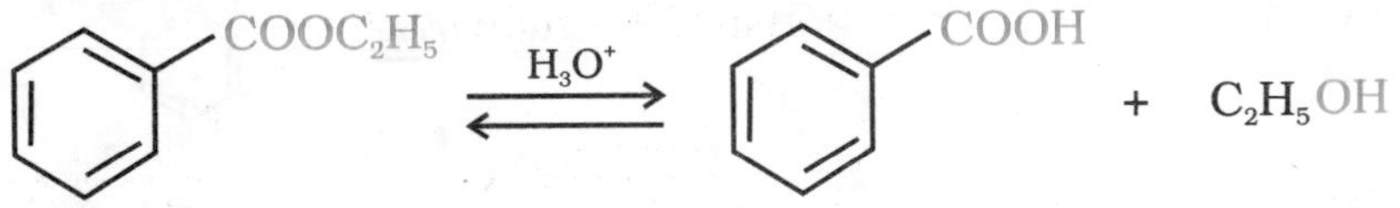

$$C_6H_5COOC_2H_5 \underset{\quad}{\overset{H_3O^+}{\rightleftharpoons}} C_6H_5COOH + C_2H_5OH$$
Ethyl benzoate   Benzoic acid

$$CH_3CH_2CH_2COOC_2H_5 \overset{NaOH}{\rightleftharpoons} CH_3CH_2CH_2COONa + C_2H_5OH$$
Ethyl butanoate

$$\downarrow H_3O^+$$

$$CH_3CH_2CH_2COOH$$
Butanoic acid

Write chemical reactions to affect the following transformations: *Example 12.5*

(i) Butan-1-ol to butanoic acid

(ii) Benzyl alcohol to phenylethanoic acid

(iii) 3-Nitrobromobenzene to 3-nitrobenzoic acid

(iv) 4-Methylacetophenone to benzene-1,4-dicarboxylic acid

(v) Cyclohexene to hexane-1,6-dioic acid

(vi) Butanal to butanoic acid.

(i) $CH_3CH_2CH_2CH_2OH \xrightarrow[\text{Jones reagent}]{CrO_3\text{-}H_2SO_4} CH_3CH_2CH_2COOH$

 Butan-1-ol   Butanoic acid

(ii) $C_6H_5CH_2OH \xrightarrow{HBr} C_6H_5CH_2Br \xrightarrow{KCN} C_6H_5CH_2CN$

 Benzyl alcohol   Benzyl bromide   Benzyl cyanide

$$\triangle \Big| H_3O^+$$

$C_6H_5CH_2COOH$

Phenylethanoic acid

(iii)

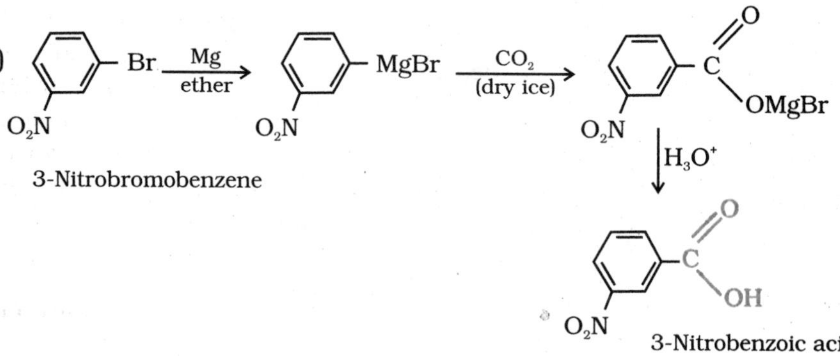

3-Nitrobromobenzene

3-Nitrobenzoic acid

(iv)

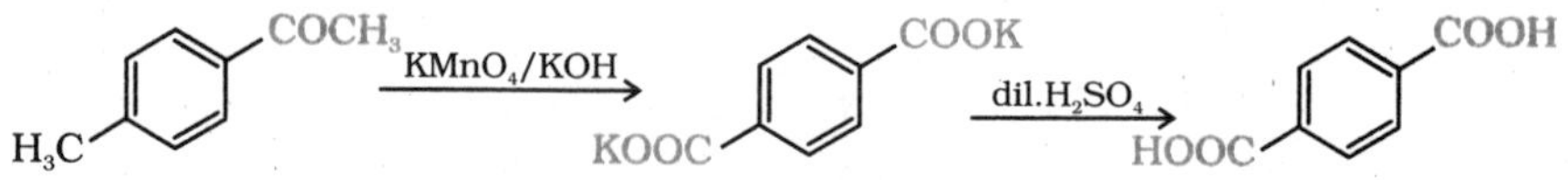

4-Methylacetophenone   Dipotassium benzene-   Benzene-1, 4-dicarboxylic
                          1, 4-dicarboxylate   acid
                                                    (Terephthalic acid)

(v)

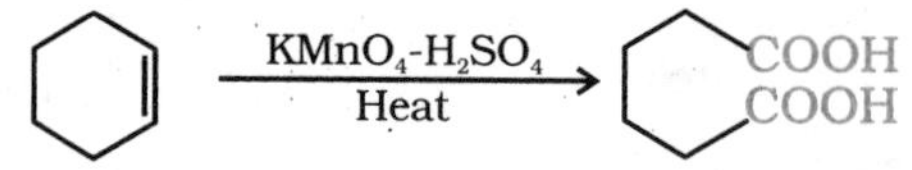

Cyclohexene   Hexane-1, 6-dioic acid (Adipic acid)

(vi) $CH_3CH_2CH_2CHO \xrightarrow[\text{(Tollens' reagent)}]{\text{Ammoniacal } AgNO_3} CH_3CH_2CH_2COOH$

 Butanal   Butanoic acid

Intext Question

12.7 Show how each of the following compounds can be converted to benzoic acid.

(i) Ethylbenzene   (ii) Acetophenone

(iii) Bromobenzene   (iv) Phenylethene (Styrene)

12.8 Physical Properties

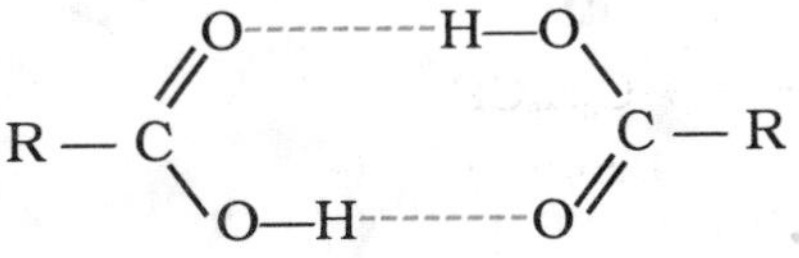

dimer

In vapour state or in aprotic solvent

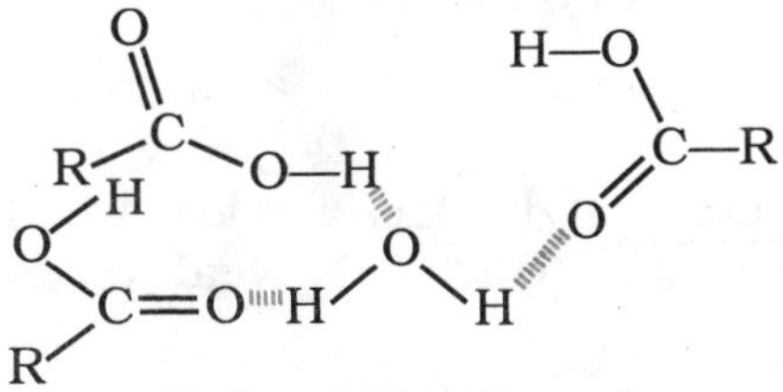

Hydrogen bonding of RCOOH with H$_2$O

Aliphatic carboxylic acids upto nine carbon atoms are colourless liquids at room temperature with unpleasant odours. The higher acids are wax like solids and are practically odourless due to their low volatility. Carboxylic acids are higher boiling liquids than aldehydes, ketones and even alcohols of comparable molecular masses. This is due to more extensive association of carboxylic acid molecules through intermolecular hydrogen bonding. The hydrogen bonds are not broken completely even in the vapour phase. In fact, most carboxylic acids exist as dimer in the vapour phase or in the aprotic solvents.

Simple aliphatic carboxylic acids having upto four carbon atoms are miscible in water due to the formation of hydrogen bonds with water. The solubility decreases with increasing number of carbon atoms. Higher carboxylic acids are practically insoluble in water due to the increased hydrophobic interaction of hydrocarbon part. Benzoic acid, the simplest aromatic carboxylic acid is nearly insoluble in cold water. Carboxylic acids are also soluble in less polar organic solvents like benzene, ether, alcohol, chloroform, etc.

12.9 Chemical Reactions

The reaction of carboxylic acids are classified as follows:

12.9.1 Reactions Involving Cleavage of O–H Bond

Acidity

Reactions with metals and alkalies

The carboxylic acids like alcohols evolve hydrogen with electropositive metals and form salts with alkalies similar to phenols. However, unlike phenols they react with weaker bases such as carbonates and hydrogencarbonates to evolve carbon dioxide. This reaction is used to detect the presence of carboxyl group in an organic compound.

$$2R\text{-COOH} + 2Na \longrightarrow 2R\text{-CO}\bar{O}Na^+ + H_2$$
$$\text{Sodium carboxylate}$$

$$R\text{-COOH} + NaOH \longrightarrow R\text{-CO}\bar{O}Na^+ + H_2O$$

$$R\text{-COOH} + NaHCO_3 \longrightarrow R\text{-CO}\bar{O}Na^+ + H_2O + CO_2$$

Carboxylic acids dissociate in water to give resonance stabilised carboxylate anions and hydronium ion.

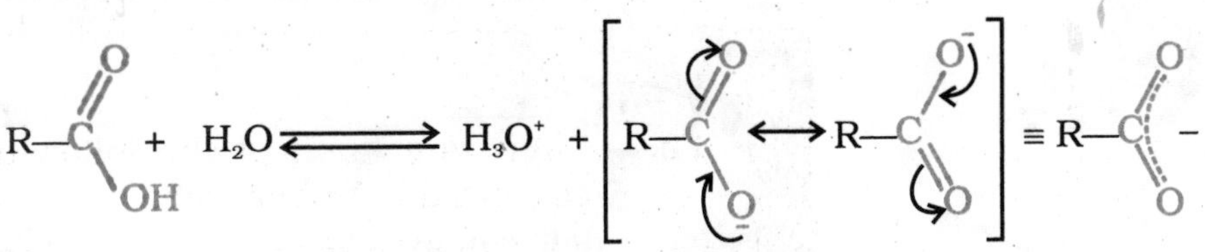

For the above reaction:

$$K_{eq} = \frac{[H_3\overset{+}{O}][RC\overset{-}{O}\overset{-}{O}]}{[H_2O][RCOOH]} \qquad K_a = K_{eq}[H_2O] = \frac{[H_3\overset{+}{O}][RC\overset{-}{O}\overset{-}{O}]}{[RCOOH]}$$

where K_{eq}, is equilibrium constant and K_a is the acid dissociation constant.

For convenience, the strength of an acid is generally indicated by its pK_a value rather than its K_a value.

$$pK_a = -\log K_a$$

The pK_a of hydrochloric acid is –7.0, where as pK_a of trifluoroacetic acid (the strongest carboxylic acid), benzoic acid and acetic acid are 0.23, 4.19 and 4.76, respectively.

Smaller the pK_a, the stronger the acid (the better it is as a proton donor). Strong acids have pK_a values < 1, the acids with pK_a values between 1 and 5 are considered to be moderately strong acids, weak acids have pK_a values between 5 and 15, and extremely weak acids have pK_a values >15.

Carboxylic acids are weaker than mineral acids, but they are stronger acids than alcohols and many simple phenols (pK_a is ~16 for ethanol and 10 for phenol). In fact, carboxylic acids are amongst the most acidic organic compounds you have studied so far. You already know why phenols are more acidic than alcohols. The higher acidity of carboxylic acids as compared to phenols can be understood similarly. The conjugate base of carboxylic acid, a carboxylate ion, is stabilised by two equivalent resonance structures in which the negative charge is at the more electronegative oxygen atom. The conjugate base of phenol, a phenoxide ion, has non-equivalent resonance structures in which the negative charge is at the less electronegative carbon atom. Therefore, resonance in phenoxide ion is not as important as it is in carboxylate ion. Further, the negative charge is delocalised over two electronegative oxygen atoms in carboxylate ion whereas it is less effectively delocalised over one oxygen atom and less electronegative carbon atoms in phenoxide ion (Unit 11, Class XII). Thus, the carboxylate ion is more stabilised than phenoxide ion, so carboxylic acids are more acidic than phenols.

Effect of substituents on the acidity of carboxylic acids: Substituents may affect the stability of the conjugate base and thus, also affect the acidity of the carboxylic acids. Electron withdrawing groups increase the acidity of carboxylic acids by stabilising the conjugate base through delocalisation of the negative charge by inductive and/or resonance effects. Conversely, electron donating groups decrease the acidity by destabilising the conjugate base.

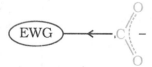   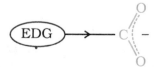

Electron withdrawing group (EWG) stabilises the carboxylate anion and strengthens the acid   Electron donating group (EDG) destabilises the carboxylate anion and weakens the acid

The effect of the following groups in increasing acidity order is

$$Ph < I < Br < Cl < F < CN < NO_2 < CF_3$$

Thus, the following acids are arranged in order of increasing acidity (based on pK_a values):

$$CF_3COOH > CCl_3COOH > CHCl_2COOH > NO_2CH_2COOH > NC\text{-}CH_2COOH >$$
←

$$FCH_2COOH > ClCH_2COOH > BrCH_2COOH > HCOOH > ClCH_2CH_2COOH >$$
(continue) ←

$$C_6H_5COOH > C_6H_5CH_2COOH > CH_3COOH > CH_3CH_2COOH$$
(continue) ←

Direct attachment of groups such as phenyl or vinyl to the carboxylic acid, increases the acidity of corresponding carboxylic acid, contrary to the decrease expected due to resonance effect shown below:

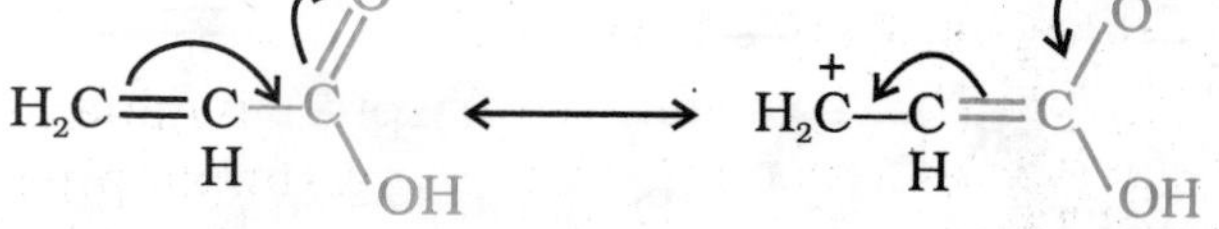

This is because of greater electronegativity of sp^2 hybridised carbon to which carboxyl carbon is attached. The presence of electron withdrawing group on the phenyl of aromatic carboxylic acid increases their acidity while electron donating groups decrease their acidity.

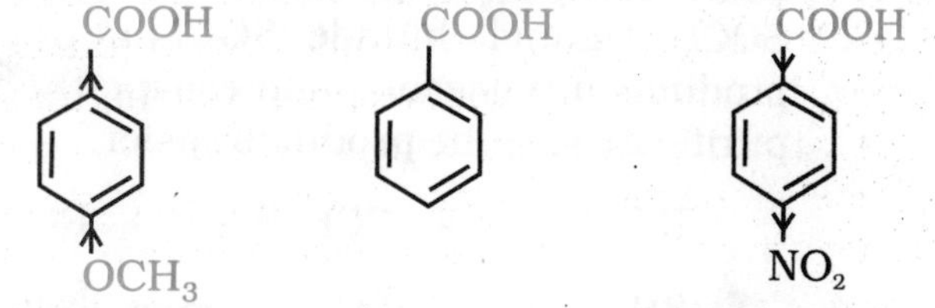

4-Methoxy
benzoic acid
(pK_a = 4.46)

Benzoic acid
(pK_a = 4.19)

4-Nitrobenzoic
acid
(pK_a = 3.41)

12.9.2 Reactions Involving Cleavage of C–OH Bond

1. Formation of anhydride

Carboxylic acids on heating with mineral acids such as H_2SO_4 or with P_2O_5 give corresponding anhydride.

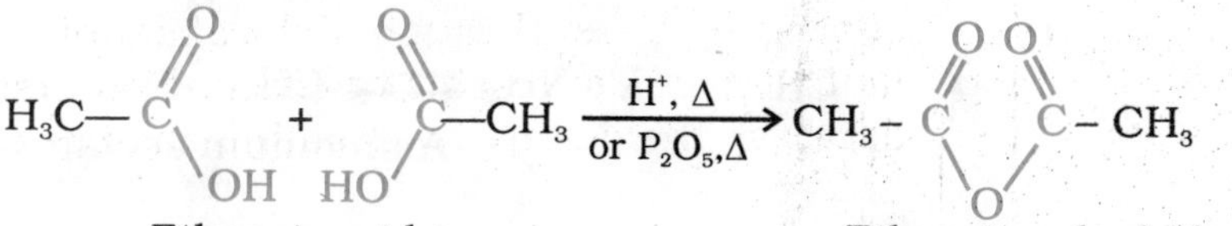

Ethanoic acid   Ethanoic anhydride

2. Esterification

Carboxylic acids are esterified with alcohols or phenols in the presence of a mineral acid such as concentrated H_2SO_4 or HCl gas as a catalyst.

$$RCOOH + R'OH \underset{}{\overset{H^+}{\rightleftharpoons}} RCOOR' + H_2O$$

Mechanism of esterification of carboxylic acids: The esterification of carboxylic acids with alcohols is a kind of nucleophilic acyl substitution. Protonation of the carbonyl oxygen activates the carbonyl group towards nucleophilic addition of the alcohol. Proton transfer in the tetrahedral intermediate converts the hydroxyl group into $-^+OH_2$ group, which, being a better leaving group, is eliminated as neutral water molecule. The protonated ester so formed finally loses a proton to give the ester.

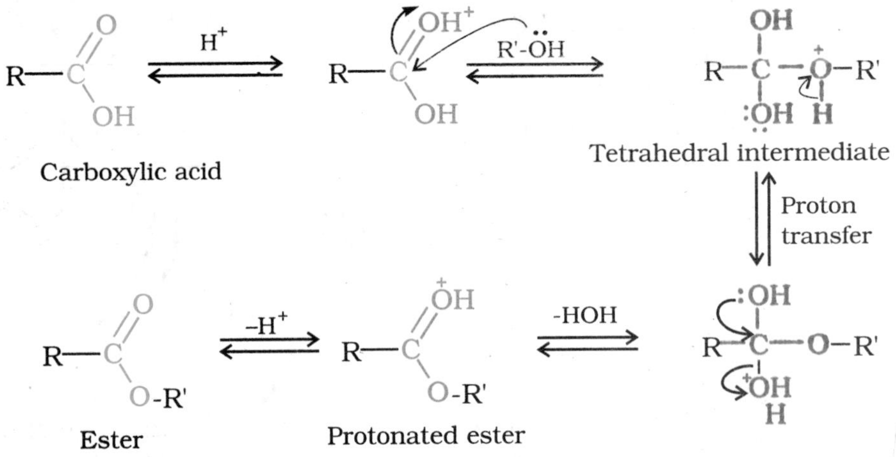

Carboxylic acid

Tetrahedral intermediate

Proton transfer

Ester

Protonated ester

3. Reactions with PCl₅, PCl₃ and SOCl₂

The hydroxyl group of carboxylic acids, behaves like that of alcohols and is easily replaced by chlorine atom on treating with PCl_5, PCl_3 or $SOCl_2$. Thionyl chloride ($SOCl_2$) is preferred because the other two products are gaseous and escape the reaction mixture making the purification of the products easier.

$$RCOOH + PCl_5 \longrightarrow RCOCl + POCl_3 + HCl$$

$$3RCOOH + PCl_3 \longrightarrow 3RCOCl + H_3PO_3$$

$$RCOOH + SOCl_2 \longrightarrow RCOCl + SO_2 + HCl$$

4. Reaction with ammonia

Carboxylic acids react with ammonia to give ammonium salt which on further heating at high temperature give amides. For example:

$$CH_3COOH + NH_3 \rightleftharpoons CH_3CO\overset{-}{O}\overset{+}{N}H_4 \xrightarrow[-H_2O]{\Delta} CH_3CONH_2$$

Ammonium acetate   Acetamide

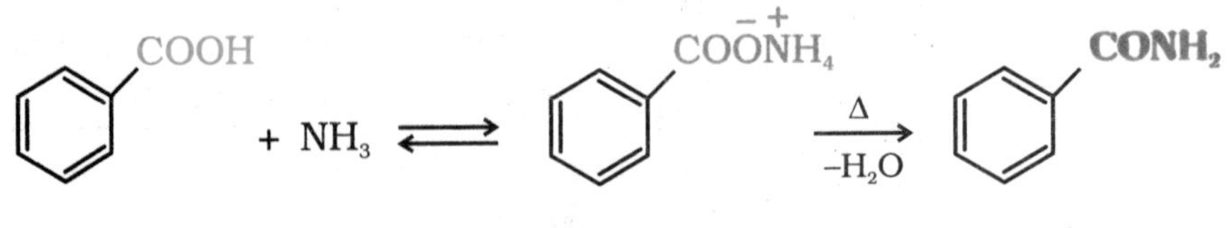

Ammonium benzoate   Benzamide

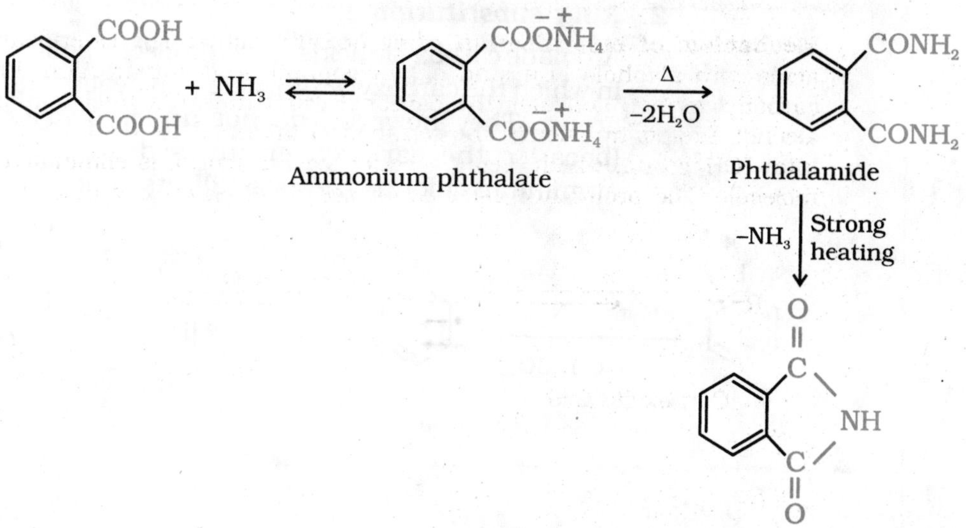

$$\text{Phthalic acid} + NH_3 \rightleftharpoons \text{Ammonium phthalate} \xrightarrow[-2H_2O]{\Delta} \text{Phthalamide}$$

Ammonium phthalate

Phthalamide

$$\xrightarrow[\text{Strong heating}]{-NH_3}$$

Phthalimide

12.9.3 Reactions Involving –COOH Group

1. Reduction

Carboxylic acids are reduced to primary alcohols by lithium aluminium hydride or better with diborane. Diborane does not easily reduce functional groups such as ester, nitro, halo, etc. Sodium borohydride does not reduce the carboxyl group.

$$R\text{-}COOH \xrightarrow[\text{(ii) } H_3O^+]{\text{(i) } LiAlH_4/\text{ether} \quad \text{or } B_2H_6} R\text{-}CH_2OH$$

2. Decarboxylation

Carboxylic acids lose carbon dioxide to form hydrocarbons when their sodium salts are heated with sodalime (NaOH and CaO in the ratio of 3 : 1). The reaction is known as decarboxylation.

$$R\text{-}COONa \xrightarrow[\text{Heat}]{\text{NaOH \& CaO}} R\text{-}H + Na_2CO_3$$

Alkali metal salts of carboxylic acids also undergo decarboxylation on electrolysis of their aqueous solutions and form hydrocarbons having twice the number of carbon atoms present in the alkyl group of the acid. The reaction is known as **Kolbe electrolysis** (Unit 13, Class XI).

12.9.4 Substitution Reactions in the Hydrocarbon Part

1. Halogenation

Carboxylic acids having an α-hydrogen are halogenated at the α-position on treatment with chlorine or bromine in the presence of small amount of red phosphorus to give α-halocarboxylic acids. The reaction is known as **Hell-Volhard-Zelinsky reaction.**

$$R\text{-}CH_2\text{-}COOH \xrightarrow[\text{(ii) } H_2O]{\text{(i) } X_2/\text{Red phosphorus}} R\text{-}\underset{\overset{|}{X}}{C}H\text{-}COOH$$

X = Cl, Br

α – Halocarboxylic acid

2. Ring substitution

Aromatic carboxylic acids undergo electrophilic substitution reactions in which the carboxyl group acts as a deactivating and meta-directing group. They however, do not undergo **Friedel-Crafts reaction** (because the carboxyl group is deactivating and the catalyst aluminium chloride (Lewis acid) gets bonded to the carboxyl group).

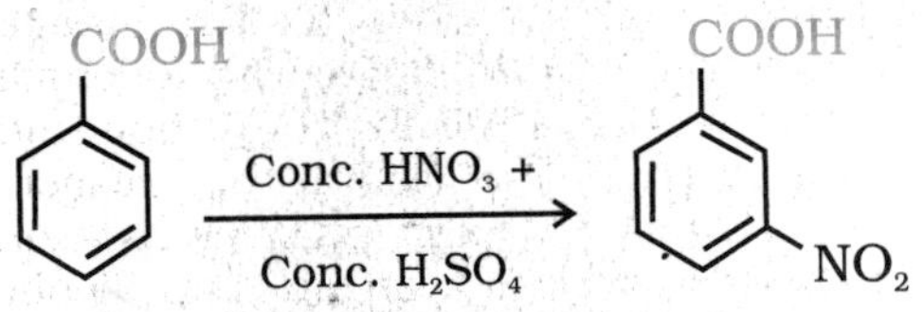

m-Nitrobenzoic acid

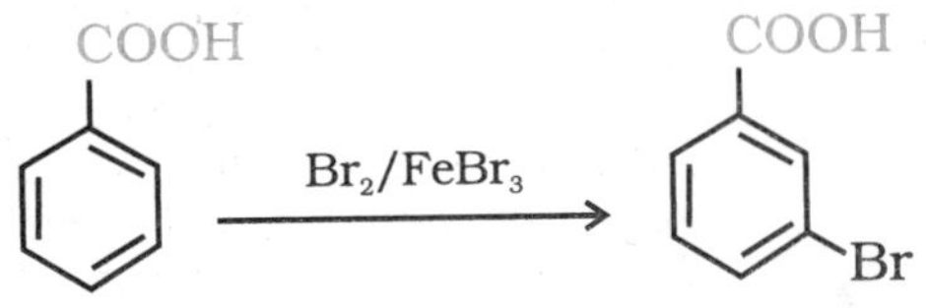

m-Bromobenzoic acid

Intext Question

12.8 Which acid of each pair shown here would you expect to be stronger?

(i) CH_3CO_2H or CH_2FCO_2H (ii) CH_2FCO_2H or CH_2ClCO_2H

(iii) $CH_2FCH_2CH_2CO_2H$ or $CH_3CHFCH_2CO_2H$

(iv) 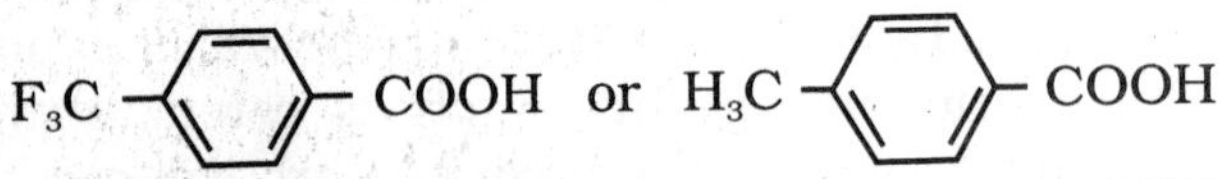 F_3C —⟨ ⟩— COOH or H_3C —⟨ ⟩— COOH

12.10 Uses of Carboxylic Acids

Methanoic acid is used in rubber, textile, dyeing, leather and electroplating industries. Ethanoic acid is used as solvent and as vinegar in food industry. Hexanedioic acid is used in the manufacture of nylon-6, 6. Esters of benzoic acid are used in perfumery. Sodium benzoate is used as a food preservative. Higher fatty acids are used for the manufacture of soaps and detergents.

Summary

Aldehydes, ketones and **carboxylic acids** are some of the important classes of organic compounds containing carbonyl group. These are highly polar molecules. Therefore, they boil at higher temperatures than the hydrocarbons and weakly polar compounds such as ethers of comparable molecular masses. The lower members are more soluble in water because they form hydrogen bonds with water. The higher members, because of large size of hydrophobic chain of carbon atoms, are insoluble in water but soluble in common organic solvents. Aldehydes are prepared by dehydrogenation or controlled oxidation of primary alcohols and controlled or selective reduction of acyl halides. Aromatic aldehydes may also be prepared by oxidation of (i) methylbenzene with chromyl chloride or CrO_3 in the presence of acetic anhydride, (ii) formylation of arenes with carbon monoxide and hydrochloric acid in the presence of anhydrous aluminium chloride, and (iii) cuprous chloride or by hydrolysis of benzal chloride. Ketones are prepared by oxidation of secondary alcohols and hydration of alkynes. Ketones are also prepared by reaction of acyl chloride with dialkylcadmium. A good method for the preparation of aromatic ketones is the **Friedel-Crafts acylation** of aromatic hydrocarbons with acyl chlorides or anhydrides. Both aldehydes and ketones can be prepared by ozonolysis of alkenes. Aldehydes and ketones undergo nucleophilic addition reactions onto the carbonyl group with a number of nucleophiles such as, HCN, $NaHSO_3$, alcohols (or diols), ammonia derivatives, and **Grignard reagents**. The α-hydrogens in aldehydes and ketones are acidic. Therefore, aldehydes and ketones having at least one α-hydrogen, undergo **Aldol condensation** in the presence of a base to give α-hydroxyaldehydes (aldol) and α-hydroxyketones(ketol), respectively. Aldehydes having no α-hydrogen undergo **Cannizzaro reaction** in the presence of concentrated alkali. Aldehydes and ketones are reduced to alcohols with $NaBH_4$, $LiAlH_4$, or by catalytic hydrogenation. The carbonyl group of aldehydes and ketones can be reduced to a methylene group by **Clemmensen reduction** or **Wolff-Kishner reduction**. Aldehydes are easily oxidised to carboxylic acids by mild oxidising reagents such as **Tollens' reagent** and **Fehling's reagent**. These oxidation reactions are used to distinguish aldehydes from ketones. Carboxylic acids are prepared by the oxidation of primary alcohols, aldehydes and alkenes by hydrolysis of nitriles, and by treatment of Grignard reagents with carbon dioxide. Aromatic carboxylic acids are also prepared by side-chain oxidation of alkylbenzenes. Carboxylic acids are considerably more acidic than alcohols and most of simple phenols. Carboxylic acids are reduced to primary alcohols with $LiAlH_4$, or better with diborane in ether solution and also undergo α-halogenation with Cl_2 and Br_2 in the presence of red phosphorus (**Hell-Volhard Zelinsky reaction**). Methanal, ethanal, propanone, benzaldehyde, formic acid, acetic acid and benzoic acid are highly useful compounds in industry.

Exercises

12.1 What is meant by the following terms ? Give an example of the reaction in each case.

(i) Cyanohydrin   (ii) Acetal   (iii) Semicarbazone

(iv) Aldol   (v) Hemiacetal   (vi) Oxime

(vii) Ketal   (vii) Imine   (ix) 2,4-DNP-derivative

(x) Schiff's base

12.2 Name the following compounds according to IUPAC system of nomenclature:

(i) $CH_3CH(CH_3)CH_2CH_2CHO$ (ii) $CH_3CH_2COCH(C_2H_5)CH_2CH_2Cl$

(iii) $CH_3CH=CHCHO$ (iv) $CH_3COCH_2COCH_3$

(v) $CH_3CH(CH_3)CH_2C(CH_3)_2COCH_3$ (vi) $(CH_3)_3CCH_2COOH$

(vii) $OHCC_6H_4CHO$-p

12.3 Draw the structures of the following compounds.

(i) 3-Methylbutanal   (ii) p-Nitropropiophenone

(iii) p-Methylbenzaldehyde   (iv) 4-Methylpent-3-en-2-one

(v) 4-Chloropentan-2-one   (vi) 3-Bromo-4-phenylpentanoic acid

(vii) p,p'-Dihydroxybenzophenone   (viii) Hex-2-en-4-ynoic acid

12.4 Write the IUPAC names of the following ketones and aldehydes. Wherever possible, give also common names.

(i) $CH_3CO(CH_2)_4CH_3$ (ii) $CH_3CH_2CHBrCH_2CH(CH_3)CHO$

(iii) $CH_3(CH_2)_5CHO$ (iv) Ph-CH=CH-CHO

(v)

(vi) PhCOPh

12.5 Draw structures of the following derivatives.

(i) The 2,4-dinitrophenylhydrazone of benzaldehyde

(ii) Cyclopropanone oxime

(iii) Acetaldehydedimethylacetal

(iv) The semicarbazone of cyclobutanone

(v) The ethylene ketal of hexan-3-one

(vi) The methyl hemiacetal of formaldehyde

12.6 Predict the products formed when cyclohexanecarbaldehyde reacts with following reagents.

(i) PhMgBr and then H_3O^+ (ii) Tollens' reagent

(iii) Semicarbazide and weak acid   (iv) Excess ethanol and acid

(v) Zinc amalgam and dilute hydrochloric acid

12.7 Which of the following compounds would undergo aldol condensation, which the Cannizzaro reaction and which neither? Write the structures of the expected products of aldol condensation and Cannizzaro reaction.

(i) Methanal   (ii) 2-Methylpentanal   (iii) Benzaldehyde

(iv) Benzophenone   (v) Cyclohexanone   (vi) 1-Phenylpropanone

(vii) Phenylacetaldehyde   (viii) Butan-1-ol   (ix) 2,2-Dimethylbutanal

12.8 How will you convert ethanal into the following compounds?

(i) Butane-1,3-diol   (ii) But-2-enal   (iii) But-2-enoic acid

12.9 Write structural formulas and names of four possible aldol condensation products from propanal and butanal. In each case, indicate which aldehyde acts as nucleophile and which as electrophile.

12.10 An organic compound with the molecular formula $C_9H_{10}O$ forms 2,4-DNP derivative, reduces Tollens' reagent and undergoes Cannizzaro reaction. On vigorous oxidation, it gives 1,2-benzenedicarboxylic acid. Identify the compound.

12.11 An organic compound (A) (molecular formula $C_8H_{16}O_2$) was hydrolysed with dilute sulphuric acid to give a carboxylic acid (B) and an alcohol (C). Oxidation of (C) with chromic acid produced (B). (C) on dehydration gives but-1-ene. Write equations for the reactions involved.

12.12 Arrange the following compounds in increasing order of their property as indicated:

(i) Acetaldehyde, Acetone, Di-*tert*-butyl ketone, Methyl *tert*-butyl ketone (reactivity towards HCN)

(ii) $CH_3CH_2CH(Br)COOH$, $CH_3CH(Br)CH_2COOH$, $(CH_3)_2CHCOOH$, $CH_3CH_2CH_2COOH$ (acid strength)

(iii) Benzoic acid, 4-Nitrobenzoic acid, 3,4-Dinitrobenzoic acid, 4-Methoxybenzoic acid (acid strength)

12.13 Give simple chemical tests to distinguish between the following pairs of compounds.

(i) Propanal and Propanone   (ii) Acetophenone and Benzophenone

(iii) Phenol and Benzoic acid   (iv) Benzoic acid and Ethyl benzoate

(v) Pentan-2-one and Pentan-3-one   (vi) Benzaldehyde and Acetophenone

(vii) Ethanal and Propanal

12.14 How will you prepare the following compounds from benzene? You may use any inorganic reagent and any organic reagent having not more than one carbon atom

(i) Methyl benzoate   (ii) *m*-Nitrobenzoic acid

(iii) *p*-Nitrobenzoic acid   (iv) Phenylacetic acid

(v) *p*-Nitrobenzaldehyde.

12.15 How will you bring about the following conversions in not more than two steps?

(i) Propanone to Propene   (ii) Benzoic acid to Benzaldehyde

(iii) Ethanol to 3-Hydroxybutanal   (iv) Benzene to *m*-Nitroacetophenone

(v) Benzaldehyde to Benzophenone   (vi) Bromobenzene to 1-Phenylethanol

(vii) Benzaldehyde to 3-Phenylpropan-1-ol

(viii) Benazaldehyde to α-Hydroxyphenylacetic acid

(ix) Benzoic acid to *m*- Nitrobenzyl alcohol

12.16 Describe the following:

(i) Acetylation   (ii) Cannizzaro reaction

(iii) Cross aldol condensation   (iv) Decarboxylation

12.17 Complete each synthesis by giving missing starting material, reagent or products

(i) $\xrightarrow[\text{KOH, heat}]{\text{KMnO}_4}$

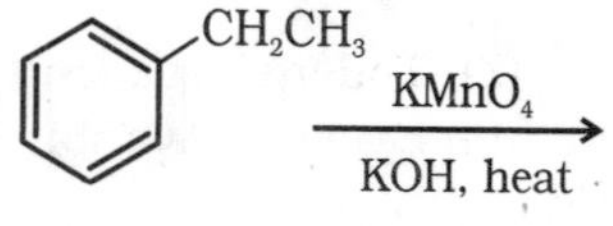

(ii) $\xrightarrow[\text{heat}]{\text{SOCl}_2}$

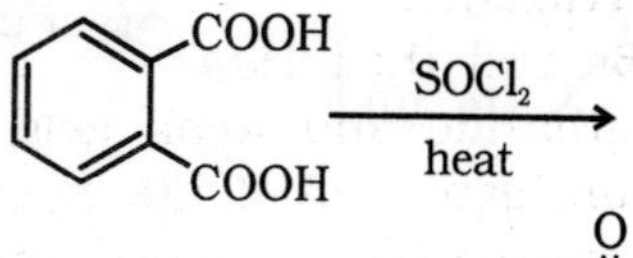

(iii) $C_6H_5CHO \xrightarrow{H_2NCONHNH_2}$

(iv)

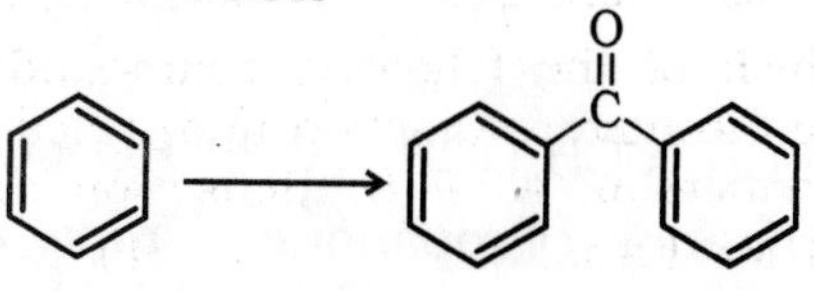

(v) $\xrightarrow{[\text{Ag(NH}_3)_2]^+}$

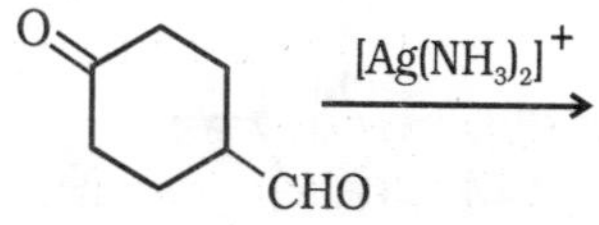

(vi) $\xrightarrow{\text{NaCN / HCl}}$

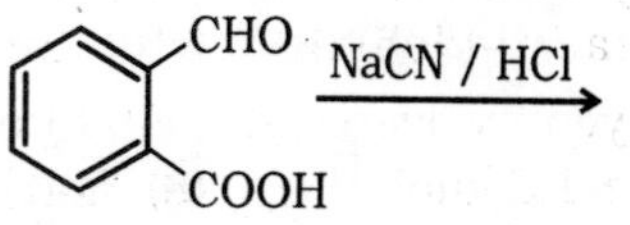

(vii) C_6H_5CHO
  +
CH_3CH_2CHO $\xrightarrow{\text{dil.NaOH}}$

(viii) $CH_3COCH_2COOC_2H_5 \xrightarrow[\text{(ii) H}^+]{\text{(i) NaBH}_4}$

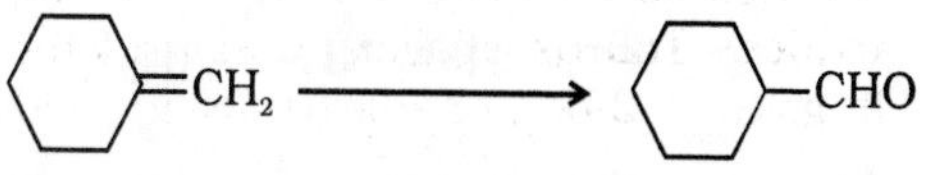

(ix) $-OH \xrightarrow{\text{CrO}_3}$

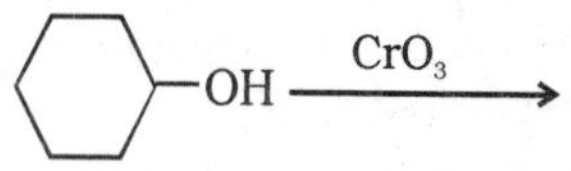

(x) $=CH_2 \longrightarrow$ $-CHO$

(xi) $\xrightarrow[\text{(ii) Zn-H}_2\text{O}]{\text{(i) O}_3}$ 2 $=O$

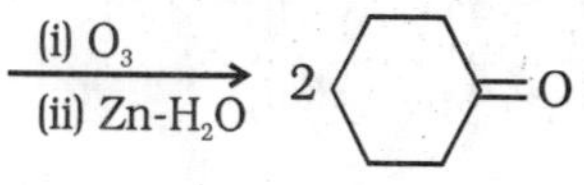

12.18 Give plausible explanation for each of the following:

(i) Cyclohexanone forms cyanohydrin in good yield but 2,2,6-trimethylcyclo-hexanone does not.

(ii) There are two –NH_2 groups in semicarbazide. However, only one is involved in the formation of semicarbazones.

(iii) During the preparation of esters from a carboxylic acid and an alcohol in the presence of an acid catalyst, the water or the ester should be removed as soon as it is formed.

12.19 An organic compound contains 69.77% carbon, 11.63% hydrogen and rest oxygen. The molecular mass of the compound is 86. It does not reduce Tollens' reagent but forms an addition compound with sodium hydrogensulphite and give positive iodoform test. On vigorous oxidation it gives ethanoic and propanoic acid. Write the possible structure of the compound.

12.20 Although phenoxide ion has more number of resonating structures than carboxylate ion, carboxylic acid is a stronger acid than phenol. Why?

Answers to Some Intext Questions

12.1

(i) $\underset{\underset{CH_3}{|}}{H_3C}-\overset{\overset{O}{||}}{CH}-\overset{O}{C}-H$

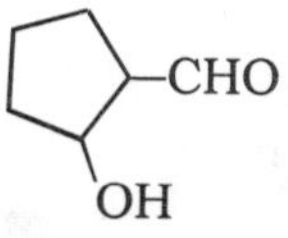

(iv) $CH_3-\overset{\overset{O}{||}}{C}-CH_2-CH_2-CHO$

(ii) $H_3C-\underset{\underset{OH}{|}}{CH}-CH_2-\overset{\overset{O}{||}}{C}-H$

(v) $CH_3CH_2\underset{\underset{CH_3}{|}}{CH}-\overset{\overset{O}{||}}{C}-\underset{\underset{CH_3}{|}}{CH}-CH_2CH_3$

(iii) $-CHO$ $\underset{OH}{}$

(vi) $F-$$-\overset{\overset{O}{||}}{C}-CH_3$

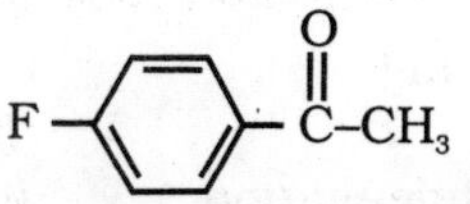

12.2 (i) 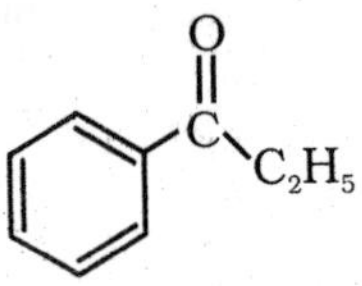 $C_6H_5-CO-C_2H_5$ (ii) 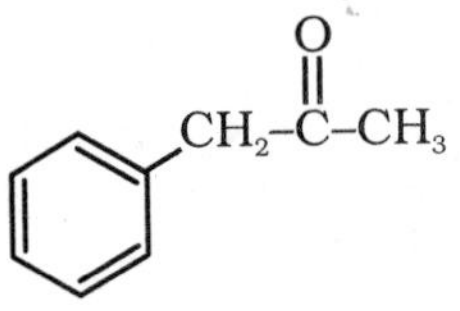 $C_6H_5-CH_2-CO-CH_3$ (iii) 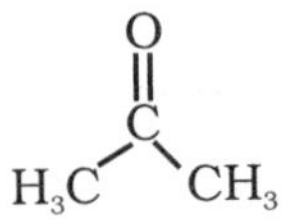 $H_3C-CO-CH_3$ (iv) 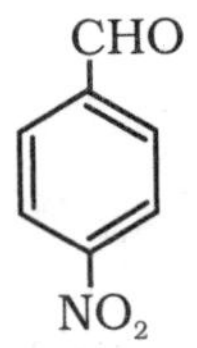 p-nitrobenzaldehyde (CHO with NO$_2$)

12.3 $CH_3CH_2CH_3 < CH_3OCH_3 < CH_3CHO < CH_3CH_2OH$

12.4 (i) Butanone < Propanone < Propanal < Ethanal

(ii) Acetophenone < p-Tolualdehyde , Benzaldehyde < p-Nitrobenzaldehyde.

12.5 (i) 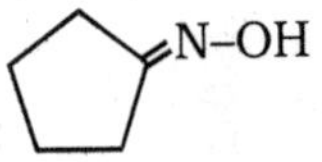 cyclopentanone N–OH (oxime)

(ii) 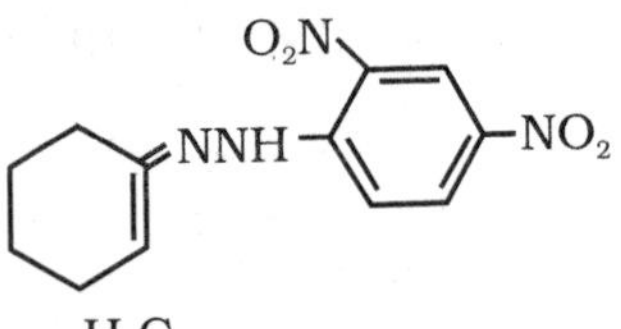 cyclohexene ring =NNH–(2,4-dinitrophenyl) with O_2N and NO_2

(iii) $R-CH=CH-CH=N-NH-\overset{O}{\underset{}{C}}-NH_2$

(iv) 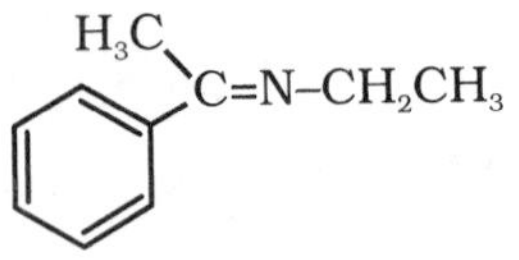 $C_6H_5-\overset{H_3C}{\underset{}{C}}=N-CH_2CH_3$

12.6 (i) 3-Phenylpropanoic acid   (ii) 3-Methylbut-2-enoic acid
(iii) 2-Methylcyclopentanecarboxylic acid.   (iv) 2,4,6-Trinitrobenzoic acid

12.7

(i) 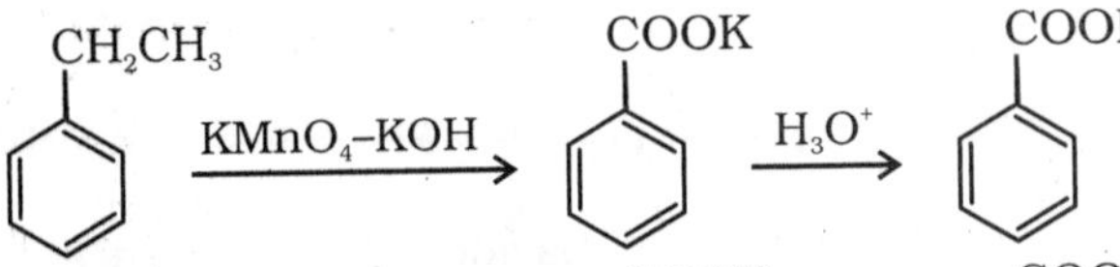 Ethylbenzene (CH_2CH_3) $\xrightarrow{KMnO_4-KOH}$ COOK (benzene) $\xrightarrow{H_3O^+}$ COOH (benzene)

(ii) 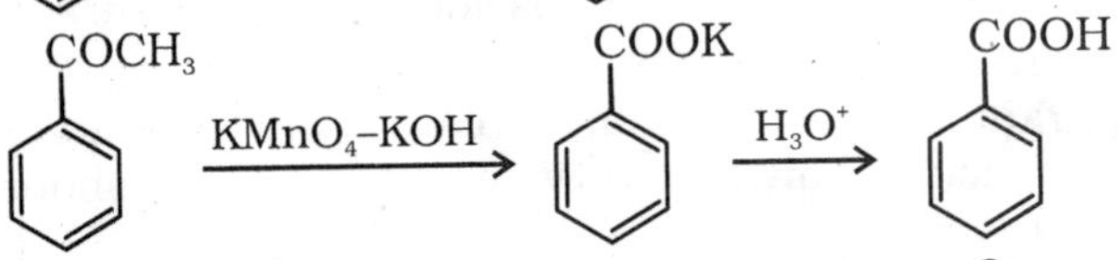 Acetophenone ($COCH_3$) $\xrightarrow{KMnO_4-KOH}$ COOK $\xrightarrow{H_3O^+}$ COOH

(iii) 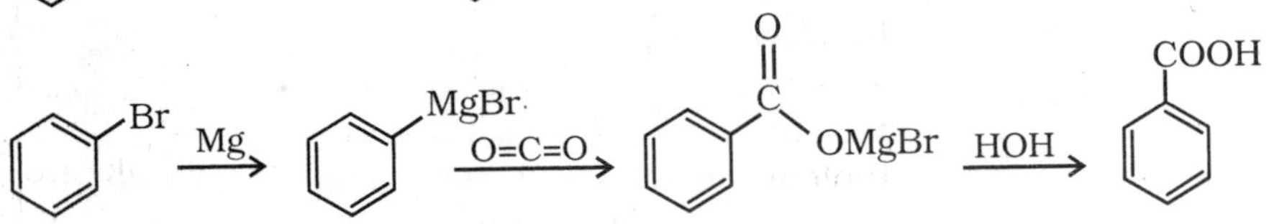 Bromobenzene (Br) $\xrightarrow{Mg}$ phenyl MgBr $\xrightarrow{O=C=O}$ $C_6H_5-CO-OMgBr$ $\xrightarrow{HOH}$ COOH (benzoic acid)

(iv) 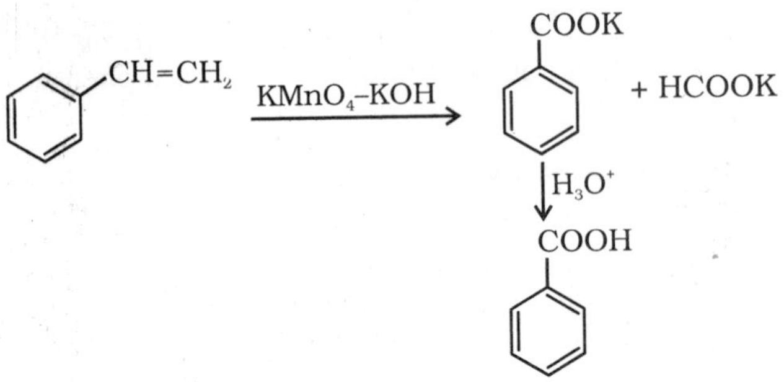 Styrene ($CH=CH_2$) $\xrightarrow{KMnO_4-KOH}$ COOK + HCOOK $\xrightarrow{H_3O^+}$ COOH (benzoic acid)

12.8 (i) CH_3COOH (ii) CH_2FCOOH (iii) CH_3CHFCH_2COOH (iv) 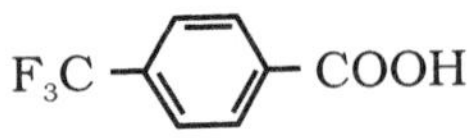 $F_3C-C_6H_4-COOH$

Chemistry 380

Objectives

After studying this Unit, you will be able to

- describe amines as derivatives of ammonia having a pyramidal structure;
- classify amines as primary, secondary and tertiary;
- name amines by common names and IUPAC system;
- describe some of the important methods of preparation of amines;
- explain the properties of amines;
- distinguish between primary, secondary and tertiary amines;
- describe the method of preparation of diazonium salts and their importance in the synthesis of a series of aromatic compounds including azo dyes.

"The chief commercial use of amines is as intermediates in the synthesis of medicines and fibres".

Amines constitute an important class of organic compounds derived by replacing one or more hydrogen atoms of ammonia molecule by alkyl/aryl group(s). In nature, they occur among proteins, vitamins, alkaloids and hormones. Synthetic examples include polymers, dyestuffs and drugs. Two biologically active compounds, namely adrenaline and ephedrine, both containing secondary amino group, are used to increase blood pressure. Novocain, a synthetic amino compound, is used as an anaesthetic in dentistry. Benadryl, a well known antihistaminic drug also contains tertiary amino group. Quaternary ammonium salts are used as surfactants. Diazonium salts are intermediates in the preparation of a variety of aromatic compounds including dyes. In this Unit, you will learn about amines and diazonium salts.

I. AMINES

Amines can be considered as derivatives of ammonia, obtained by replacement of one, two or all the three hydrogen atoms by alkyl and/or aryl groups.

For example:

$$CH_3-NH_2, \quad C_6H_5-NH_2, \quad CH_3-NH-CH_3, \quad CH_3-N\begin{smallmatrix}CH_3\\CH_3\end{smallmatrix}$$

13.1 Structure of Amines

Like ammonia, nitrogen atom of amines is trivalent and carries an unshared pair of electrons. Nitrogen orbitals in amines are therefore, sp^3 hybridised and the geometry of amines is pyramidal. Each of the three sp^3 hybridised orbitals of nitrogen overlap with orbitals of hydrogen or carbon depending upon the composition of the amines. The fourth orbital of nitrogen in all amines contains an unshared pair of electrons. Due to the presence of unshared pair of electrons, the angle C–N–E, (where E is

C or H) is less than 109.5°; for instance, it is 108° in case of trimethylamine as shown in Fig. 13.1.

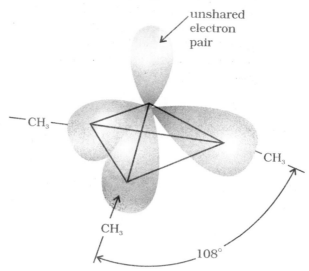

Fig. 13.1 *Pyramidal shape of trimethylamine*

13.2 Classification

Amines are classified as primary (1°), secondary (2°) and tertiary (3°) depending upon the number of hydrogen atoms replaced by alkyl or aryl groups in ammonia molecule. If one hydrogen atom of ammonia is replaced by R or Ar , we get RNH_2 or $ArNH_2$, a primary amine (1°). If two hydrogen atoms of ammonia or one hydrogen atom of $R-NH_2$ are replaced by another alkyl/aryl(R') group, what would you get? You get R-NHR', secondary amine. The second alkyl/aryl group may be same or different. Replacement of another hydrogen atom by alkyl/aryl group leads to the formation of tertiary amine. Amines are said to be 'simple' when all the alkyl or aryl groups are the same, and 'mixed' when they are different.

$$NH_3 \rightarrow \quad RNH_2 \rightarrow \quad \underset{R'}{\overset{R}{\diagdown}}N-H \rightarrow \quad \underset{R'}{\overset{R}{\diagdown}}N-R''$$

Primary(1°) Secondary(2°) Tertiary(3°)

13.3 Nomenclature

In common system, an aliphatic amine is named by prefixing alkyl group to amine, i.e., alkylamine as one word (e.g., methylamine). In secondary and tertiary amines, when two or more groups are the same, the prefix di or tri is appended before the name of alkyl group. In IUPAC system, amines are named as **alkanamines**, derived by replacement of 'e' of alkane by the word amine. For example, CH_3NH_2 is named as methanamine. In case, more than one amino group is present at different positions in the parent chain, their positions are specified by giving numbers to the carbon atoms bearing $-NH_2$ groups and suitable prefix such as di, tri, etc. is attached to the amine. The letter 'e' of the suffix of the hydrocarbon part is retained. For example, $H_2N-CH_2-CH_2-NH_2$ is named as ethane-1, 2-diamine.

In arylamines, $-NH_2$ group is directly attached to the benzene ring. $C_6H_5NH_2$ is the simplest example of arylamine. In common system, it is known as aniline. It is also an accepted IUPAC name. While naming arylamines according to IUPAC system, suffix 'e' of arene is replaced by 'amine'. Thus in IUPAC system, $C_6H_5-NH_2$ is named as benzenamine. Common and IUPAC names of some alkylamines and arylamines are given in Table 13.1.

Table 13.1: Nomenclature of Some Alkylamines and Arylamines

Amine	Common name	IUPAC name
$CH_3-CH_2-NH_2$	Ethylamine	Ethanamine
$CH_3-CH_2-CH_2-NH_2$	n-Propylamine	Propan-1-amine
$CH_3-\overset{\displaystyle }{\underset{\displaystyle NH_2}{CH}}-CH_3$	Isopropylamine	Propan-2-amine
$CH_3-\underset{\displaystyle H}{N}-CH_2-CH_3$	Ethylmethylamine	N-Methylethanamine
$CH_3-\underset{\displaystyle CH_3}{N}-CH_3$	Trimethylamine	N,N-Dimethylmethanamine
$C_2H_5-\underset{\displaystyle C_2H_5}{N}-\overset{1}{C}H_2-\overset{2}{C}H_2-\overset{3}{C}H_2-\overset{4}{C}H_3$	N,N-Diethylbutylamine	N,N-Diethylbutan-1-amine
$NH_2-\overset{1}{C}H_2-\overset{2}{C}H=\overset{3}{C}H_2$	Allylamine	Prop-2-en-1-amine
$NH_2-(CH_2)_6-NH_2$	Hexamethylenediamine	Hexane-1,6-diamine
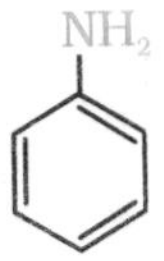	Aniline	Aniline or Benzenamine
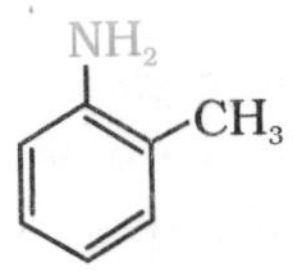	o-Toluidine	2-Aminotoluene
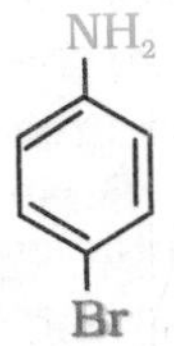	p-Bromoaniline	4-Bromobenzenamine or 4-Bromoaniline
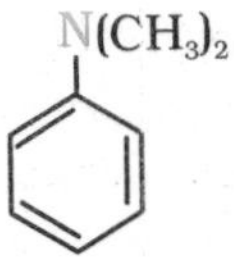	N,N-Dimethylaniline	N,N-Dimethylbenzenamine

13.4 Preparation of Amines

Amines are prepared by the following methods:

1. Reduction of nitro compounds

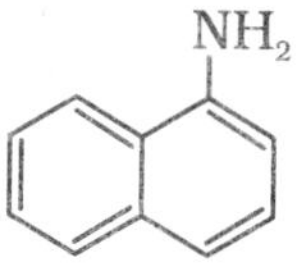

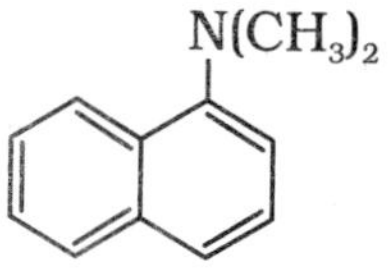

Nitro compounds are reduced to amines by passing hydrogen gas in the presence of finely divided nickel, palladium or platinum and also by reduction with metals in acidic medium. Nitroalkanes can also be similarly reduced to the corresponding alkanamines.

(i) 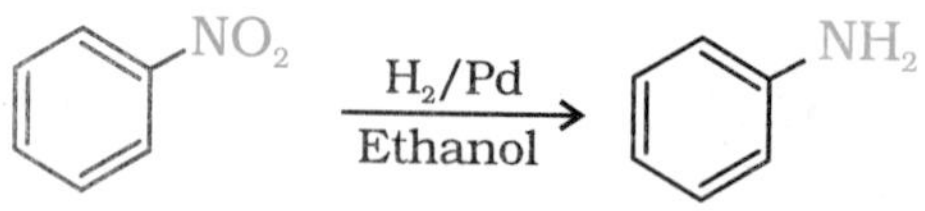 [benzene-NO$_2$] $\xrightarrow[\text{Ethanol}]{\text{H}_2/\text{Pd}}$ [benzene-NH$_2$]

(ii) 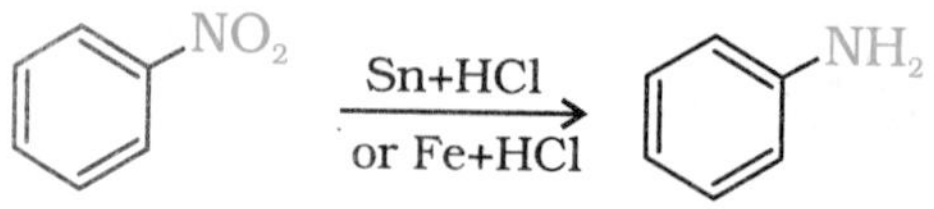 [benzene-NO$_2$] $\xrightarrow[\text{or Fe+HCl}]{\text{Sn+HCl}}$ [benzene-NH$_2$]

Reduction with iron scrap and hydrochloric acid is preferred because FeCl$_2$ formed gets hydrolysed to release hydrochloric acid during the reaction. Thus, only a small amount of hydrochloric acid is required to initiate the reaction.

2. Ammonolysis of alkyl halides

You have read (Unit 10, Class XII) that the carbon - halogen bond in alkyl or benzyl halides can be easily cleaved by a nucleophile. Hence, an alkyl or benzyl halide on reaction with an ethanolic solution of ammonia undergoes nucleophilic substitution reaction in which the halogen atom is replaced by an amino (–NH$_2$) group. This process of cleavage of the C–X bond by ammonia molecule is known as **ammonolysis**. The reaction is carried out in a sealed tube at 373 K. The primary amine thus obtained behaves as a nucleophile and can further react with alkyl halide to form secondary and tertiary amines, and finally quaternary ammonium salt.

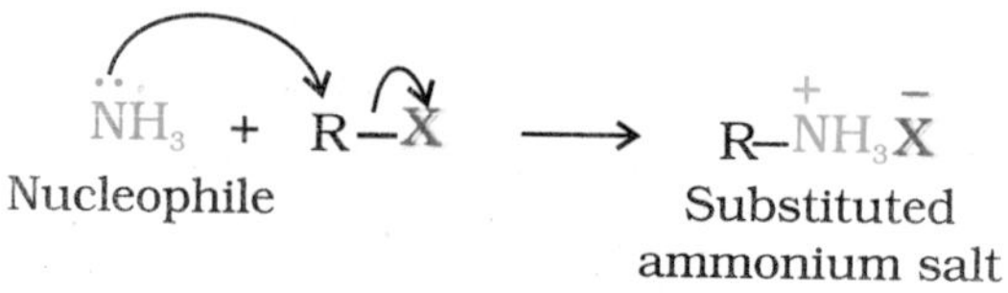

$$\overset{..}{N}H_3 + R-X \longrightarrow R-\overset{+}{N}H_3\overset{-}{X}$$

Nucleophile   Substituted ammonium salt

$$RNH_2 \xrightarrow{\text{RX}} R_2NH \xrightarrow{\text{RX}} R_3N \xrightarrow{\text{RX}} R_4\overset{+}{N}\overset{-}{X}$$

(1°) (2°) (3°) Quaternary
ammonium salt

The free amine can be obtained from the ammonium salt by treatment with a strong base:

$$R-\overset{+}{N}H_3\overset{-}{X} + NaOH \longrightarrow R-NH_2 + H_2O + Na\overset{-}{X}$$

Ammonolysis has the disadvantage of yielding a mixture of primary, secondary and tertiary amines and also a quaternary ammonium salt. However, primary amine is obtained as a major product by taking large excess of ammonia.

The order of reactivity of halides with amines is RI > RBr > RCl.

Write chemical equations for the following reactions: *Example 13.1*
  (i) Reaction of ethanolic NH_3 with C_2H_5Cl.
  (ii) Ammonolysis of benzyl chloride and reaction of amine so formed with two moles of CH_3Cl.

Solution

(i) $C_2H_5-Cl \xrightarrow{NH_3} C_2H_5-NH_2 \xrightarrow{C_2H_5-Cl} C_2H_5-\overset{\overset{H}{|}}{N}-C_2H_5 \xrightarrow{C_2H_5-Cl} C_2H_5-\underset{\underset{C_2H_5}{|}}{N}-C_2H_5 \xrightarrow{C_2H_5Cl} (C_2H_5)_3\overset{+}{N}\overset{-}{Cl}$

Chloroethane Ethanamine N-Ethylethanamine N,N-Diethylethanamine Quaternary ammonium Salt

(ii) $C_6H_5-CH_2-Cl \xrightarrow{NH_3} C_6H_5-CH_2NH_2 \xrightarrow{2CH_3Cl} C_6H_5-CH_2-\underset{\underset{CH_3}{|}}{N}-CH_3$

Benzylchloride Benzylamine N,N-Dimethylphenylmethanamine

---

3. Reduction of nitriles

Nitriles on reduction with lithium aluminium hydride ($LiAlH_4$) or catalytic hydrogenation produce primary amines. This reaction is used for ascent of amine series, i.e., for preparation of amines containing one carbon atom more than the starting amine.

$$R-C\equiv N \xrightarrow[\text{Na(Hg)/}C_2H_5OH]{H_2/Ni} R-CH_2-NH_2$$

4. Reduction of amides

The amides on reduction with lithium aluminium hydride yield amines.

$$R-\overset{\overset{O}{\|}}{C}-NH_2 \xrightarrow[\text{(ii) }H_2O]{\text{(i) }LiAlH_4} R-CH_2-NH_2$$

5. Gabriel phthalimide synthesis

Gabriel synthesis is used for the preparation of primary amines. Phthalimide on treatment with ethanolic potassium hydroxide forms potassium salt of phthalimide which on heating with alkyl halide followed by alkaline hydrolysis produces the corresponding primary amine. Aromatic primary amines cannot be prepared by this method because aryl halides do not undergo nucleophilic substitution with the anion formed by phthalimide.

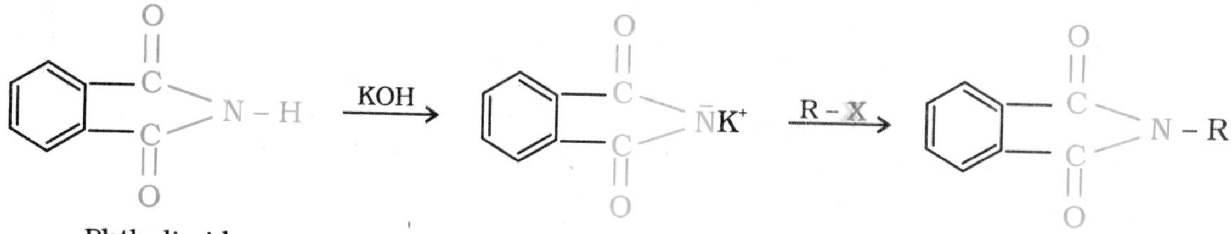

Phthalimide   N-Alkylphthalimide

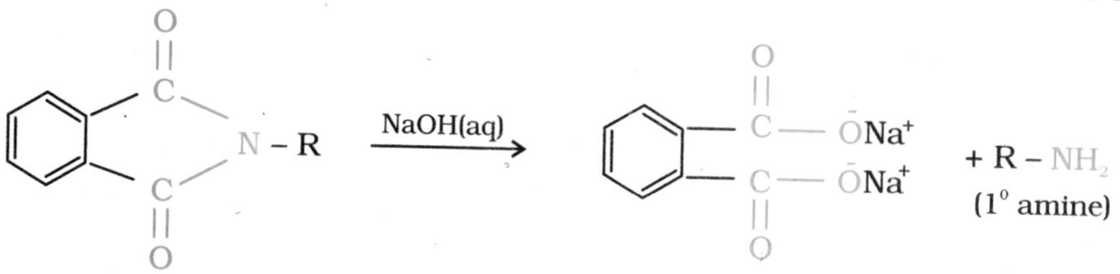

$+ R - NH_2$
(1° amine)

6. Hoffmann bromamide degradation reaction

Hoffmann developed a method for preparation of primary amines by treating an amide with bromine in an aqueous or ethanolic solution of sodium hydroxide. In this degradation reaction, migration of an alkyl or aryl group takes place from carbonyl carbon of the amide to the nitrogen atom. The amine so formed contains one carbon less than that present in the amide.

$$R - \overset{\overset{\displaystyle O}{||}}{C} - NH_2 + Br_2 + 4NaOH \longrightarrow R - NH_2 + Na_2CO_3 + 2NaBr + 2H_2O$$

Example 13.2   Write chemical equations for the following conversions:

(i) CH_3-CH_2-Cl into $CH_3-CH_2-CH_2-NH_2$

(ii) $C_6H_5-CH_2-Cl$ into $C_6H_5-CH_2-CH_2-NH_2$

Solution

(i) $CH_3-CH_2-Cl \xrightarrow{\text{Ethanolic NaCN}} CH_3-CH_2-C\equiv N \xrightarrow{\text{reduction}} CH_3-CH_2-CH_2-NH_2$

Chloroethane   Propanenitrile   Propan-1-amine

(ii) $C_6H_5-CH_2-Cl \xrightarrow{\text{Ethanolic NaCN}} C_6H_5-CH_2-C\equiv N \xrightarrow{H_2/Ni} C_6H_5-CH_2-CH_2-NH_2$

Chlorophenylmethane   Phenylethanenitrile   2-Phenylethanamine
(Benzyl chloride)   (Benzyl cyanide)

Example 13.3

Write structures and IUPAC names of

(i) the amide which gives propanamine by Hoffmann bromamide reaction.

(ii) the amine produced by the Hoffmann degradation of benzamide.

(i) Propanamine contains three carbons. Hence, the amide molecule must contain four carbon atoms. Structure and IUPAC name of the starting amide with four carbon atoms are given below:

$$CH_3-CH_2-CH_2-\underset{\underset{O}{||}}{C}-NH_2 \qquad \text{Butanamide}$$

(ii) Benzamide is an aromatic amide containing seven carbon atoms. Hence, the amine formed from benzamide is aromatic primary amine containing six carbon atoms.

Aniline or benzenamine

13.3 How will you convert

(i) Benzene into aniline (ii) Benzene into N, N-dimethylaniline

(iii) $Cl-(CH_2)_4-Cl$ into hexan-1,6-diamine?

13.5 Physical Properties

The lower aliphatic amines are gases with fishy odour. Primary amines with three or more carbon atoms are liquid and still higher ones are solid. Aniline and other arylamines are usually colourless but get coloured on storage due to atmospheric oxidation.

Lower aliphatic amines are soluble in water because they can form hydrogen bonds with water molecules. However, solubility decreases with increase in molar mass of amines due to increase in size of the hydrophobic alkyl part. Higher amines are essentially insoluble in water. Considering the electronegativity of nitrogen of amine and oxygen of alcohol as 3.0 and 3.5 respectively, you can predict the pattern of solubility of amines and alcohols in water. Out of butan-1-ol and butan-1-amine, which will be more soluble in water and why? Amines are soluble in organic solvents like alcohol, ether and benzene. You may remember that alcohols are more polar than amines and form stronger intermolecular hydrogen bonds than amines.

Primary and secondary amines are engaged in intermolecular association due to hydrogen bonding between nitrogen of one and hydrogen of another molecule. This intermolecular association is more in primary amines than in secondary amines as there are two hydrogen atoms available for hydrogen bond formation in it. Tertiary amines do not have intermolecular association due to the absence of hydrogen atom available for hydrogen bond formation. Therefore, the order of boiling points of isomeric amines is as follows:

387 Amines

Primary > Secondary > Tertiary

Intermolecular hydrogen bonding in primary amines is shown in Fig. 13.2.

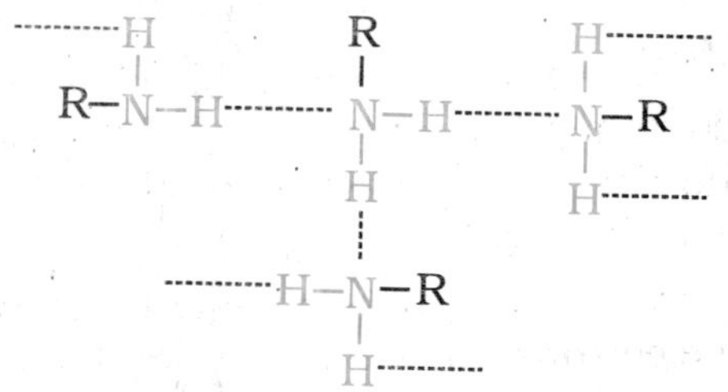

Fig. 13.2 *Intermolecular hydrogen bonding in primary amines*

Boiling points of amines, alcohols and alkanes of almost the same molar mass are shown in Table 13.2.

Table 13.2: **Comparison of Boiling Points of Amines, Alcohols and Alkanes of Similar Molecular Masses**

Sl. No.	Compound	Molar mass	b.p./K
1.	n-$C_4H_9NH_2$	73	350.8
2.	$(C_2H_5)_2NH$	73	329.3
3.	$C_2H_5N(CH_3)_2$	73	310.5
4.	$C_2H_5CH(CH_3)_2$	72	300.8
5.	n-C_4H_9OH	74	390.3

13.6 Chemical Reactions

Difference in electronegativity between nitrogen and hydrogen atoms and the presence of unshared pair of electrons over the nitrogen atom makes amines reactive. The number of hydrogen atoms attached to nitrogen atom also decides the course of reaction of amines; that is why primary $(-NH_2)$, secondary $\left(\begin{array}{c}\diagdown\\ \diagup\end{array}N-H\right)$ and tertiary amines $\left(\begin{array}{c}\diagdown\\ \diagup\end{array}N-\right)$ differ in many reactions. Moreover, amines behave as nucleophiles due to the presence of unshared electron pair. Some of the reactions of amines are described below:

1. Basic character of amines

Amines, being basic in nature, react with acids to form salts.

$$R - \overset{..}{NH_2} + H\mathbf{X} \rightleftharpoons R - \overset{+}{NH_3}\ \bar{\mathbf{X}} \quad \text{(Salt)}$$

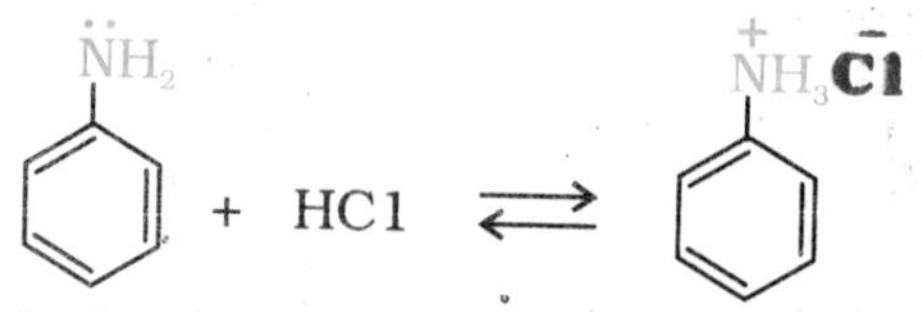

Aniline   +   HCl $\rightleftharpoons$ Anilinium chloride

Amine salts on treatment with a base like NaOH, regenerate the parent amine.

$$R\overset{+}{N}H_3\,\bar{X} + \bar{O}H \longrightarrow R\ddot{N}H_2 + H_2O + \bar{X}$$

Amine salts are soluble in water but insoluble in organic solvents like ether. This reaction is the basis for the separation of amines from the non basic organic compounds insoluble in water.

The reaction of amines with mineral acids to form ammonium salts shows that these are basic in nature. Amines have an unshared pair of electrons on nitrogen atom due to which they behave as **Lewis base.** Basic character of amines can be better understood in terms of their K_b and pK_b values as explained below:

$$R - NH_2 + H_2O \rightleftharpoons R - \overset{+}{N}H_3 + \bar{O}H$$

$$K = \frac{\left[R - \overset{+}{N}H_3\right]\left[\bar{O}H\right]}{[R - NH_2][H_2O]}$$

$$\text{or } K[H_2O] = \frac{\left[R - \overset{+}{N}H_3\right]\left[\bar{O}H\right]}{[R - NH_2]}$$

$$\text{or } K_b = \frac{\left[R - \overset{+}{N}H_3\right]\left[\bar{O}H\right]}{[R - NH_2]}$$

$$pK_b = -\log K_b$$

Larger the value of K_b or smaller the value of pK_b, stronger is the base. The pK_b values of few amines are given in Table 13.3.

pK_b value of ammonia is 4.75. Aliphatic amines are stronger bases than ammonia due to +I effect of alkyl groups leading to high electron density on the nitrogen atom. Their pK_b values lie in the range of 3 to 4.22. On the other hand, aromatic amines are weaker bases than ammonia due to the electron withdrawing nature of the aryl group.

Table 13.3: pK_b Values of Amines in Aqueous Phase

Name of amine	pK_b
Methanamine	3.38
N-Methylmethanamine	3.27
N,N-Dimethylmethanamine	4.22
Ethanamine	3.29
N-Ethylethanamine	3.00
N,N-Diethylethanamine	3.25
Benzenamine	9.38
Phenylmethanamine	4.70
N-Methylaniline	9.30
N,N-Dimethylaniline	8.92

You may find some discrepancies while trying to interpret the K_b values of amines on the basis of +I or –I effect of the substituents present in amines. Besides inductive effect, there are other effects like solvation effect, steric hinderance, etc., which affect the basic strength of amines. Just ponder over. You may get the answer in the following paragraphs.

Structure-basicity relationship of amines

Basicity of amines is related to their structure. Basic character of an amine depends upon the ease of formation of the cation by accepting a proton from the acid. The more stable the cation is relative to the amine, more basic is the amine.

(a) Alkanamines versus ammonia

Let us consider the reaction of an alkanamine and ammonia with a proton to compare their basicity.

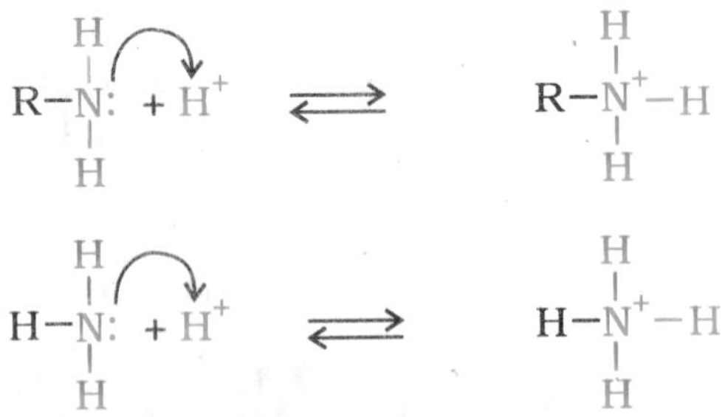

Due to the electron releasing nature of alkyl group, it (R) pushes electrons towards nitrogen and thus makes the unshared electron pair more available for sharing with the proton of the acid. Moreover, the substituted ammonium ion formed from the amine gets stabilised due to dispersal of the positive charge by the +I effect of the alkyl group. Hence, alkylamines are stronger bases than ammonia. Thus, the basic nature of aliphatic amines should increase with increase in the number of alkyl groups. This trend is followed in the gaseous phase. The order of basicity of amines in the gaseous phase follows the expected order: tertiary amine > secondary amine > primary amine > NH_3. The trend is not regular in the aqueous state as evident by their pK_b values given in Table 13.3. In the aqueous phase, the substituted ammonium cations get stabilised not only by electron releasing effect of the alkyl group (+I) but also by solvation with water molecules. The greater the size of the ion, lesser will be the solvation and the less stabilised is the ion. The order of stability of ions are as follows:

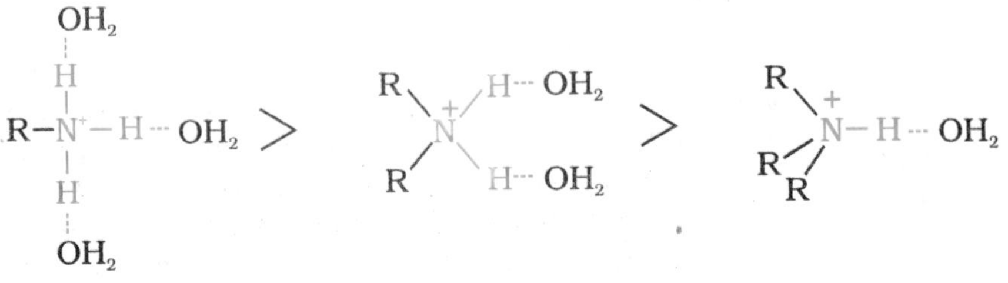

Decreasing order of extent of H-bonding in water and order of stability of ions by solvation.

Greater is the stability of the substituted ammonium cation, stronger should be the corresponding amine as a base. Thus, the order of basicity of aliphatic amines should be: primary > secondary > tertiary, which is opposite to the inductive effect based order. Secondly, when the alkyl group is small, like $-CH_3$ group, there is no steric hindrance to H-bonding. In case the alkyl group is bigger than CH_3 group, there will be steric hinderance to H-bonding. Therefore, the change of nature of the alkyl group, e.g., from $-CH_3$ to $-C_2H_5$ results in change of the order of basic strength. Thus, there is a subtle interplay of the inductive effect, solvation effect and steric hinderance of the alkyl group which decides the basic strength of alkyl amines in the aqueous state. The order of basic strength in case of methyl substituted amines and ethyl substituted amines in aqueous solution is as follows:

$$(C_2H_5)_2NH > (C_2H_5)_3N > C_2H_5NH_2 > NH_3$$
$$(CH_3)_2NH > CH_3NH_2 > (CH_3)_3N > NH_3$$

(b) Arylamines versus ammonia

pK_b value of aniline is quite high. Why is it so? It is because in aniline or other arylamines, the $-NH_2$ group is attached directly to the benzene ring. It results in the unshared electron pair on nitrogen atom to be in conjugation with the benzene ring and thus making it less available for protonation. If you write different resonating structures of aniline, you will find that aniline is a resonance hybrid of the following five structures.

I   II   III   IV   V

On the other hand, anilinium ion obtained by accepting a proton can have only two resonating structures (kekule).

I   II

We know that greater the number of resonating structures, greater is the stability. Thus you can infer that aniline (five resonating structures) is more stable than anilinium ion. Hence, the proton acceptability or the basic nature of aniline or other aromatic amines would be less than that of ammonia. In case of substituted aniline, it is observed that electron releasing groups like $-OCH_3$, $-CH_3$ increase basic strength whereas electron withdrawing groups like $-NO_2$, $-SO_3H$, $-COOH$, $-X$ decrease it.

Example 13.4 Arrange the following in decreasing order of their basic strength:
$C_6H_5NH_2$, $C_2H_5NH_2$, $(C_2H_5)_2NH$, NH_3

Solution The decreasing order of basic strength of the above amines and ammonia follows the following order:
$(C_2H_5)_2NH > C_2H_5NH_2 > NH_3 > C_6H_5NH_2$

2. *Alkylation*

Amines undergo alkylation on reaction with alkyl halides (refer Unit 10, Class XII).

3. *Acylation*

Aliphatic and aromatic primary and secondary amines react with acid chlorides, anhydrides and esters by nucleophilic substitution reaction. This reaction is known as acylation. You can consider this reaction as the replacement of hydrogen atom of $-NH_2$ or >N–H group by the acyl group. The products obtained by acylation reaction are known as amides. The reaction is carried out in the presence of a base stronger than the amine, like pyridine, which removes HCl so formed and shifts the equilibrium to the right hand side.

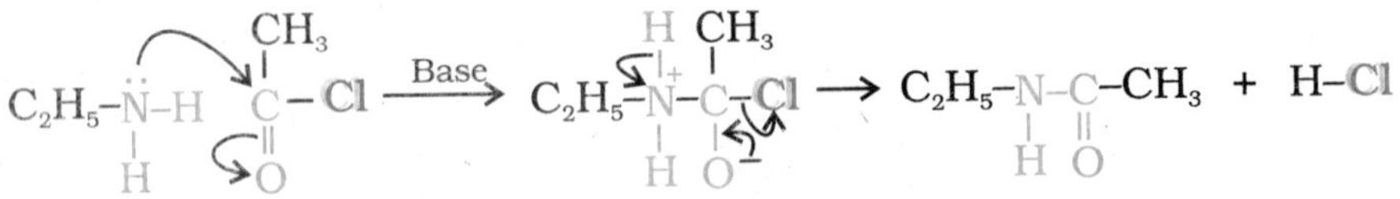

Ethanamine N-Ethylethanamide

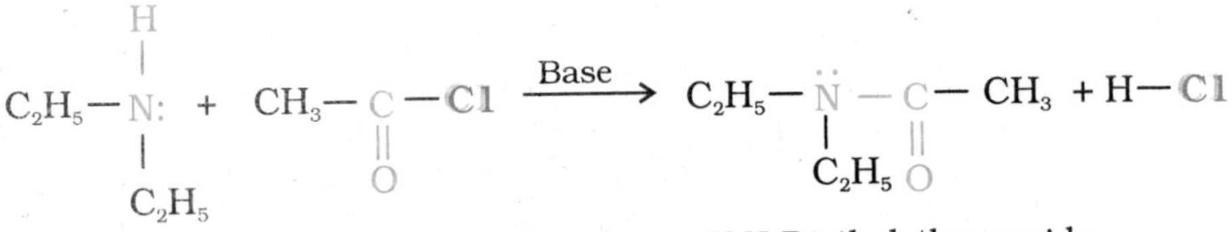

N-Ethylethanamine N,N-Diethylethanamide

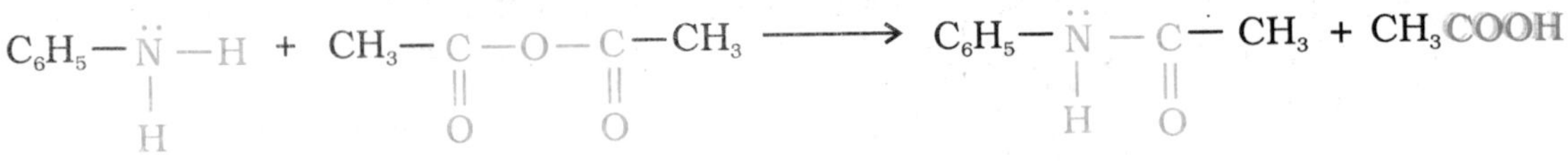

Benzenamine Ethanoic anhydride N-Phenylethanamide or Acetanilide

Amines also react with benzoyl chloride (C_6H_5COCl). This reaction is known as benzoylation.

$$CH_3NH_2 + C_6H_5COCl \rightarrow CH_3NHCOC_6H_5 + HCl$$

Methanamine Benzoyl chloride N – Methylbenzamide

What do you think is the product of the reaction of amines with carboxylic acids ? They form salts with amines at room temperature.

4. Carbylamine reaction

Aliphatic and aromatic primary amines on heating with chloroform and ethanolic potassium hydroxide form isocyanides or carbylamines which are foul smelling substances. Secondary and tertiary amines do not show this reaction. This reaction is known as carbylamine reaction or isocyanide test and is used as a test for primary amines.

$$R-NH_2 + CHCl_3 + 3KOH \xrightarrow{\text{Heat}} R-NC + 3KCl + 3H_2O$$

5. Reaction with nitrous acid

Three classes of amines react differently with nitrous acid which is prepared *in situ* from a mineral acid and sodium nitrite.

(a) Primary aliphatic amines react with nitrous acid to form aliphatic diazonium salts which being unstable, liberate nitrogen gas quantitatively and alcohols. Quantitative evolution of nitrogen is used in estimation of amino acids and proteins.

$$R-NH_2 + HNO_2 \xrightarrow{NaNO_2 + HCl} [R-\overset{+}{N_2}\overset{-}{Cl}] \xrightarrow{H_2O} ROH + N_2 + HCl$$

(b) Aromatic amines react with nitrous acid at low temperatures (273-278 K) to form diazonium salts, a very important class of compounds used for synthesis of a variety of aromatic compounds discussed in Section 13.7.

$$C_6H_5 - NH_2 \xrightarrow[273 - 278\ K]{NaNO_2 + 2HCl} C_6H_5 - \overset{+}{N_2}\overset{-}{Cl} + NaCl + 2H_2O$$

Aniline   Benzenediazonium
chloride

Secondary and tertiary amines react with nitrous acid in a different manner.

6. Reaction with arylsulphonyl chloride

Benzenesulphonyl chloride ($C_6H_5SO_2Cl$), which is also known as Hinsberg's reagent, reacts with primary and secondary amines to form sulphonamides.

(a) The reaction of benzenesulphonyl chloride with primary amine yields N-ethylbenzenesulphonyl amide.

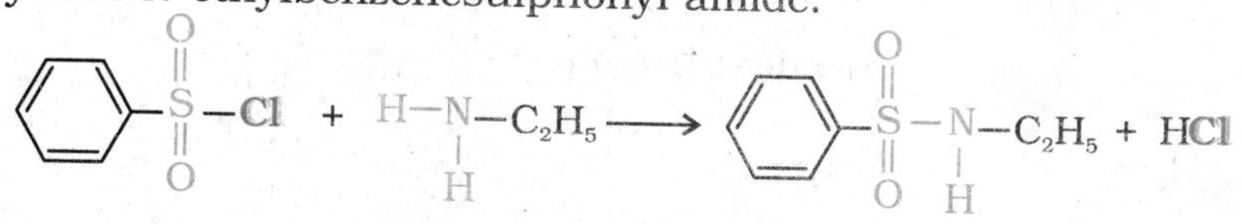

N-Ethylbenzenesulphonamide
(soluble in alkali)

The hydrogen attached to nitrogen in sulphonamide is strongly acidic due to the presence of strong electron withdrawing sulphonyl group. Hence, it is soluble in alkali.

(b) In the reaction with secondary amine, N,N-diethyl-benzenesulphonamide is formed.

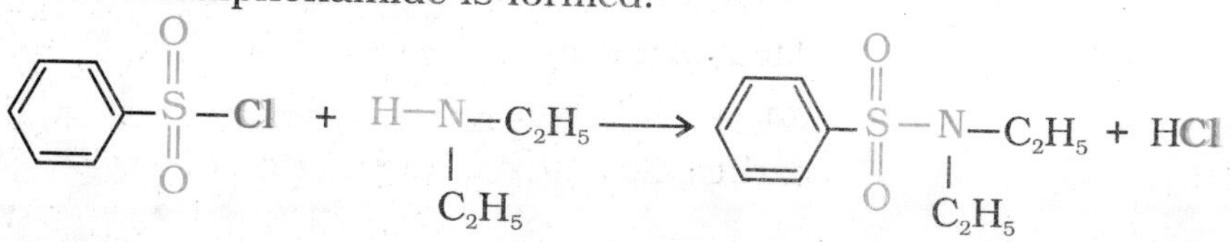

N,N-Diethylbenzenesulphonamide

Since N, N-diethylbenzene sulphonamide does not contain any hydrogen atom attached to nitrogen atom, it is not acidic and hence insoluble in alkali.

(c) Tertiary amines do not react with benzenesulphonyl chloride. This property of amines reacting with benzenesulphonyl chloride in a different manner is used for the distinction of primary, secondary and tertiary amines and also for the separation of a mixture of amines. However, these days benzenesulphonyl chloride is replaced by p-toluenesulphonyl chloride.

7. Electrophilic substitution

You have read earlier that aniline is a resonance hybrid of five structures. Where do you find the maximum electron density in these structures? Ortho- and para-positions to the $-NH_2$ group become centres of high electron density. Thus $-NH_2$ group is ortho and para directing and a powerful activating group.

(a) Bromination: Aniline reacts with bromine water at room temperature to give a white precipitate of 2,4,6-tribromoaniline.

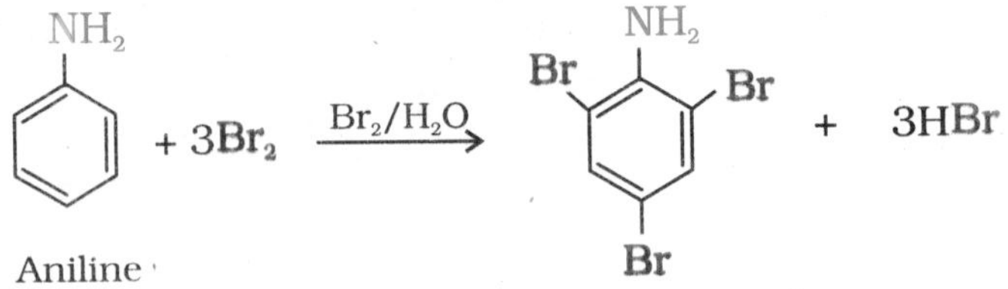

Aniline   2,4,6-Tribromoaniline

The main problem encountered during electrophilic substitution reactions of aromatic amines is that of their very high reactivity. Substitution tends to occur at ortho- and para-positions. If we have to prepare monosubstituted aniline derivative, how can the activating effect of $-NH_2$ group be controlled ? This can be done by protecting the $-NH_2$ group by acetylation with acetic anhydride, then carrying out the desired substitution followed by hydrolysis of the substituted amide to the substituted amine.

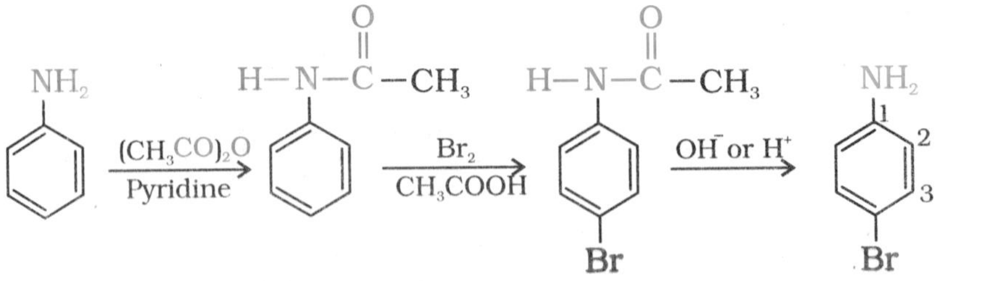

Aniline   N-Phenylethanamide   (Major)   4-Bromoaniline
            (Acetanilide)

The lone pair of electrons on nitrogen of acetanilide interacts with oxygen atom due to resonance as shown below:

Hence, the lone pair of electrons on nitrogen is less available for donation to benzene ring by resonance. Therefore, activating effect of –NHCOCH$_3$ group is less than that of amino group.

(b) **Nitration:** Direct nitration of aniline yields tarry oxidation products in addition to the nitro derivatives. Moreover, in the strongly acidic medium, aniline is protonated to form the anilinium ion which is *meta* directing. That is why besides the *ortho* and *para* derivatives, significant amount of *meta* derivative is also formed.

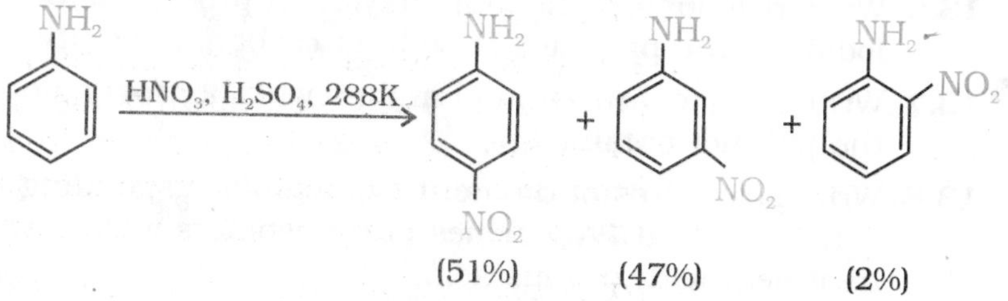

However, by protecting the –NH$_2$ group by acetylation reaction with acetic anhydride, the nitration reaction can be controlled and the *p*-nitro derivative can be obtained as the major product.

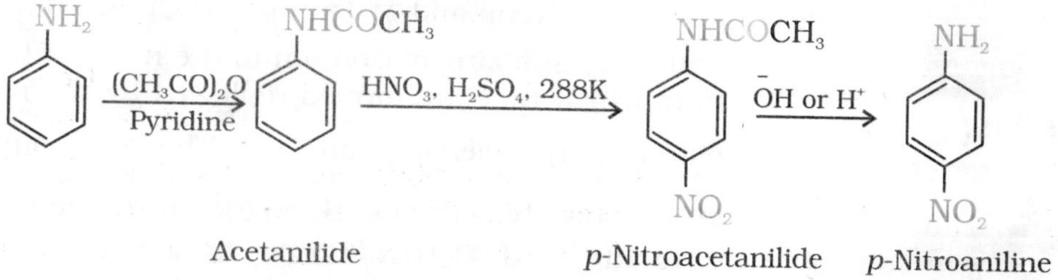

(c) **Sulphonation:** Aniline reacts with concentrated sulphuric acid to form anilinium hydrogensulphate which on heating with sulphuric acid at 453-473K produces p-aminobenzene sulphonic acid, commonly known as sulphanilic acid, as the major product.

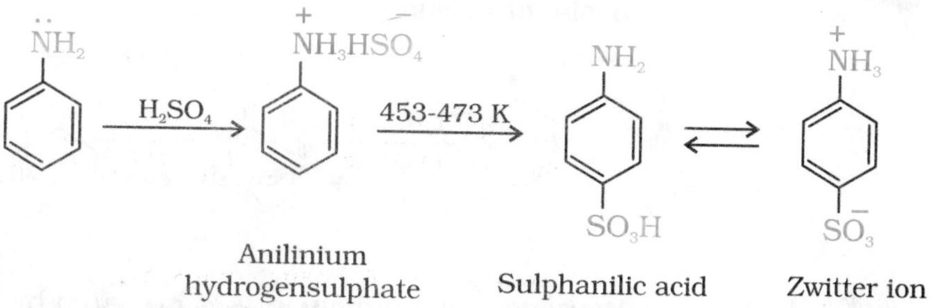

Aniline does not undergo Friedel-Crafts reaction (alkylation and acetylation) due to salt formation with aluminium chloride, the Lewis acid, which is used as a catalyst. Due to this, nitrogen of aniline acquires positive charge and hence acts as a strong deactivating group for further reaction.

Intext Questions

13.4 Arrange the following in increasing order of their basic strength:

    (i) $C_2H_5NH_2$, $C_6H_5NH_2$, NH_3, $C_6H_5CH_2NH_2$ and $(C_2H_5)_2NH$

    (ii) $C_2H_5NH_2$, $(C_2H_5)_2NH$, $(C_2H_5)_3N$, $C_6H_5NH_2$

    (iii) CH_3NH_2, $(CH_3)_2NH$, $(CH_3)_3N$, $C_6H_5NH_2$, $C_6H_5CH_2NH_2$.

13.5 Complete the following acid-base reactions and name the products:

    (i) $CH_3CH_2CH_2NH_2 + HCl \rightarrow$ (ii) $(C_2H_5)_3N + HCl \rightarrow$

13.6 Write reactions of the final alkylation product of aniline with excess of methyl iodide in the presence of sodium carbonate solution.

13.7 Write chemical reaction of aniline with benzoyl chloride and write the name of the product obtained.

13.8 Write structures of different isomers corresponding to the molecular formula, C_3H_9N. Write IUPAC names of the isomers which will liberate nitrogen gas on treatment with nitrous acid.

II. DIAZONIUM SALTS

The diazonium salts have the general formula $R\overset{+}{N_2}\overset{-}{X}$ where R stands for an aryl group and $\overset{-}{X}$ ion may be $\overset{-}{Cl}$ $\overset{-}{Br}$, HSO_4^-, BF_4^-, etc. They are named by suffixing diazonium to the name of the parent hydrocarbon from which they are formed, followed by the name of anion such as chloride, hydrogensulphate, etc. The $\overset{+}{N_2}$ group is called diazonium group. For example, $C_6H_5\overset{+}{N_2}\overset{-}{Cl}$ is named as benzenediazonium chloride and $C_6H_5N_2^+HSO_4^-$ is known as benzenediazonium hydrogensulphate.

Primary aliphatic amines form highly unstable alkyldiazonium salts (refer to Section 13.6). Primary aromatic amines form arenediazonium salts which are stable for a short time in solution at low temperatures (273-278 K). The stability of arenediazonium ion is explained on the basis of resonance.

13.7 Method of Preparation of Diazonium Salts

Benzenediazonium chloride is prepared by the reaction of aniline with nitrous acid at 273-278K. Nitrous acid is produced in the reaction mixture by the reaction of sodium nitrite with hydrochloric acid. The conversion of primary aromatic amines into diazonium salts is known as **diazotisation**. Due to its instability, the diazonium salt is not generally stored and is used immediately after its preparation.

$$C_6H_5NH_2 + NaNO_2 + 2HCl \xrightarrow{273-278K} C_6H_5\overset{+}{N_2}\overset{-}{Cl} + NaCl + 2H_2O$$

13.8 Physical Properties

Benzenediazonium chloride is a colourless crystalline solid. It is readily soluble in water and is stable in cold but reacts with water when warmed. It decomposes easily in the dry state. Benzenediazonium fluoroborate is water insoluble and stable at room temperature.

13.9 Chemical Reactions

The reactions of diazonium salts can be broadly divided into two categories, namely (A) reactions involving displacement of nitrogen and (B) reactions involving retention of diazo group.

A. Reactions involving displacement of nitrogen

Diazonium group being a very good leaving group, is substituted by other groups such as Cl^-, Br^- I^- CN^- and OH^- which displace nitrogen from the aromatic ring. The nitrogen formed escapes from the reaction mixture as a gas.

1. *Replacement by halide or cyanide ion*: The Cl^-, Br^- and CN^- nucleophiles can easily be introduced in the benzene ring in the presence of Cu(I) ion. This reaction is called **Sandmeyer reaction**.

$$Ar \overset{+}{N_2} \overset{-}{X} \begin{array}{l} \xrightarrow{Cu_2 Cl_2/H Cl} Ar Cl + N_2 \\ \xrightarrow{Cu_2 Br_2/H Br} Ar Br + N_2 \\ \xrightarrow{Cu CN /K CN} Ar CN + N_2 \end{array}$$

Alternatively, chlorine or bromine can also be introduced in the benzene ring by treating the diazonium salt solution with corresponding halogen acid in the presence of copper powder. This is referred as **Gatterman reaction**.

$$Ar \overset{+}{N_2} \overset{-}{X} \begin{array}{l} \xrightarrow{Cu/H Cl} Ar Cl + N_2 + Cu X \\ \xrightarrow{Cu/H Br} Ar Br + N_2 + Cu X \end{array}$$

The yield in Sandmeyer reaction is found to be better than Gattermann reaction.

2. *Replacement by iodide ion*: Iodine is not easily introduced into the benzene ring directly, but, when the diazonium salt solution is treated with potassium iodide, iodobenzene is formed.

$$Ar \overset{+}{N_2} \overset{-}{Cl} + K I \longrightarrow Ar I + K Cl + N_2$$

3. *Replacement by fluoride ion*: When arenediazonium chloride is treated with fluoroboric acid, arene diazonium fluoroborate is precipitated which on heating decomposes to yield aryl fluoride.

$$Ar \overset{+}{N_2} \overset{-}{Cl} + HB F_4 \longrightarrow Ar - \overset{+}{N_2} B \overset{-}{F_4} \xrightarrow{\Delta} Ar - F + B F_3 + N_2$$

4. *Replacement by ·H*: Certain mild reducing agents like hypophosphorous acid (phosphinic acid) or ethanol reduce diazonium salts to arenes and themselves get oxidised to phosphorous acid and ethanal, respectively.

$$Ar\overset{+}{N_2}\overset{-}{Cl} + H_3PO_2 + H_2O \longrightarrow ArH + N_2 + H_3PO_3 + HCl$$

$$Ar\overset{+}{N_2}\overset{-}{Cl} + CH_3CH_2OH \longrightarrow ArH + N_2 + CH_3CHO + HCl$$

5. *Replacement by hydroxyl group*: If the temperature of the diazonium salt solution is allowed to rise upto 283 K, the salt gets hydrolysed to phenol.

$$Ar\overset{+}{N_2}\overset{-}{Cl} + H_2O \longrightarrow ArOH + N_2 + HCl$$

6. *Replacement by* $-NO_2$ *group*: When diazonium fluoroborate is heated with aqueous sodium nitrite solution in the presence of copper, the diazonium group is replaced by $-NO_2$ group.

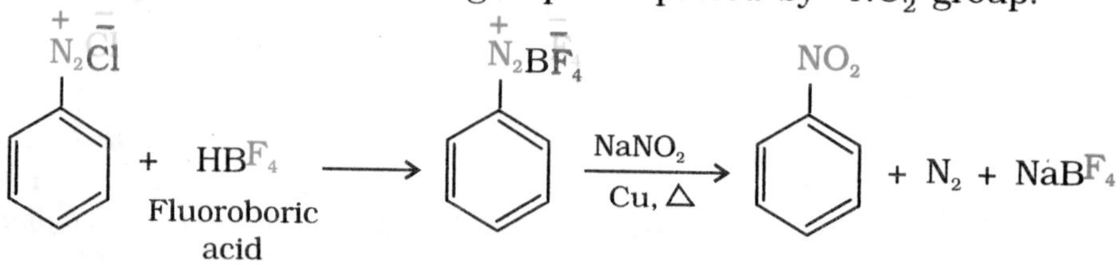

B. Reactions involving retention of diazo group

coupling reactions

The azo products obtained have an extended conjugate system having both the aromatic rings joined through the $-N=N-$ bond. These compounds are often coloured and are used as dyes. Benzene diazonium chloride reacts with phenol in which the phenol molecule at its para position is coupled with the diazonium salt to form *p*-hydroxyazobenzene. This type of reaction is known as coupling reaction. Similarly the reaction of diazonium salt with aniline yields *p*-aminoazobenzene. This is an example of electrophilic substitution reaction.

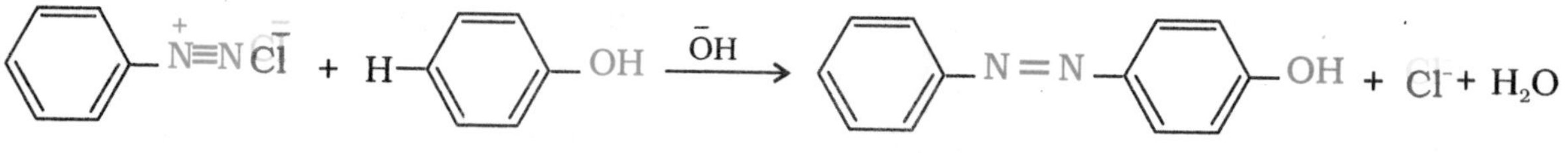

p-Hydroxyazobenzene (orange dye)

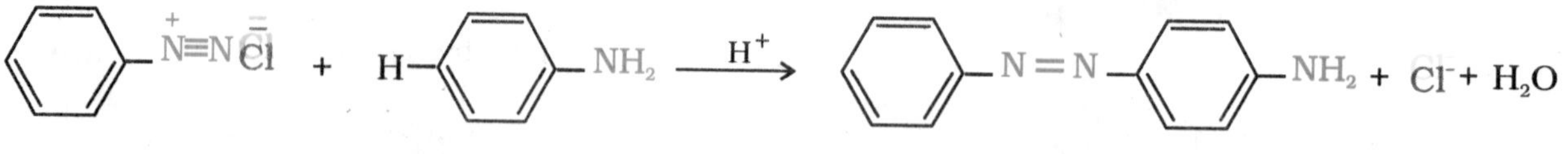

p-Aminoazobenzene
(yellow dye)

13.10 *Importance of Diazonium Salts in Synthesis of Aromatic Compounds*

From the above reactions, it is clear that the diazonium salts are very good intermediates for the introduction of $-F$, $-Cl$, $-Br$, $-I$, $-CN$, $-OH$, $-NO_2$ groups into the aromatic ring.

Aryl fluorides and iodides cannot be prepared by direct halogenation. The cyano group cannot be introduced by nucleophilic substitution of chlorine in chlorobenzene but cyanobenzene can be easily obtained from diazonium salt.

Thus, the replacement of diazo group by other groups is helpful in preparing those substituted aromatic compounds which cannot be prepared by direct substitution in benzene or substituted benzene.

Example 13.5

How will you convert 4-nitrotoluene to 2-bromobenzoic acid ?

Solution

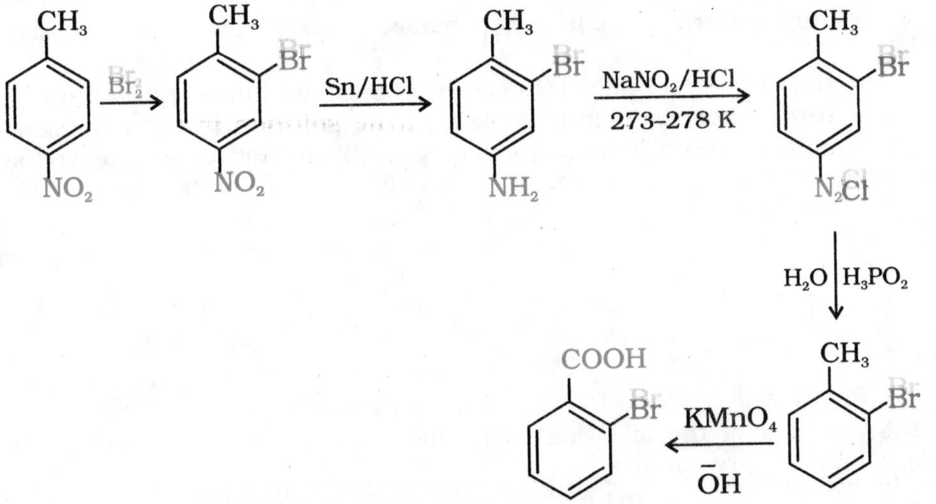

Intext Question

13.9 Convert

(i) 3-Methylaniline into 3-nitrotoluene.

(ii) Aniline into 1,3,5 - tribromobenzene.

Summary

Amines can be considered as derivatives of ammonia obtained by replacement of hydrogen atoms with alkyl or aryl groups. Replacement of one hydrogen atom of ammonia gives rise to structure of the type **R-NH$_2$**, known as **primary amine**. **Secondary amines** are characterised by the structure **R$_2$NH** or **R-NHR′** and **tertiary amines** by **R$_3$N, RNR′R″** or **R$_2$NR′**. Secondary and tertiary amines are known as simple amines if the alkyl or aryl groups are the same and mixed amines if the groups are different. Like ammonia, all the three types of amines have one unshared electron pair on nitrogen atom due to which they behave as **Lewis bases**.

Amines are usually formed from nitro compounds, halides, amides, imides, etc. They exhibit hydrogen bonding which influence their physical properties. In **alkylamines**, a combination of electron releasing, steric and H-bonding factors influence the stability of the substituted ammonium cations in protic polar solvents and thus affect the basic nature of amines. Alkyl amines are found to be stronger bases than ammonia. In **aromatic amines**, electron releasing and withdrawing groups, respectively increase and decrease their basic character. **Aniline** is a weaker base than ammonia. Reactions of amines are governed by availability of the unshared pair of electrons on nitrogen. Influence of the number of hydrogen atoms at nitrogen atom on the type of reactions and nature of products is responsible for identification and distinction between primary, secondary and tertiary amines. p-Toluenesulphonyl chloride is used for the identification of primary, secondary and tertiary amines. Presence of amino group in aromatic ring enhances reactivity of the aromatic amines. Reactivity of aromatic amines can be controlled by **acylation** process, i.e., by treating with acetyl chloride or acetic anhydride. Tertiary amines like **trimethylamine** are used as insect attractants.

Aryldiazonium salts, usually obtained from arylamines, undergo replacement of the diazonium group with a variety of nucleophiles to provide advantageous methods for producing aryl halides, cyanides, phenols and arenes by reductive removal of the diazo group. Coupling reaction of aryldiazonium salts with phenols or arylamines give rise to the formation of **azo dyes**.

Exercises

13.1 Write IUPAC names of the following compounds and classify them into primary, secondary and tertiary amines.

(i) $(CH_3)_2CHNH_2$ (ii) $CH_3(CH_2)_2NH_2$ (iii) $CH_3NHCH(CH_3)_2$

(iv) $(CH_3)_3CNH_2$ (v) $C_6H_5NHCH_3$ (vi) $(CH_3CH_2)_2NCH_3$

(vii) $m\text{--}BrC_6H_4NH_2$

13.2 Give one chemical test to distinguish between the following pairs of compounds.

(i) Methylamine and dimethylamine   (ii) Secondary and tertiary amines

(iii) Ethylamine and aniline   (iv) Aniline and benzylamine

(v) Aniline and N-methylaniline.

13.3 Account for the following:

(i) pK_b of aniline is more than that of methylamine.

(ii) Ethylamine is soluble in water whereas aniline is not.

(iii) Methylamine in water reacts with ferric chloride to precipitate hydrated ferric oxide.

(iv) Although amino group is o– and p– directing in aromatic electrophilic substitution reactions, aniline on nitration gives a substantial amount of m-nitroaniline.

(v) Aniline does not undergo Friedel-Crafts reaction.

(vi) Diazonium salts of aromatic amines are more stable than those of aliphatic amines.

(vii) Gabriel phthalimide synthesis is preferred for synthesising primary amines.

13.4 Arrange the following:

(i) In decreasing order of the pK_b values:

$C_2H_5NH_2$, $C_6H_5NHCH_3$, $(C_2H_5)_2NH$ and $C_6H_5NH_2$

(ii) In increasing order of basic strength:

$C_6H_5NH_2$, $C_6H_5N(CH_3)_2$, $(C_2H_5)_2NH$ and CH_3NH_2

(iii) In increasing order of basic strength:

(a) Aniline, p-nitroaniline and p-toluidine

(b) $C_6H_5NH_2$, $C_6H_5NHCH_3$, $C_6H_5CH_2NH_2$.

(iv) In decreasing order of basic strength in gas phase:

$C_2H_5NH_2$, $(C_2H_5)_2NH$, $(C_2H_5)_3N$ and NH_3

(v) In increasing order of boiling point:

C_2H_5OH, $(CH_3)_2NH$, $C_2H_5NH_2$

(vi) In increasing order of solubility in water:

$C_6H_5NH_2$, $(C_2H_5)_2NH$, $C_2H_5NH_2$.

13.5 How will you convert:

(i) Ethanoic acid into methanamine

(ii) Hexanenitrile into 1-aminopentane

(iii) Methanol to ethanoic acid

(iv) Ethanamine into methanamine

(v) Ethanoic acid into propanoic acid

(vi) Methanamine into ethanamine

(vii) Nitromethane into dimethylamine

(viii) Propanoic acid into ethanoic acid?

13.6 Describe a method for the identification of primary, secondary and tertiary amines. Also write chemical equations of the reactions involved.

13.7 Write short notes on the following:

(i) Carbylamine reaction

(ii) Diazotisation

(iii) Hofmann's bromamide reaction

(iv) Coupling reaction

(v) Ammonolysis

(vi) Acetylation

(vii) Gabriel phthalimide synthesis.

13.8 Accomplish the following conversions:

(i) Nitrobenzene to benzoic acid

(ii) Benzene to *m*-bromophenol

(iii) Benzoic acid to aniline

(iv) Aniline to 2,4,6-tribromofluorobenzene

(v) Benzyl chloride to 2-phenylethanamine

(vi) Chlorobenzene to *p*-chloroaniline

(vii) Aniline to *p*-bromoaniline

(viii) Benzamide to toluene

(ix) Aniline to benzyl alcohol.

13.9 Give the structures of A, B and C in the following reactions:

(i) $CH_3CH_2I \xrightarrow{\text{NaCN}} A \xrightarrow[\text{Partial hydrolysis}]{\text{OH}^-} B \xrightarrow{\text{NaOH+Br}_2} C$

(ii) $C_6H_5N_2Cl \xrightarrow{\text{CuCN}} A \xrightarrow{\text{H}_2\text{O/H}^+} B \xrightarrow[\Delta]{\text{NH}_3} C$

(iii) $CH_3CH_2Br \xrightarrow{\text{KCN}} A \xrightarrow{\text{LiAlH}_4} B \xrightarrow[0°C]{\text{HNO}_2} C$

(iv) $C_6H_5NO_2 \xrightarrow{\text{Fe/HCl}} A \xrightarrow[273\ K]{\text{NaNO}_2 + \text{HCl}} B \xrightarrow[\Delta]{\text{H}_2\text{O/H}^+} C$

(v) $CH_3COOH \xrightarrow[\Delta]{\text{NH}_3} A \xrightarrow{\text{NaOBr}} B \xrightarrow{\text{NaNO}_2 / \text{HCl}} C$

(vi) $C_6H_5NO_2 \xrightarrow{\text{Fe/HCl}} A \xrightarrow[273K]{\text{HNO}_2} B \xrightarrow{\text{C}_6\text{H}_5\text{OH}} C$

13.10 An aromatic compound 'A' on treatment with aqueous ammonia and heating forms compound 'B' which on heating with Br_2 and KOH forms a compound 'C' of molecular formula C_6H_7N. Write the structures and IUPAC names of compounds A, B and C.

13.11 Complete the following reactions:

(i) $C_6H_5NH_2 + CHCl_3 + alc.KOH \rightarrow$

(ii) $C_6H_5N_2Cl + H_3PO_2 + H_2O \rightarrow$

(iii) $C_6H_5NH_2 + H_2SO_4 \text{(conc.)} \rightarrow$

(iv) $C_6H_5N_2Cl + C_2H_5OH \rightarrow$

(v) $C_6H_5NH_2 + Br_2 \text{(aq)} \rightarrow$

(vi) $C_6H_5NH_2 + (CH_3CO)_2 O \rightarrow$

(vii) $C_6H_5N_2Cl \xrightarrow[\text{(ii)NaNO}_2 / \text{Cu}, \Delta]{\text{(i)HBF}_4}$

13.12 Why cannot aromatic primary amines be prepared by Gabriel phthalimide synthesis?

13.13 Write the reactions of (i) aromatic and (ii) aliphatic primary amines with nitrous acid.

13.14 Give plausible explanation for each of the following:

(i) Why are amines less acidic than alcohols of comparable molecular masses?

(ii) Why do primary amines have higher boiling point than tertiary amines?

(iii) Why are aliphatic amines stronger bases than aromatic amines?

Answers to Some Intext Questions

13.4 (i) $C_6H_5NH_2 < NH_3 < C_6H_5CH_2NH_2 < C_2H_5NH_2 < (C_2H_5)_2NH$

(ii) $C_6H_5NH_2 < C_2H_5NH_2 < (C_2H_5)_3N < (C_2H_5)_2NH$

(iii) $C_6H_5NH_2 < C_6H_5CH_2NH_2 < (CH_3)_3N < CH_3NH_2 < (CH_3)_2NH$

Objectives

After studying this Unit, you will be able to

- define the biomolecules like carbohydrates, proteins and nucleic acids;
- classify carbohydrates, proteins, nucleic acids and vitamins on the basis of their structures;
- explain the difference between DNA and RNA;
- appreciate the role of biomolecules in biosystem.

"It is the harmonious and synchronous progress of chemical reactions in body which leads to life".

A living system grows, sustains and reproduces itself. The most amazing thing about a living system is that it is composed of non-living atoms and molecules. The pursuit of knowledge of what goes on chemically within a living system falls in the domain of *biochemistry*. Living systems are made up of various complex biomolecules like carbohydrates, proteins, nucleic acids, lipids, etc. Proteins and carbohydrates are essential constituents of our food. These biomolecules interact with each other and constitute the molecular logic of life processes. In addition, some simple molecules like vitamins and mineral salts also play an important role in the functions of organisms. Structures and functions of some of these biomolecules are discussed in this Unit.

14.1 Carbohydrates

Carbohydrates are primarily produced by plants and form a very large group of naturally occurring organic compounds. Some common examples are cane sugar, glucose, starch, etc. Most of them have a general formula, $C_x(H_2O)_y$, and were considered as hydrates of carbon from where the name carbohydrate was derived. For example, the molecular formula of glucose ($C_6H_{12}O_6$) fits into this general formula, $C_6(H_2O)_6$. But all the compounds which fit into this formula may not be classified as carbohydrates. Acetic acid (CH_3COOH) fits into this general formula, $C_2(H_2O)_2$ but is not a carbohydrate. Similarly, rhamnose, $C_6H_{12}O_5$ is a carbohydrate but does not fit in this definition. A large number of their reactions have shown that they contain specific functional groups. Chemically, *the carbohydrates may be defined as optically active polyhydroxy aldehydes or ketones or the compounds which produce such units on hydrolysis.* Some of the carbohydrates, which are sweet in taste, are also called sugars. The most common sugar, used in our homes is named as sucrose whereas the sugar present in milk is known as lactose. Carbohydrates are also called saccharides (Greek: *sakcharon* means sugar).

14.1.1 Classification of Carbohydrates

Carbohydrates are classified on the basis of their behaviour on hydrolysis. They have been broadly divided into following three groups.

(i) *Monosaccharides*: A carbohydrate that cannot be hydrolysed further to give simpler unit of polyhydroxy aldehyde or ketone is called a monosaccharide. About 20 monosaccharides are known to occur in nature. Some common examples are glucose, fructose, ribose, etc.

(ii) *Oligosaccharides*: Carbohydrates that yield two to ten monosaccharide units, on hydrolysis, are called oligosaccharides. They are further classified as disaccharides, trisaccharides, tetrasaccharides, etc., depending upon the number of monosaccharides, they provide on hydrolysis. Amongst these the most common are disaccharides. The two monosaccharide units obtained on hydrolysis of a disaccharide may be same or different. For example, sucrose on hydrolysis gives one molecule each of glucose and fructose whereas maltose gives two molecules of glucose only.

(iii) *Polysaccharides*: Carbohydrates which yield a large number of monosaccharide units on hydrolysis are called polysaccharides. Some common examples are starch, cellulose, glycogen, gums, etc. Polysaccharides are not sweet in taste, hence they are also called non-sugars.

The carbohydrates may also be classified as either reducing or non-reducing sugars. All those carbohydrates which reduce Fehling's solution and Tollens' reagent are referred to as reducing sugars. All monosaccharides whether aldose or ketose are *reducing sugars*.

In disaccharides, if the reducing groups of monosaccharides i.e., aldehydic or ketonic groups are bonded, these are non-reducing sugars e.g. sucrose. On the other hand, sugars in which these functional groups are free, are called reducing sugars, for example, maltose and lactose.

14.1.2 Monosaccharides

Monosaccharides are further classified on the basis of number of carbon atoms and the functional group present in them. If a monosaccharide contains an aldehyde group, it is known as an aldose and if it contains a keto group, it is known as a ketose. Number of carbon atoms constituting the monosaccharide is also introduced in the name as is evident from the examples given in Table 14.1

Table 14.1: Different Types of Monosaccharides

Carbon atoms	General term	Aldehyde	Ketone
3	Triose	Aldotriose	Ketotriose
4	Tetrose	Aldotetrose	Ketotetrose
5	Pentose	Aldopentose	Ketopentose
6	Hexose	Aldohexose	Ketohexose
7	Heptose	Aldoheptose	Ketoheptose

I Glucose

Glucose occurs freely in nature as well as in the combined form. It is present in sweet fruits and honey. Ripe grapes also contain glucose in large amounts. It is prepared as follows:

14.1.3 Preparation of Glucose

1. *From sucrose (Cane sugar):* If sucrose is boiled with dilute HCl or H_2SO_4 in alcoholic solution, glucose and fructose are obtained in equal amounts.

$$C_{12}H_{22}O_{11} + H_2O \xrightarrow{\ H^+\ } C_6H_{12}O_6 + C_6H_{12}O_6$$

Sucrose Glucose Fructose

2. *From starch:* Commercially glucose is obtained by hydrolysis of starch by boiling it with dilute H_2SO_4 at 393 K under pressure.

$$(C_6H_{10}O_5)_n + nH_2O \xrightarrow[393\,K;\ 2\text{-}3\ atm]{H^+} nC_6H_{12}O_6$$

Starch or cellulose Glucose

14.1.4 Structure of Glucose

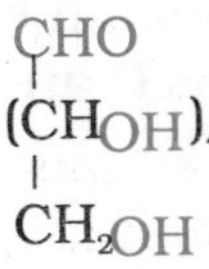

Glucose is an aldohexose and is also known as dextrose. It is the monomer of many of the larger carbohydrates, namely starch, cellulose. It is probably the most abundant organic compound on earth. It was assigned the structure given below on the basis of the following evidences:

CHO
|
(CHOH)$_4$
|
CH$_2$OH

Glucose

1. Its molecular formula was found to be $C_6H_{12}O_6$.

2. On prolonged heating with HI, it forms n-hexane, suggesting that all the six carbon atoms are linked in a straight chain.

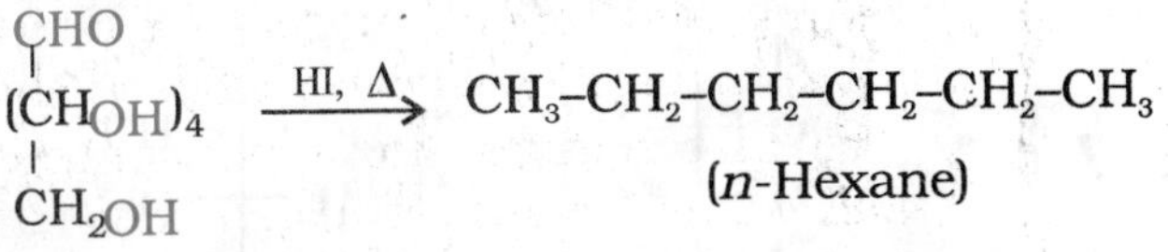

CHO
|
(CHOH)$_4$ $\xrightarrow{HI,\ \Delta}$ $CH_3-CH_2-CH_2-CH_2-CH_2-CH_3$
|
CH$_2$OH

(*n*-Hexane)

3. Glucose reacts with hydroxylamine to form an oxime and adds a molecule of hydrogen cyanide to give cyanohydrin. These reactions confirm the presence of a carbonyl group (>C = O) in glucose.

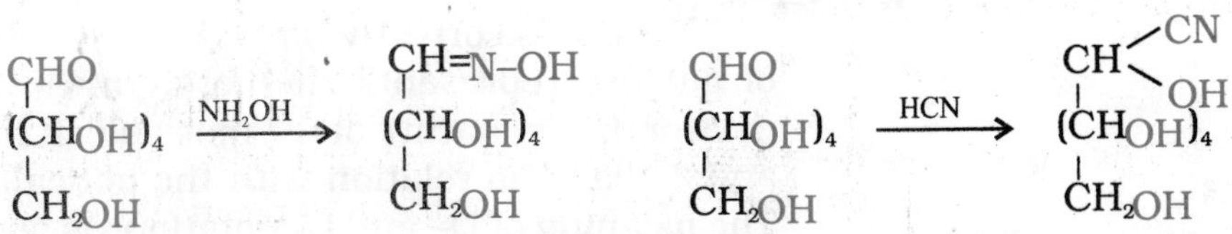

CHO
|
(CHOH)$_4$ $\xrightarrow{NH_2OH}$
|
CH$_2$OH

CH=N–OH
|
(CHOH)$_4$
|
CH$_2$OH

CHO
|
(CHOH)$_4$ $\xrightarrow{HCN}$
|
CH$_2$OH

CH<$\begin{smallmatrix}CN\\OH\end{smallmatrix}$
|
(CHOH)$_4$
|
CH$_2$OH

4. Glucose gets oxidised to six carbon carboxylic acid (gluconic acid) on reaction with a mild oxidising agent like bromine water. This indicates that the carbonyl group is present as an aldehydic group.

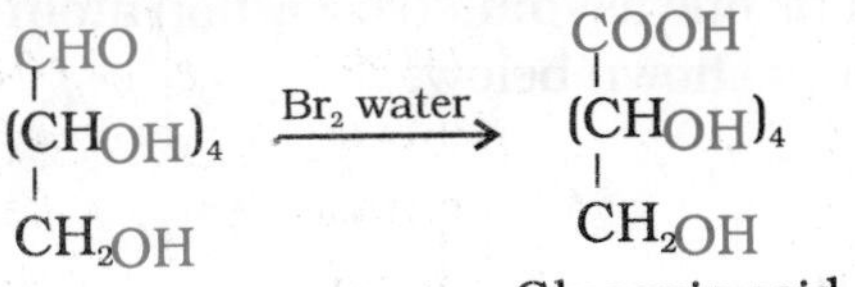

CHO
|
(CHOH)$_4$ $\xrightarrow{Br_2\ water}$
|
CH$_2$OH

COOH
|
(CHOH)$_4$
|
CH$_2$OH
Gluconic acid

5. Acetylation of glucose with acetic anhydride gives glucose pentaacetate which confirms the presence of five –OH groups. Since it exists as a stable compound, five –OH groups should be attached to different carbon atoms.

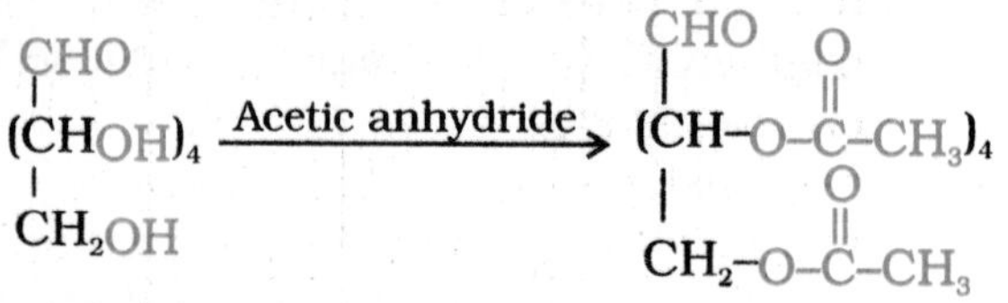

$$\begin{array}{c} CHO \\ | \\ (CHOH)_4 \\ | \\ CH_2OH \end{array} \xrightarrow{\text{Acetic anhydride}} \begin{array}{c} CHO \quad\; O \\ | \qquad\; \| \\ (CH-O-C-CH_3)_4 \\ | \qquad\; O \\ \qquad\qquad \| \\ CH_2-O-C-CH_3 \end{array}$$

6. On oxidation with nitric acid, glucose as well as gluconic acid both yield a dicarboxylic acid, saccharic acid. This indicates the presence of a primary alcoholic (–OH) group in glucose.

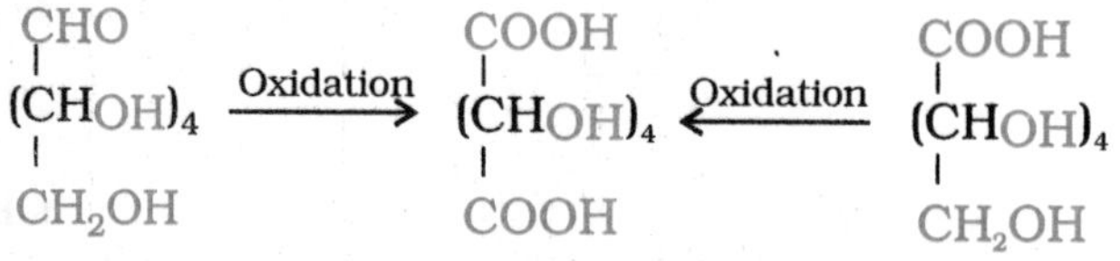

$$\begin{array}{c} CHO \\ | \\ (CHOH)_4 \\ | \\ CH_2OH \end{array} \xrightarrow{\text{Oxidation}} \begin{array}{c} COOH \\ | \\ (CHOH)_4 \\ | \\ COOH \end{array} \xleftarrow{\text{Oxidation}} \begin{array}{c} COOH \\ | \\ (CHOH)_4 \\ | \\ CH_2OH \end{array}$$

Saccharic   Gluconic

acid   acid

The exact spatial arrangement of different —OH groups was given by Fischer after studying many other properties. Its configuration is correctly represented as **I**. So gluconic acid is represented as **II** and saccharic acid as **III**.

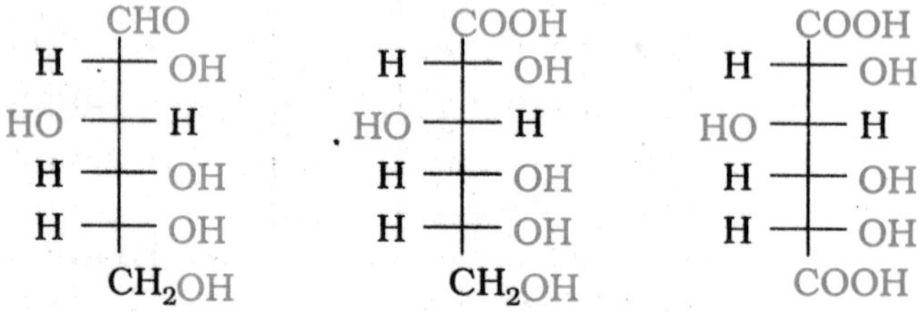

Glucose is correctly named as D(+)-glucose. 'D' before the name of glucose represents the configuration whereas '(+)' represents dextrorotatory nature of the molecule. It may be remembered that 'D' and 'L' have no relation with the optical activity of the compound. The meaning of D– and L– notations is given as follows.

The letters 'D' or 'L' before the name of any compound indicate the relative configuration of a particular stereoisomer. This refers to their relation with a particular isomer of glyceraldehyde. Glyceraldehyde contains one asymmetric carbon atom and exists in two enantiomeric forms as shown below.

All those compounds which can be chemically correlated to (+) isomer of glyceraldehyde are said to have D-configuration whereas those which can be correlated to (–) isomer of glyceraldehyde are said to have L—configuration. For assigning the configuration of monosaccharides, it is the lowest asymmetric carbon atom (as shown below) which is compared. As in (+) glucose, —OH on the lowest asymmetric carbon is on the right side which is comparable to (+) glyceraldehyde, so it is assigned D-configuration. For this comparison, the structure is written in a way that most oxidised carbon is at the top.

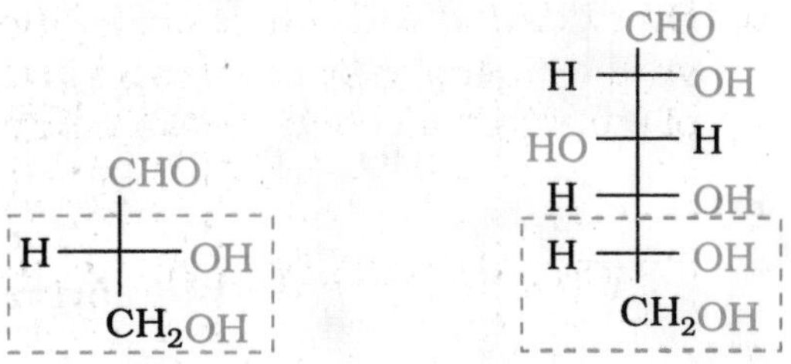

D– (+) – Glyceraldehyde   D–(+) – Glucose

14.1.5 Cyclic Structure of Glucose

The structure (I) of glucose explained most of its properties but the following reactions and facts could not be explained by this structure.

1. Despite having the aldehyde group, glucose does not give Schiff's test and it does not form the hydrogensulphite addition product with $NaHSO_3$.

2. The pentaacetate of glucose does not react with hydroxylamine indicating the absence of free —CHO group.

3. Glucose is found to exist in two different crystalline forms which are named as α and β. The α-form of glucose (m.p. 419 K) is obtained by crystallisation from concentrated solution of glucose at 303 K while the β-form (m.p. 423 K) is obtained by crystallisation from hot and saturated aqueous solution at 371 K.

This behaviour could not be explained by the open chain structure (I) for glucose. It was proposed that one of the —OH groups may add to the —CHO group and form a cyclic hemiacetal structure. It was found that glucose forms a six-membered ring in which —OH at C-5 is involved in ring formation. This explains the absence of —CHO group and also existence of glucose in two forms as shown below. These two cyclic forms exist in equilibrium with open chain structure.

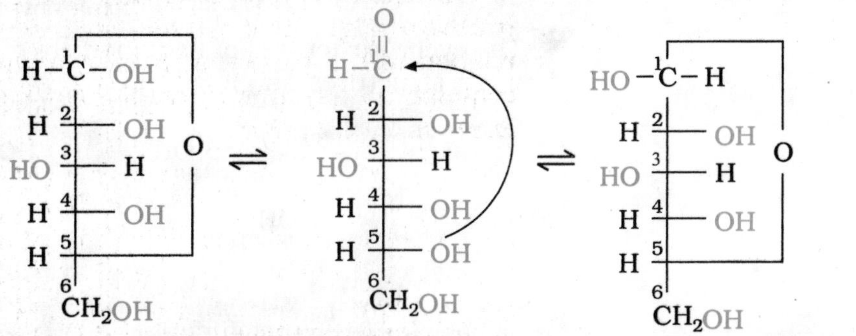

α – D – (+) – Glucose   β – D– (+) – Glucose

The two cyclic hemiacetal forms of glucose differ only in the configuration of the hydroxyl group at C1, called *anomeric carbon* (the aldehyde carbon before cyclisation). Such isomers, i.e., α-form and β-form, are called **anomers**. The six membered cyclic structure of glucose is called **pyranose structure** (α– or β–), in analogy with pyran. Pyran is a cyclic organic compound with one oxygen atom and five carbon atoms in the ring. The cyclic structure of glucose is more correctly represented by Haworth structure as given below.

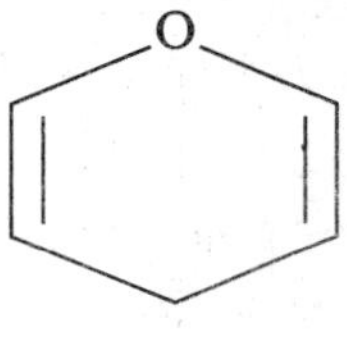

Pyran

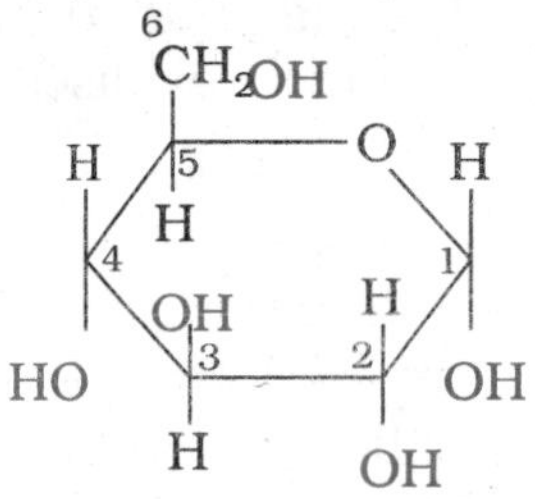

α – D – (+) – Glucopyranose 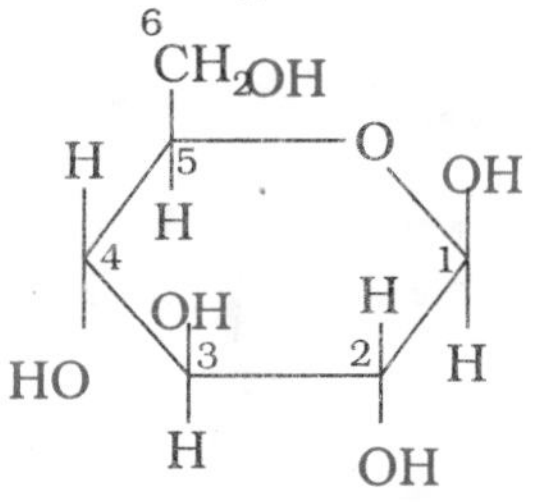   β – D – (+) – Glucopyranose

II. Fructose

Fructose is an important ketohexose. It is obtained along with glucose by the hydrolysis of disaccharide, sucrose.

14.1.6 Structure of Fructose

Fructose also has the molecular formula $C_6H_{12}O_6$ and on the basis of its reactions it was found to contain a ketonic functional group at carbon number 2 and six carbons in straight chain as in the case of glucose. It belongs to D-series and is a laevorotatory compound. It is appropriately written as D-(–)-fructose. Its open chain structure is as shown.

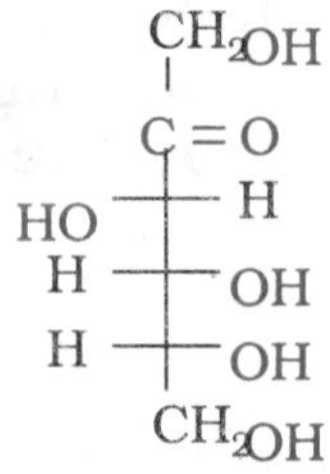

D – (–) – Fructose

It also exists in two cyclic forms which are obtained by the addition of —OH at C5 to the ($>$C=O) group. The ring, thus formed is a five membered ring and is named as furanose with analogy to the compound furan. Furan is a five membered cyclic compound with one oxygen and four carbon atoms.

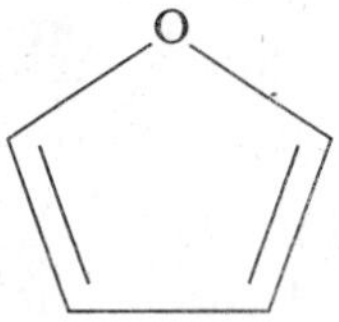

Furan

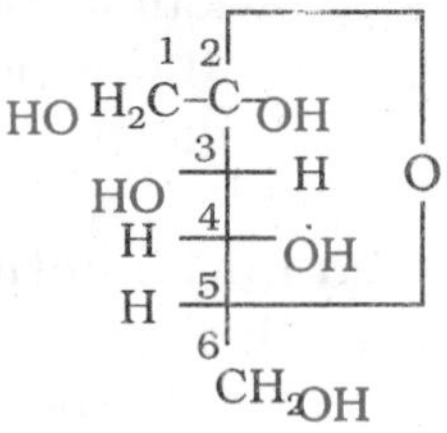

α – D – (–) – Fructofuranose 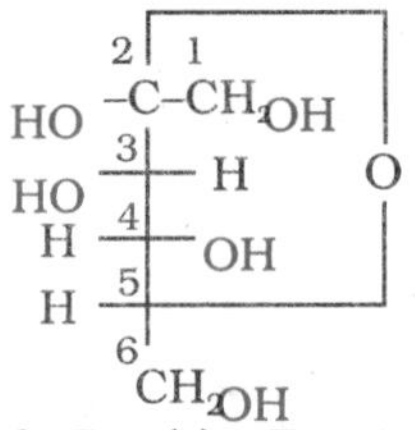   β – D – (–) – Fructofuranose

The cyclic structures of two anomers of fructose are represented by Haworth structures as given.

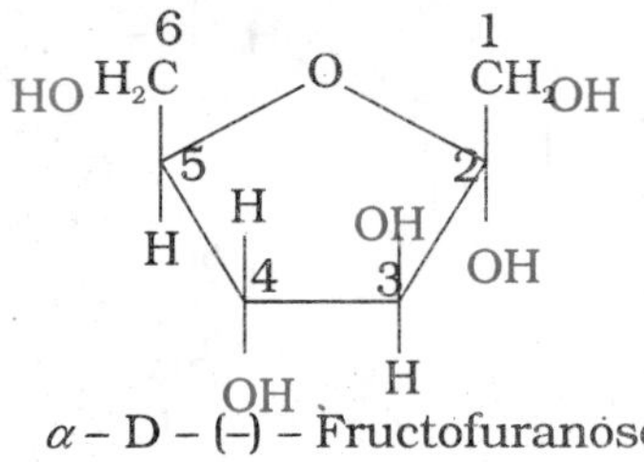

α – D – (–) – Fructofuranose 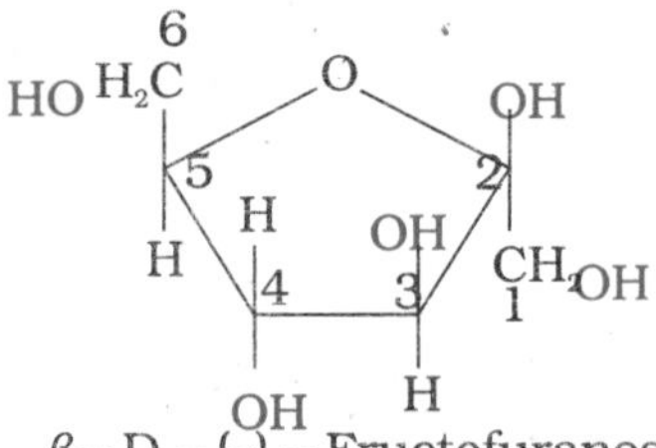   β – D – (–) – Fructofuranose

14.1.7 Disaccharides

You have already read that disaccharides on hydrolysis with dilute acids or enzymes yield two molecules of either the same or different monosaccharides. The two monosaccharides are joined together by an oxide linkage formed by the loss of a water molecule. Such a linkage between two monosaccharide units through oxygen atom is called *glycosidic linkage.*

(i) *Sucrose*: One of the common disaccharides is **sucrose** which on hydrolysis gives equimolar mixture of D-(+)-glucose and D-(–) fructose.

$$C_{12}H_{22}O_{11} + H_2O \longrightarrow C_6H_{12}O_6 + C_6H_{12}O_6$$

Sucrose   D-(+)-Glucose   D-(–)-Fructose

These two monosaccharides are held together by a glycosidic linkage between C1 of α-glucose and C2 of β-fructose. Since the reducing groups of glucose and fructose are involved in glycosidic bond formation, sucrose is a non reducing sugar.

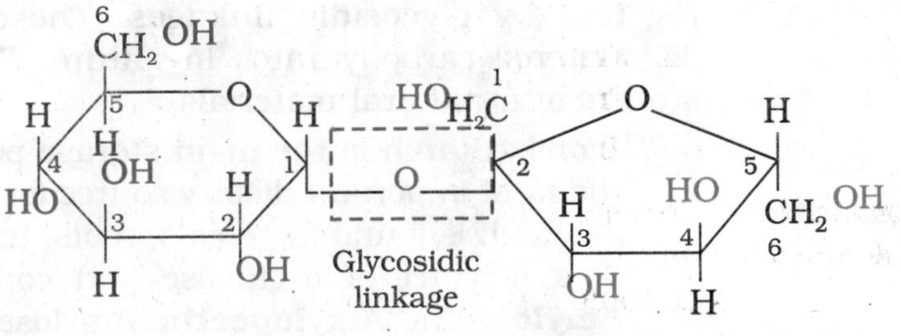

α – D – Glucose   β – D – Fructose

Sucrose

Sucrose is dextrorotatory but after hydrolysis gives dextrorotatory glucose and laevorotatory fructose. Since the laevorotation of fructose (–92.4°) is more than dextrorotation of glucose (+ 52.5°), the mixture is laevorotatory. Thus, hydrolysis of sucrose brings about a change in the sign of rotation, from dextro (+) to laevo (–) and the product is named as **invert sugar**.

(ii) *Maltose*: Another disaccharide, maltose is composed of two α-D-glucose units in which C1 of one glucose (I) is linked to C4 of another glucose unit (II). The free aldehyde group can be produced at C1 of second glucose in solution and it shows reducing properties so it is a reducing sugar.

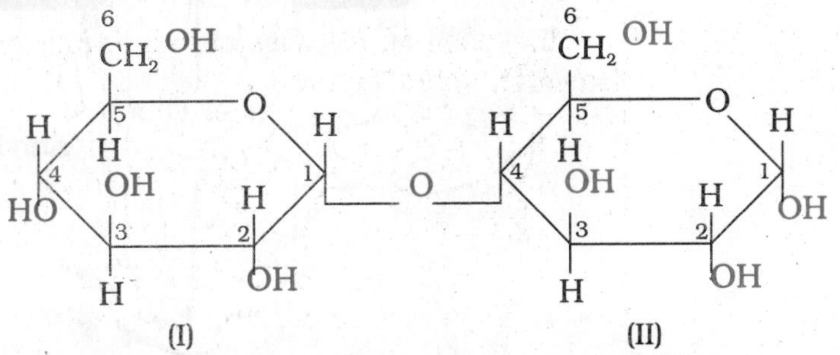

(I)   (II)

α – D – Glucose   α – D – Glucose

Maltose

(iii) *Lactose*: It is more commonly known as milk sugar since this disaccharide is found in milk. It is composed of β-D-galactose and β-D-glucose. The linkage is between C1 of galactose and C4 of glucose. Hence it is also a reducing sugar.

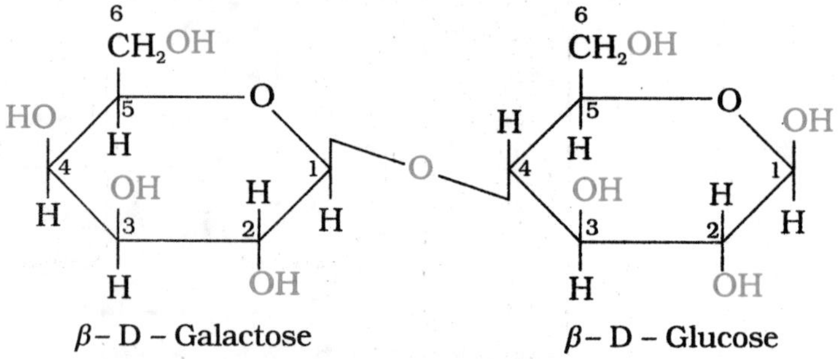

β– D – Galactose   β– D – Glucose

Lactose

14.1.8 Polysaccharides

Polysaccharides contain a large number of monosaccharide units joined together by glycosidic linkages. These are the most commonly encountered carbohydrates in nature. They mainly act as the food storage or structural materials.

(i) *Starch*: Starch is the main storage polysaccharide of plants. It is the most important dietary source for human beings. High content of starch is found in cereals, roots, tubers and some vegetables. It is a polymer of α-glucose and consists of two components— **Amylose** and **Amylopectin**. Amylose is water soluble component which constitutes about 15-20% of starch. Chemically amylose is a long unbranched chain with 200-1000 α-D-(+)-glucose units held by C1– C4 glycosidic linkage.

Amylopectin is insoluble in water and constitutes about 80-85% of starch. It is a branched chain polymer of α-D-glucose units in which chain is formed by C1–C4 glycosidic linkage whereas branching occurs by C1–C6 glycosidic linkage.

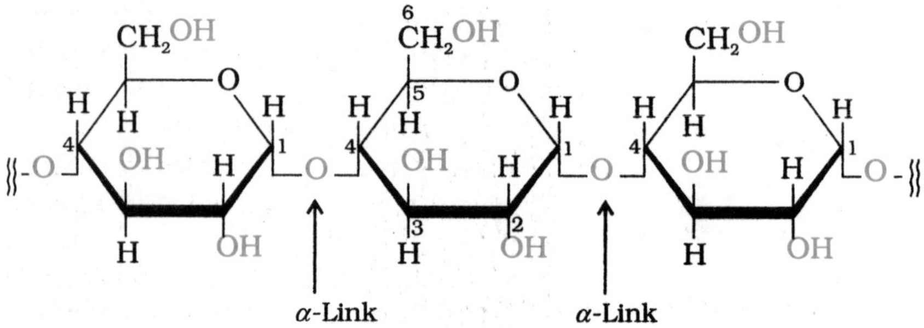

α-Link   α-Link

Amylose

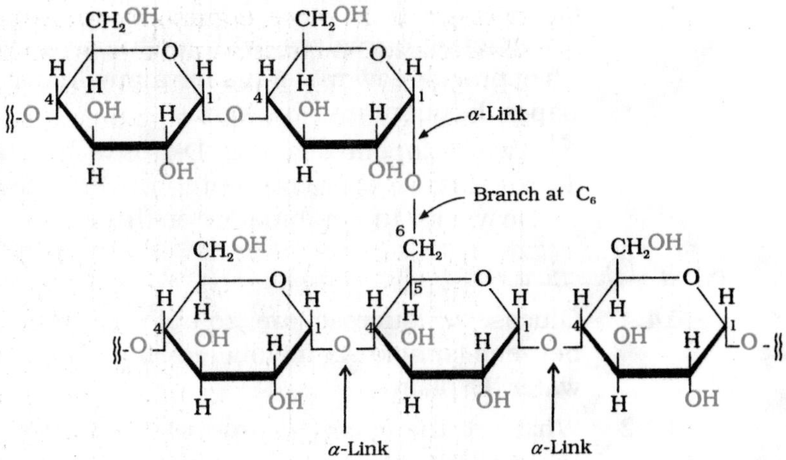

CH$_2$OH CH$_2$OH

H H H H H H

§-O $\overset{4}{}$ OH H $\overset{1}{}$ O $\overset{4}{}$ OH H $\overset{1}{}$ — α-Link

H OH H OH

— Branch at C$_6$

CH$_2$OH $\overset{6}{}$CH$_2$ CH$_2$OH

H H H H$\overset{5}{}$H H H H H

§-O $\overset{4}{}$ OH H $\overset{1}{}$ O $\overset{4}{}$ OH H $\overset{1}{}$ O $\overset{4}{}$ OH H $\overset{1}{}$ O-§

H OH H OH H OH

α-Link α-Link

Amylopectin

(ii) *Cellulose*: Cellulose occurs exclusively in plants and it is the most abundant organic substance in plant kingdom. It is a predominant constituent of cell wall of plant cells. Cellulose is a straight chain

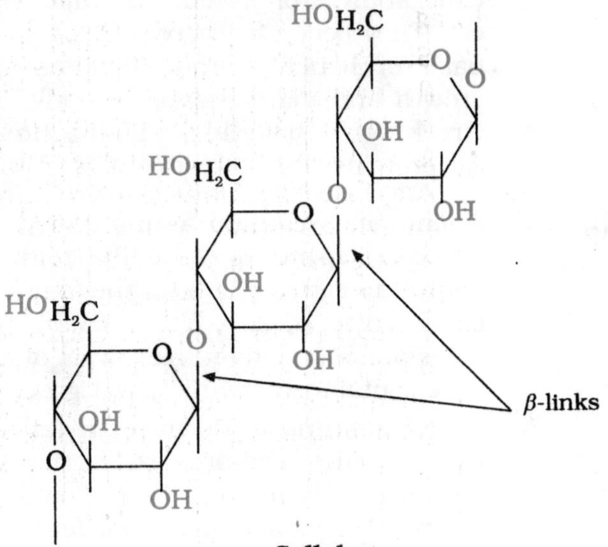

HOH$_2$C

OH

OH

HOH$_2$C

OH

OH

HOH$_2$C

OH

OH

β-links

Cellulose

polysaccharide composed only of β-D-glucose units which are joined by glycosidic linkage between C1 of one glucose unit and C4 of the next glucose unit.

(iii) *Glycogen*: The carbohydrates are stored in animal body as glycogen. It is also known as *animal starch* because its structure is similar to amylopectin and is rather more highly branched. It is present in liver, muscles and brain. When the body needs glucose, enzymes break the glycogen down to glucose. Glycogen is also found in yeast and fungi.

14.1.9 Importance of Carbohydrates

Carbohydrates are essential for life in both plants and animals. They form a major portion of our food. Honey has been used for a long time as an instant source of energy by 'Vaids' in ayurvedic system of medicine. Carbohydrates are used as storage molecules as starch in plants and **glycogen** in animals. Cell wall of bacteria and plants is made up of cellulose. We build furniture, etc. from cellulose in the form of wood and clothe ourselves with cellulose in the form of cotton fibre. They provide raw materials for many important industries like textiles, paper, lacquers and breweries.

Two aldopentoses viz. D-ribose and 2-deoxy-D-ribose (Section 14.5.1, Class XII) are present in nucleic acids. Carbohydrates are found in biosystem in combination with many proteins and lipids.

Intext Questions

14.1 Glucose or sucrose are soluble in water but cyclohexane or benzene (simple six membered ring compounds) are insoluble in water. Explain.

14.2 What are the expected products of hydrolysis of lactose?

14.3 How do you explain the absence of aldehyde group in the pentaacetate of D-glucose?

14.2 Proteins

Proteins are the most abundant biomolecules of the living system. Chief sources of proteins are milk, cheese, pulses, peanuts, fish, meat, etc. They occur in every part of the body and form the fundamental basis of structure and functions of life. They are also required for growth and maintenance of body. The word protein is derived from Greek word, **"proteios"** which means primary or of prime importance. All proteins are polymers of α-amino acids.

14.2.1 Amino Acids

Amino acids contain amino ($-NH_2$) and carboxyl ($-COOH$) functional groups. Depending upon the relative position of amino group with respect to carboxyl group, the amino acids can be classified as α, β, γ, δ and so on. Only α-amino acids are obtained on hydrolysis of proteins. They may contain other functional groups also.

$$R-CH-COOH$$
$$\overset{|}{NH_2}$$

α-amino acid
(R = side chain)

All α-amino acids have trivial names, which usually reflect the property of that compound or its source. Glycine is so named since it has sweet taste (in Greek *glykos* means sweet) and tyrosine was first obtained from cheese (in Greek, *tyros* means cheese.) Amino acids are generally represented by a three letter symbol, sometimes one letter symbol is also used. Structures of some commonly occurring amino acids along with their 3-letter and 1-letter symbols are given in Table 14.2.

Table 14.2: Natural Amino Acids

$$H_2N \overset{COOH}{\underset{R}{\vert\vert}} H$$

Name of the amino acids	Characteristic feature of side chain, R	Three letter symbol	One letter code
1. Glycine	H	Gly	G
2. Alanine	$- CH_3$	Ala	A
3. Valine*	$(H_3C)_2CH-$	Val	V
4. Leucine*	$(H_3C)_2CH-CH_2-$	Leu	L

5. Isoleucine*	$H_3C\text{-}CH_2\text{-}CH\text{-}$ $\quad\quad\quad\quad\quad \vert$ $\quad\quad\quad\quad CH_3$	Ile	I
6. Arginine*	$HN{=}C\text{-}NH\text{-}(CH_2)_3\text{-}$ $\quad\quad \vert$ $\quad\quad NH_2$	Arg	R
7. Lysine*	$H_2N\text{-}(CH_2)_4\text{-}$	Lys	K
8. Glutamic acid	$HOOC\text{-}CH_2\text{-}CH_2\text{-}$	Glu	E
9. Aspartic acid	$HOOC\text{-}CH_2\text{-}$	Asp	D
10. Glutamine	$\quad\quad\quad O$ $\quad\quad\quad \Vert$ $H_2N\text{-}C\text{-}CH_2\text{-}CH_2\text{-}$	Gln	Q
11. Asparagine	$\quad\quad\quad O$ $\quad\quad\quad \Vert$ $H_2N\text{-}C\text{-}CH_2\text{-}$	Asn	N
12. Threonine*	$H_3C\text{-}CHOH\text{-}$	Thr	T
13. Serine	$HO\text{-}CH_2\text{-}$	Ser	S
14. Cysteine	$HS\text{-}CH_2\text{-}$	Cys	C
15. Methionine*	$H_3C\text{-}S\text{-}CH_2\text{-}CH_2\text{-}$	Met	M
16. Phenylalanine*	$C_6H_5\text{-}CH_2\text{-}$	Phe	F
17. Tyrosine	$(p)HO\text{-}C_6H_4\text{-}CH_2\text{-}$	Tyr	Y
18. Tryptophan*	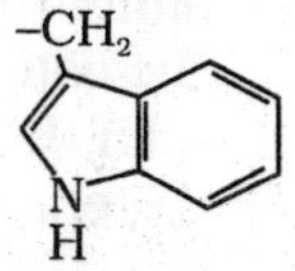	Trp	W
19. Histidine*	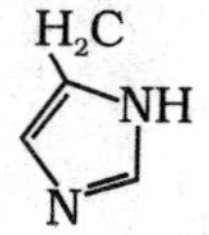	His	H
20. Proline	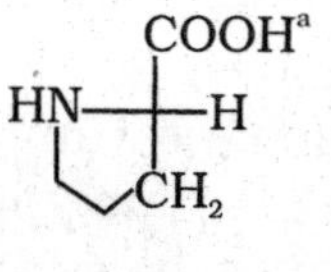	Pro	P

* *essential amino acid, a = entire structure*

14.2.2 Classification of Amino Acids

Amino acids are classified as acidic, basic or neutral depending upon the relative number of amino and carboxyl groups in their molecule. Equal number of amino and carboxyl groups makes it neutral; more number of amino than carboxyl groups makes it basic and more carboxyl groups as compared to amino groups makes it acidic. The amino acids, which can be synthesised in the body, are known as **non-essential amino acids.** On the other hand, those which cannot be synthesised in the body and must be obtained through diet, are known as **essential amino acids** (marked with asterisk in Table 14.2).

Amino acids are usually colourless, crystalline solids. These are water-soluble, high melting solids and behave like salts rather than simple amines or carboxylic acids. This behaviour is due to the presence of both acidic (carboxyl group) and basic (amino group) groups in the same molecule. In aqueous solution, the carboxyl group can lose a proton and amino group can accept a proton, giving rise to a dipolar ion known as *zwitter ion*. This is neutral but contains both positive and negative charges.

$$R-\underset{\underset{:NH_2}{|}}{CH}-\overset{\overset{O}{||}}{C}-O-H \rightleftharpoons R-\underset{\underset{^+NH_3}{|}}{CH}-\overset{\overset{O}{||}}{C}-O^-$$

(Zwitter ion)

In zwitter ionic form, amino acids show amphoteric behaviour as they react both with acids and bases.

Except glycine, all other naturally occurring α-amino acids are optically active, since the α-carbon atom is asymmetric. These exist both in 'D' and 'L' forms. Most naturally occurring amino acids have L-configuration. L-Aminoacids are represented by writing the –NH$_2$ group on left hand side.

14.2.3 Structure of Proteins

You have already read that proteins are the polymers of α-amino acids and they are connected to each other by **peptide bond** or **peptide linkage.** Chemically, peptide linkage is an amide formed between –COOH group and –NH$_2$ group. The reaction between two molecules of similar or different amino acids, proceeds through the combination of the amino group of one molecule with the carboxyl group of the other. This results in the elimination of a water molecule and formation of a peptide bond –CO–NH–. The product of the reaction is called a dipeptide because it is made up of two amino acids. For example, when carboxyl group of glycine combines with the amino group of alanine we get a **dipeptide**, glycylalanine.

$$H_2N-CH_2-COOH + H_2N-\underset{\underset{CH_3}{|}}{CH}-COOH$$

$$\underset{-H_2O}{\downarrow}$$

$$H_2N-CH_2-\boxed{CO-NH}-\underset{\underset{CH_3}{|}}{CH}-COOH$$

Peptide linkage

Glycylalanine (Gly-Ala)

If a third amino acid combines to a dipeptide, the product is called a **tripeptide**. A tripeptide contains three amino acids linked by two peptide linkages. Similarly when four, five or six amino acids are linked, the respective products are known as **tetrapeptide, pentapeptide or hexapeptide**, respectively. When the number of such amino acids is more than ten, then the products are called **polypeptides**. A polypeptide with more than hundred amino acid residues, having molecular mass higher than 10,000u is called a protein. However, the distinction between a polypeptide and a protein is not very sharp. Polypeptides with fewer amino acids are likely to be called proteins if they ordinarily have a well defined conformation of a protein such as insulin which contains 51 amino acids.

Proteins can be classified into two types on the basis of their molecular shape.

(a) Fibrous proteins

When the polypeptide chains run parallel and are held together by hydrogen and disulphide bonds, then fibre– like structure is formed. Such proteins are generally insoluble in water. Some common examples are keratin (present in hair, wool, silk) and myosin (present in muscles), etc.

(b) Globular proteins

This structure results when the chains of polypeptides coil around to give a spherical shape. These are usually soluble in water. Insulin and albumins are the common examples of globular proteins.

Structure and shape of proteins can be studied at four different levels, i.e., primary, secondary, tertiary and quaternary, each level being more complex than the previous one.

(i) Primary structure of proteins: Proteins may have one or more polypeptide chains. Each polypeptide in a protein has amino acids linked with each other in a specific sequence and it is this sequence of amino acids that is said to be the primary structure of that protein. Any change in this primary structure i.e., the sequence of amino acids creates a different protein.

(ii) Secondary structure of proteins: The secondary structure of protein refers to the shape in which a long polypeptide chain can exist. They are found to exist in two different types of structures viz. α-helix and β-pleated sheet structure. These structures arise due to the regular folding of the backbone of the polypeptide chain due to hydrogen bonding between $-\overset{\text{O}}{\overset{\|}{C}}-$ and –NH– groups of the peptide bond.

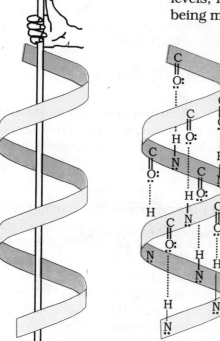

Fig. 14.1: *α-Helix structure of proteins*

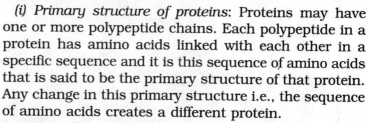

α-Helix is one of the most common ways in which a polypeptide chain forms all possible hydrogen bonds by twisting into a right handed screw (helix) with the –NH group of each amino acid residue hydrogen bonded to the $>$C=O of an adjacent turn of the helix as shown in Fig.14.1.

In β-structure all peptide chains are stretched out to nearly maximum extension and then laid side by side which are held together by intermolecular hydrogen bonds. The structure resembles the pleated folds of drapery and therefore is known as β-pleated sheet.

(iii) Tertiary structure of proteins: The tertiary structure of proteins represents overall folding of the polypeptide chains i.e., further folding of the secondary structure. It gives rise to two major molecular shapes viz. fibrous and globular. The main forces which stabilise the 2° and 3° structures of proteins are hydrogen bonds, disulphide linkages, van der Waals and electrostatic forces of attraction.

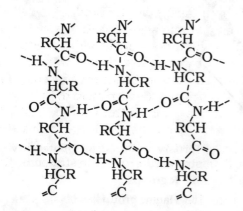

Fig. 14.2: *β-Pleated sheet structure of proteins*

(iv) Quaternary structure of proteins: Some of the proteins are composed of two or more polypeptide chains referred to as sub-units. The spatial arrangement of these subunits with respect to each other is known as quaternary structure.

A diagrammatic representation of all these four structures is given in Figure 14.3 where each coloured ball represents an amino acid.

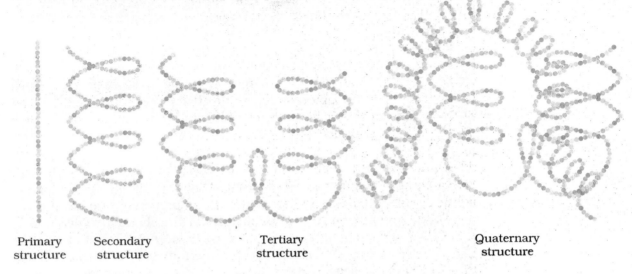

Primary structure   Secondary structure   Tertiary structure   Quaternary structure

Fig. 14.3: Diagrammatic representation of protein structure (two sub-units of two types in quaternary structure)

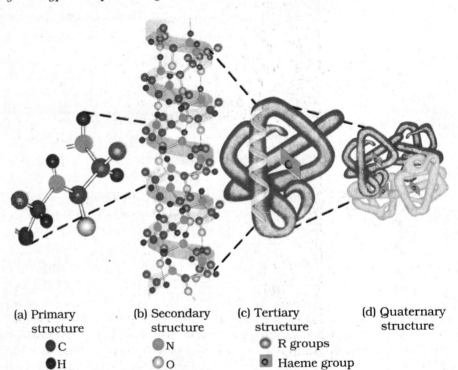

Fig. 14.4: Primary, secondary, tertiary and quaternary structures of haemoglobin

(a) Primary structure
    ● C
    ● H

(b) Secondary structure
    ● N
    ○ O

(c) Tertiary structure
    R groups
    Haeme group

(d) Quaternary structure

14.2.4 Denaturation of Proteins

Protein found in a biological system with a unique three-dimensional structure and biological activity is called a native protein. When a protein in its native form, is subjected to physical change like change in temperature or chemical change like change in pH, the hydrogen bonds are disturbed. Due to this, globules unfold and helix get uncoiled and protein loses its biological activity. This is called **denaturation** of protein. During denaturation 2° and 3° structures are destroyed but 1° structure remains intact. The coagulation of egg white on boiling is a common example of denaturation. Another example is curdling of milk which is caused due to the formation of lactic acid by the bacteria present in milk.

14.4 The melting points and solubility in water of amino acids are generally higher than that of the corresponding halo acids. Explain.

14.5 Where does the water present in the egg go after boiling the egg?

14.3 Enzymes

Life is possible due to the coordination of various chemical reactions in living organisms. An example is the digestion of food, absorption of appropriate molecules and ultimately production of energy. This process involves a sequence of reactions and all these reactions occur in the body under very mild conditions. This occurs with the help of certain biocatalysts called **enzymes.** Almost all the enzymes are globular proteins. Enzymes are very specific for a particular reaction and for a particular substrate. They are generally named after the compound or class of compounds upon which they work. For example, the enzyme that catalyses hydrolysis of maltose into glucose is named as *maltase.*

$$\underset{\text{Maltose}}{C_{12}H_{22}O_{11}} \xrightarrow{\text{Maltase}} \underset{\text{Glucose}}{2\ C_6H_{12}O_6}$$

Sometimes enzymes are also named after the reaction, where they are used. For example, the enzymes which catalyse the oxidation of one substrate with simultaneous reduction of another substrate are named as **oxidoreductase** enzymes. The ending of the name of an enzyme is **-ase.**

14.3.1 Mechanism of Enzyme Action

Enzymes are needed only in small quantities for the progress of a reaction. Similar to the action of chemical catalysts, enzymes are said to reduce the magnitude of activation energy. For example, activation energy for acid hydrolysis of sucrose is 6.22 kJ mol^{-1}, while the activation energy is only 2.15 kJ mol^{-1} when hydrolysed by the enzyme, sucrase. Mechanism for the enzyme action has been discussed in Unit 5.

14.4 Vitamins

It has been observed that certain organic compounds are required in small amounts in our diet but their deficiency causes specific diseases. These compounds are called **vitamins.** Most of the vitamins cannot be synthesised in our body but plants can synthesise almost all of them, so they are considered as essential food factors. However, the bacteria of the gut can produce some of the vitamins required by us. All the vitamins are generally available in our diet. Different vitamins belong to various chemical classes and it is difficult to define them on the basis of structure. They are generally regarded as **organic compounds required in the diet in small amounts to perform specific biological functions for normal maintenance of optimum growth** and health of the organism. Vitamins are designated by alphabets A, B, C, D, etc. Some of them are further named as sub-groups e.g. B_1, B_2, B_6, B_{12}, etc. Excess of vitamins is also harmful and vitamin pills should not be taken without the advice of doctor.

The term "**Vitamine**" was coined from the word vital + amine since the earlier identified compounds had amino groups. Later work showed that most of them did not contain amino groups, so the letter 'e' was dropped and the term **vitamin** is used these days.

14.4.1
Classification of Vitamins

Vitamins are classified into two groups depending upon their solubility in water or fat.

(i) *Fat soluble vitamins*: Vitamins which are soluble in fat and oils but insoluble in water are kept in this group. These are vitamins A, D, E and K. They are stored in liver and adipose (fat storing) tissues.

(ii) *Water soluble vitamins*: B group vitamins and vitamin C are soluble in water so they are grouped together. Water soluble vitamins must be supplied regularly in diet because they are readily excreted in urine and cannot be stored (except vitamin B_{12}) in our body.

Some important vitamins, their sources and diseases caused by their deficiency are listed in Table 14.3.

Table 14.3: Some important Vitamins, their Sources and their Deficiency Diseases

Sl. No.	Name of Vitamins	Sources	Deficiency diseases
1.	Vitamin A	Fish liver oil, carrots, butter and milk	Xerophthalmia (hardening of cornea of eye) Night blindness
2.	Vitamin B_1 (Thiamine)	Yeast, milk, green vegetables and cereals	Beri beri (loss of appetite, retarded growth)
3.	Vitamin B_2 (Riboflavin)	Milk, eggwhite, liver, kidney	Cheilosis (fissuring at corners of mouth and lips), digestive disorders and burning sensation of the skin.
4.	Vitamin B_6 (Pyridoxine)	Yeast, milk, egg yolk, cereals and grams	Convulsions
5.	Vitamin B_{12}	Meat, fish, egg and curd	Pernicious anaemia (RBC deficient in haemoglobin)
6.	Vitamin C (Ascorbic acid)	Citrus fruits, amla and green leafy vegetables	Scurvy (bleeding gums)
7.	Vitamin D	Exposure to sunlight, fish and egg yolk	Rickets (bone deformities in children) and osteomalacia (soft bones and joint pain in adults)

8. Vitamin E	Vegetable oils like wheat germ oil, sunflower oil, etc.	Increased fragility of RBCs and muscular weakness
9. Vitamin K	Green leafy vegetables	Increased blood clotting time

14.5: Nucleic Acids

Every generation of each and every species resembles its ancestors in many ways. How are these characteristics transmitted from one generation to the next? It has been observed that nucleus of a living cell is responsible for this transmission of inherent characters, also called **heredity**. The particles in nucleus of the cell, responsible for heredity, are called chromosomes which are made up of proteins and another type of biomolecules called **nucleic acids.** These are mainly of two types, the **deoxyribonucleic acid (DNA) and ribonucleic acid (RNA).** Since nucleic acids are long chain polymers of **nucleotides,** so they are also called polynucleotides.

James Dewey Watson

Born in Chicago, Illinois, in 1928, Dr Watson received his Ph.D. (1950) from Indiana University in Zoology. He is best known for his discovery of the structure of DNA for which he shared with Francis Crick and Maurice Wilkins the 1962 Nobel prize in Physiology and Medicine. They proposed that DNA molecule takes the shape of a double helix, an elegantly simple structure that resembles a gently twisted ladder. The rails of the ladder are made of alternating units of phosphate and the sugar deoxyribose; the rungs are each composed of a pair of purine/ pyrimidine bases. This research laid the foundation for the emerging field of **molecular biology**. The complementary pairing of nucleotide bases explains how identical copies of parental DNA pass on to two daughter cells. This research launched a revolution in biology that led to modern recombinant DNA techniques.

14.5.1 Chemical Composition of Nucleic Acids

Complete hydrolysis of DNA (or RNA) yields a pentose sugar, phosphoric acid and nitrogen containing heterocyclic compounds (called bases). In DNA molecules, the sugar moiety is β-D-2-deoxyribose whereas in RNA molecule, it is β-D-ribose.

β–D–ribose β–D–2–deoxyribose

DNA contains four bases viz. adenine (A), guanine (G), cytosine (C) and thymine (T). RNA also contains four bases, the first three bases are same as in DNA but the fourth one is uracil (U).

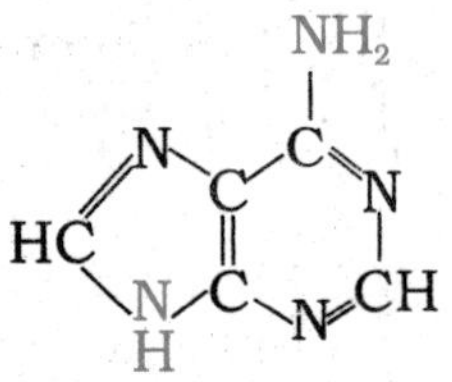

Adenine (A)

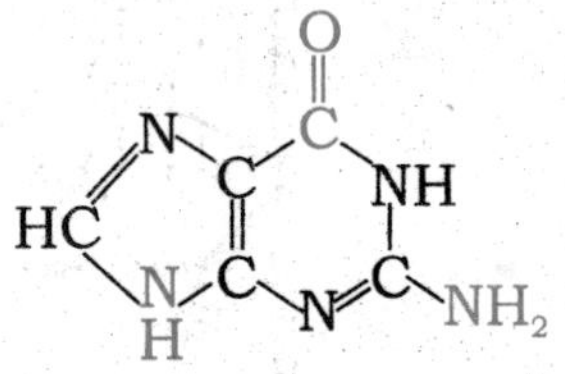

Guanine (G)

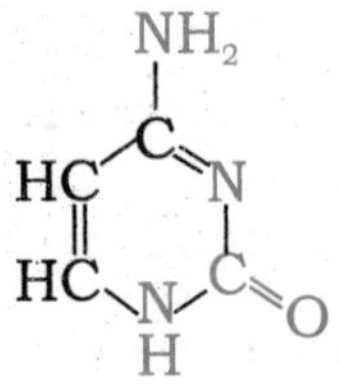

Cytosine (C)

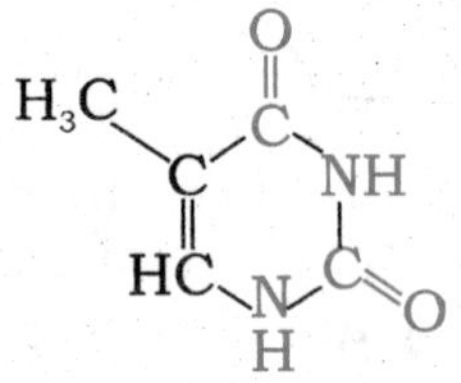

Thymine (T)

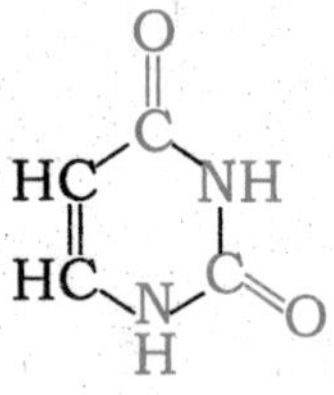

Uracil (U)

14.5.2 Structure of Nucleic Acids

A unit formed by the attachment of a base to 1′ position of sugar is known as **nucleoside.** In nucleosides, the sugar carbons are numbered as 1′, 2′, 3′, etc. in order to distinguish these from the bases (Fig. 14.5a). When nucleoside is linked to phosphoric acid at 5′-position of sugar moiety, we get a nucleotide (Fig. 14.5).

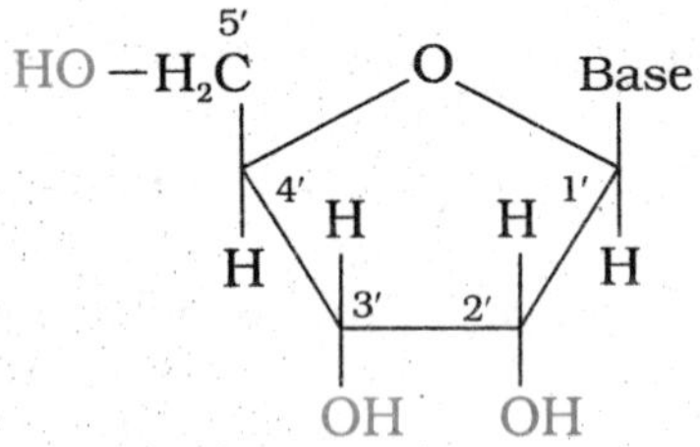

(a)

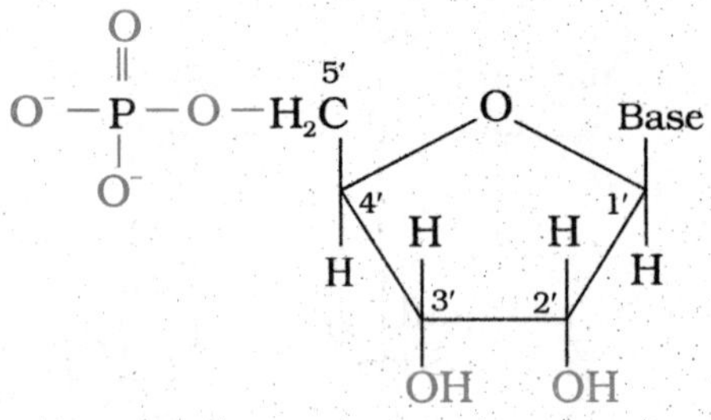

(b)

Fig. 14.5: *Structure of (a) a nucleoside and (b) a nucleotide*

Nucleotides are joined together by phosphodiester linkage between 5′ and 3′ carbon atoms of the pentose sugar. The formation of a typical dinucleotide is shown in Fig. 14.6.

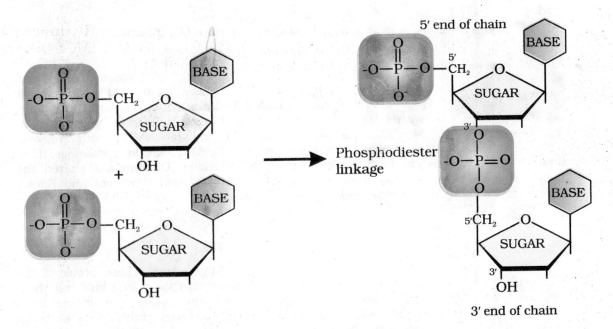

Fig. 14.6: *Formation of a dinucleotide*

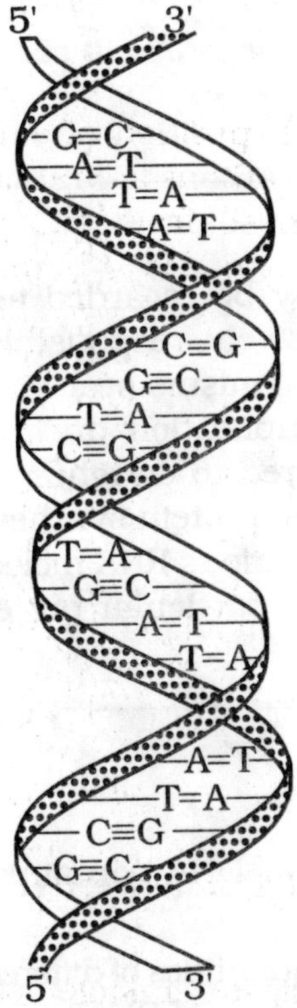

A simplified version of nucleic acid chain is as shown below.

$$\text{—Sugar — Phosphate} \left\lbrace \underset{|}{\overset{\text{Base}}{\text{Sugar}}} \text{— Phosphate} \right\rbrace_n \underset{|}{\overset{\text{Base}}{\text{Sugar}}} \text{—}$$

Information regarding the sequence of nucleotides in the chain of a nucleic acid is called its primary structure. Nucleic acids have a secondary structure also. James Watson and Francis Crick gave a double strand helix structure for DNA (Fig. 14.7). Two nucleic acid chains are wound about each other and held together by hydrogen bonds between pairs of bases. The two strands are complementary to each other because the hydrogen bonds are formed between specific pairs of bases. Adenine forms hydrogen bonds with thymine whereas cytosine forms hydrogen bonds with guanine.

In secondary structure of RNA, helices are present which are only single stranded. Sometimes they fold back on themselves to form a double helix structure. RNA molecules are of three types and they perform different functions. They are named as **messenger RNA (m-RNA), ribosomal RNA (r-RNA) and transfer RNA (t-RNA).**

Fig. 14.7: Double strand helix structure for DNA

Har Gobind Khorana

Har Gobind Khorana, was born in 1922. He obtained his M.Sc. degree from Punjab University in Lahore. He worked with Professor Vladimir Prelog, who moulded Khorana's thought and philosophy towards science, work and effort. After a brief stay in India in 1949, Khorana went back to England and worked with Professor G.W. Kenner and Professor A.R.Todd. It was at Cambridge, U.K. that he got interested in both proteins and nucleic acids. Dr Khorana shared the Nobel Prize for Medicine and Physiology in 1968 with Marshall Nirenberg and Robert Holley for cracking the genetic code.

DNA Fingerprinting

It is known that every individual has unique fingerprints. These occur at the tips of the fingers and have been used for identification for a long time but these can be altered by surgery. A sequence of bases on DNA is also unique for a person and information regarding this is called DNA fingerprinting. It is same for every cell and cannot be altered by any known treatment. DNA fingerprinting is now used

(i) in forensic laboratories for identification of criminals.

(ii) to determine paternity of an individual.

(iii) to identify the dead bodies in any accident by comparing the DNA's of parents or children.

(iv) to identify racial groups to rewrite biological evolution.

14.5.3 Biological Functions of Nucleic Acids

DNA is the chemical basis of heredity and may be regarded as the reserve of genetic information. DNA is exclusively responsible for maintaining the identity of different species of organisms over millions of years. A DNA molecule is capable of self duplication during cell division and identical DNA strands are transferred to daughter cells. Another important function of nucleic acids is the protein synthesis in the cell. Actually, the proteins are synthesised by various RNA molecules in the cell but the message for the synthesis of a particular protein is present in DNA.

Intext Questions

14.6 Why cannot vitamin C be stored in our body?

14.7 What products would be formed when a nucleotide from DNA containing thymine is hydrolysed?

14.8 When RNA is hydrolysed, there is no relationship among the quantities of different bases obtained. What does this fact suggest about the structure of RNA?

Summary

Carbohydrates are optically active polyhydroxy aldehydes or ketones or molecules which provide such units on hydrolysis. They are broadly classified into three groups — **monosaccharides**, **disaccharides** and **polysaccharides**. Glucose, the most important source of energy for mammals, is obtained by the digestion of starch. Monosaccharides are held together by glycosidic linkages to form disaccharides or polysaccharides.

 Proteins are the **polymers** of about twenty different **α-amino acids** which are linked by peptide bonds. Ten amino acids are called essential amino acids because they cannot be synthesised by our body, hence must be provided through diet. Proteins perform various structural and dynamic functions in the organisms. Proteins which contain only α-amino acids are called simple proteins. The **secondary** or **tertiary structure of proteins** get disturbed on change of pH or temperature and they are not able to perform their functions. This is called **denaturation of proteins**. Enzymes are **biocatalysts** which speed up the reactions in biosystems. They are very specific and selective in their action and chemically all **enzymes** are proteins.

 Vitamins are accessory food factors required in the diet. They are classified as fat soluble (A, D, E and K) and water soluble (B group and C). Deficiency of vitamins leads to many diseases.

 Nucleic acids are the polymers of nucleotides which in turn consist of a base, a pentose sugar and phosphate moiety. Nucleic acids are responsible for the transfer of characters from parents to offsprings. There are two types of nucleic acids — **DNA** and **RNA**. DNA contains a five carbon sugar molecule called **2-deoxyribose** whereas RNA contains ribose. Both DNA and RNA contain adenine, guanine and cytosine. The fourth base is thymine in DNA and uracil in RNA. The structure of DNA is a double strand whereas RNA is a single strand molecule. DNA is the chemical basis of heredity and have the coded message for proteins to be synthesised in the cell. There are three types of RNA — mRNA, rRNA and tRNA which actually carry out the protein synthesis in the cell.

Exercises

14.1 What are monosaccharides?

14.2 What are reducing sugars?

14.3 Write two main functions of carbohydrates in plants.

14.4 Classify the following into monosaccharides and disaccharides.
   Ribose, 2-deoxyribose, maltose, galactose, fructose and lactose.

14.5 What do you understand by the term glycosidic linkage?

14.6 What is glycogen? How is it different from starch?

14.7 What are the hydrolysis products of
   (i) sucrose and   (ii) lactose?

14.8 What is the basic structural difference between starch and cellulose?

14.9 What happens when D-glucose is treated with the following reagents?
   (i) HI   (ii) Bromine water   (iii) HNO_3

14.10 Enumerate the reactions of D-glucose which cannot be explained by its open chain structure.

14.11 What are essential and non-essential amino acids? Give two examples of each type.

14.12 Define the following as related to proteins
   (i) Peptide linkage   (ii) Primary structure   (iii) Denaturation.

14.13 What are the common types of secondary structure of proteins?

14.14 What type of bonding helps in stabilising the α-helix structure of proteins?

14.15 Differentiate between globular and fibrous proteins.

14.16 How do you explain the amphoteric behaviour of amino acids?

14.17 What are enzymes?

14.18 What is the effect of denaturation on the structure of proteins?

14.19 How are vitamins classified? Name the vitamin responsible for the coagulation of blood.

14.20 Why are vitamin A and vitamin C essential to us? Give their important sources.

14.21 What are nucleic acids? Mention their two important functions.

14.22 What is the difference between a nucleoside and a nucleotide?

14.23 The two strands in DNA are not identical but are complementary. Explain.

14.24 Write the important structural and functional differences between DNA and RNA.

14.25 What are the different types of RNA found in the cell?

Objectives

After studying this Unit, you will be able to

- explain the terms - monomer, polymer and polymerisation and appreciate their importance;

- distinguish between various classes of polymers and different types of polymerisation processes;

- appreciate the formation of polymers from mono- and bi-functional monomer molecules;

- describe the preparation of some important synthetic polymers and their properties;

- appreciate the importance of polymers in daily life.

"Copolymerisation has been used by nature in polypeptides which may contain as many as 20 different amino acids. Chemists are still far behind".

Do you think that daily life would have been easier and colourful without the discovery and varied applications of polymers? The use of polymers in the manufacture of plastic buckets, cups and saucers, children's toys, packaging bags, synthetic clothing materials, automobile tyres, gears and seals, electrical insulating materials and machine parts has completely revolutionised the daily life as well as the industrial scenario. Indeed, the polymers are the backbone of four major industries viz. plastics, elastomers, fibres and paints and varnishes.

The word 'polymer' is coined from two Greek words: *poly* means many and *mer* means unit or part. The term polymer is defined as very large molecules having high molecular mass (10^3-10^7u). These are also referred to as **macromolecules**, which are formed by joining of repeating structural units on a large scale. The repeating structural units are derived from some simple and reactive molecules known as monomers and are linked to each other by covalent bonds. This process of formation of polymers from respective monomers is called **polymerisation**. The transformation of ethene to polythene and interaction of hexamethylene diamine and adipic acid leading to the formation of Nylon 6, 6 are examples of two different types of polymerisation reactions.

(i) $nCH_2 = CH_2 \xrightarrow{\text{Polymerisation}} n\left[CH_2-CH_2\right] \longrightarrow \left[CH_2-CH_2\right]_n$

　　　Ethene　　　　　　　　　　Repeating unit　　　　　Polythene polymer

(ii) $nNH_2(CH_2)_6 NH_2 + nHOOC(CH_2)_4 COOH \xrightarrow{\text{Polymerisation}} \left[\overset{H}{\underset{|}{N}}-(CH_2)_6-\overset{H}{\underset{|}{N}}-\overset{O}{\overset{||}{C}}-(CH_2)_4-\overset{O}{\overset{||}{C}}\right]_n$

　　Hexamethylene　　　　　Adipic acid　　　　　　　　　　　　　　　Nylon 6,6
　　　diamine

15.1 Classification of Polymers

There are several ways of classification of polymers based on some special considerations. The following are some of the common classifications of polymers:

15.1.1 Classification Based on Source

Under this type of classification, there are three sub categories.

1. Natural polymers

These polymers are found in plants and animals. Examples are proteins, cellulose, starch, some resins and rubber.

2. Semi-synthetic polymers

Cellulose derivatives as cellulose acetate (rayon) and cellulose nitrate, etc. are the usual examples of this sub category.

3. Synthetic polymers

A variety of synthetic polymers as plastic (polythene), synthetic fibres (nylon 6,6) and synthetic rubbers (Buna - S) are examples of man-made polymers extensively used in daily life as well as in industry.

15.1.2 Classification Based on Structure of Polymers

There are three different types based on the structure of the polymers.

1. Linear polymers

These polymers consist of long and straight chains. The examples are high density polythene, polyvinyl chloride, etc. These are represented as:

2. Branched chain polymers

These polymers contain linear chains having some branches, e.g., low density polythene. These are depicted as follows:

3. Cross linked or Network polymers

These are usually formed from bi-functional and tri-functional monomers and contain strong covalent bonds between various linear polymer chains, e.g. bakelite, melamine, etc. These polymers are depicted as follows:

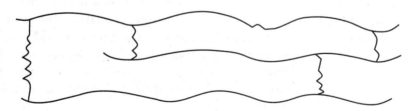

15.1.3 Classification Based on Mode of Polymerisation

Polymers can also be classified on the basis of mode of polymerisation into two sub groups.

1. Addition polymers

The addition polymers are formed by the repeated addition of monomer molecules possessing double or triple bonds, e.g., the formation of polythene from ethene and polypropene from propene. However, the addition polymers formed by the polymerisation of a single monomeric species are known as **homopolymers**, e.g., polythene.

$$n\ CH_2 = CH_2 \longrightarrow -(CH_2-CH_2)_n \text{ Homopolymer}$$

Ethene   Polythene

The polymers made by addition polymerisation from two different monomers are termed as **copolymers**, e.g., Buna-S, Buna-N, etc.

$$n\ CH_2 = CH - CH = CH_2 + n\ C_6H_5CH=CH_2 \longrightarrow -(CH_2-CH=CH-CH_2-CH_2-\underset{\underset{C_6H_5}{|}}{CH})_n$$

1, 3-Butadiene   Styrene   Butadiene-styrene copolymer
(Buna - S)

2. Condensation polymers

The condensation polymers are formed by repeated condensation reaction between two different bi-functional or tri-functional monomeric units. In these polymerisation reactions, the elimination of small molecules such as water, alcohol, hydrogen chloride, etc. take place. The examples are terylene (dacron), nylon 6, 6, nylon 6, etc. For example, nylon 6, 6 is formed by the condensation of hexamethylene diamine with adipic acid.

$$n\ H_2N\ (CH_2)_6\ NH_2 + n\ HOOC\ (CH_2)_4\ COOH$$

$$\longrightarrow -[NH\ (CH_2)_6\ NHCO(CH_2)_4CO]_n + n\ H_2O$$

Nylon 6, 6

Example 15.1

Is $+CH_2-CH(C_6H_5)+_n$ a homopolymer or a copolymer?

Solution

It is a homopolymer and the monomer from which it is obtained is styrene $C_6H_5CH = CH_2$.

15.1.4 Classification Based on Molecular Forces

A large number of polymer applications in different fields depend on their unique mechanical properties like tensile strength, elasticity, toughness, etc. These mechanical properties are governed by intermolecular forces, e.g., van der Waals forces and hydrogen bonds, present in the polymer. These forces also bind the polymer chains. Under this category, the polymers are classified into the following four sub groups on the basis of magnitude of intermolecular forces present in them.

1. Elastomers

These are rubber – like solids with elastic properties. In these

$$\left(CH_2-C=CH-CH_2 \right)_n$$
$$\quad\quad \mid$$
$$\quad\quad Cl$$

Neoprene

$$\left(\begin{array}{c} H \\ \mid \\ N-(CH_2)_6 \end{array} - \begin{array}{c} H \\ \mid \\ N \end{array} - \begin{array}{c} O \\ \parallel \\ C \end{array} (CH_2)_4 - \begin{array}{c} O \\ \parallel \\ C \end{array} \right)_n$$

Nylon 6,6

$$\left(CH_2-CH \right)_n$$
$$\quad\quad\quad \mid$$
$$\quad\quad\quad Cl$$

PVC

Bakelite

elastomeric polymers, the polymer chains are held together by the weakest intermolecular forces. These weak binding forces permit the polymer to be stretched. A few 'crosslinks' are introduced in between the chains, which help the polymer to retract to its original position after the force is released as in vulcanised rubber. The examples are buna-S, buna-N, neoprene, etc.

2. Fibres

Fibres are the thread forming solids which possess high tensile strength and high modulus. These characteristics can be attributed to the strong intermolecular forces like hydrogen bonding. These strong forces also lead to close packing of chains and thus impart crystalline nature. The examples are polyamides (nylon 6, 6), polyesters (terylene), etc.

3. Thermoplastic polymers

These are the linear or slightly branched long chain molecules capable of repeatedly softening on heating and hardening on cooling. These polymers possess intermolecular forces of attraction intermediate between elastomers and fibres. Some common thermoplastics are polythene, polystyrene, polyvinyls, etc.

4 Thermosetting polymers

These polymers are cross linked or heavily branched molecules, which on heating undergo extensive cross linking in moulds and again become infusible. These cannot be reused. Some common examples are bakelite, urea-formaldelyde resins, etc.

15.1.5 Classification Based on Growth Polymerisation

The addition and condensation polymers are nowadays also referred as chain growth polymers and step growth polymers depending on the type of polymerisation mechanism they undergo during their formation.

Intext Questions

15.1 What are polymers ?

15.2 How are polymers classified on the basis of structure?

15.2 Types of Polymerisation Reactions

There are two broad types of polymerisation reactions, *i.e.*, the addition or chain growth polymerisation and condensation or step growth polymerisation.

15.2.1 Addition Polymerisation or Chain Growth Polymerisation

In this type of polymerisation, the molecules of the same monomer or diferent monomers add together on a large scale to form a polymer. The monomers used are unsaturated compounds, *e.g.*, alkenes, alkadienes and their derivatives. This mode of polymerisation leading to an increase in chain length or chain growth can take place through the formation of either free radicals or ionic species. However, the free radical governed addition or chain growth polymerisation is the most common mode.

1. Free radical mechanism

A variety of alkenes or dienes and their derivatives are polymerised in the presence of a free radical generating initiator (catalyst) like benzoyl peroxide, acetyl peroxide, tert-butyl peroxide, etc. For example, the polymerisation of ethene to polythene consists of heating or exposing to light a mixture of ethene with a small amount of benzoyl peroxide initiator. The process starts with the addition of phenyl free radical formed by the peroxide to the ethene double bond thus generating a new and larger free radical. This step is called **chain initiating step**. As this radical reacts with another molecule of ethene, another bigger sized radical is formed. The repetition of this sequence with new and bigger radicals carries the reaction forward and the step is termed as **chain propagating step**. Ultimately, at some stage the product radical thus formed reacts with another radical to form the polymerised product. This step is called the **chain terminating step**. The sequence of steps may be depicted as follows:

Chain initiation steps

$$C_6H_5-\overset{\overset{O}{\|}}{C}-O\,\,O-\overset{\overset{O}{\|}}{C}-C_6H_5 \longrightarrow 2C_6H_5-\overset{\overset{O}{\|}}{C}-\overset{\bullet}{O} \longrightarrow 2\overset{\bullet}{C}_6H_5$$

Benzoyl peroxide   Phenyl radical

$$\overset{\bullet}{C}_6H_5 + CH_2{=}CH_2 \longrightarrow C_6H_5-CH_2-\overset{\bullet}{C}H_2$$

Chain propagating step

$$C_6H_5-CH_2-\overset{\bullet}{C}H_2 + CH_2=CH_2 \longrightarrow C_6H_5-CH_2-CH_2-CH_2-\overset{\bullet}{C}H_2$$

$$\downarrow$$

$$C_6H_5{+}CH_2-CH_2{\Big)}_n CH_2-\overset{\bullet}{C}H_2$$

Chain terminating step

For termination of the long chain, these free radicals can combine in different ways to form polythene. One mode of termination of chain is shown as under:

$$C_6H_5{+}CH_2-CH_2{\Big)}_n CH_2-\overset{\bullet}{C}H_2$$
$$C_6H_5{+}CH_2-\overset{\bullet}{C}H_2{\Big)}_n CH_2-\overset{\bullet}{C}H_2 \longrightarrow C_6H_5{+}CH_2-CH_2{\Big)}_n CH_2-CH_2-CH_2{+}CH_2-CH_2{\Big)}_n C_6H_5$$

2 Preparation of some important addition polymers

(a) Polythene

There are two types of polythene as given below:

(i) *Low density polythene*: It is obtained by the polymerisation of ethene under high pressure of 1000 to 2000 atmospheres at a temperature of 350 K to 570 K in the presence of traces of dioxygen or a peroxide initiator (catalyst). The low density polythene (LDP) obtained through the free radical addition and H-atom abstraction has highly branched structure.

Low density polythene is chemically inert and tough but flexible and a poor conductor of electricity. Hence, it is used in the insulation of electricity carrying wires and manufacture of squeeze bottles, toys and flexible pipes.

(ii) *High density polythene:* It is formed when addition polymerisation of ethene takes place in a hydrocarbon solvent in the presence of a catalyst such as triethylaluminium and titanium tetrachloride (Ziegler-Natta catalyst) at a temperature of 333 K to 343 K and under a pressure of 6-7 atmospheres. High density polythene (HDP) thus produced, consists of linear molecules and has a high density due to close packing. It is also chemically inert and more tough and hard. It is used for manufacturing buckets, dustbins, bottles, pipes, etc.

(b) Polytetrafluoroethene (Teflon)

Teflon is manufactured by heating tetrafluoroethene with a free radical or persulphate catalyst at high pressures. It is chemically inert and resistant to attack by corrosive reagents. It is used in making oil seals and gaskets and also used for non – stick surface coated utensils.

$$n\ CF_2 = CF_2 \xrightarrow[\text{High pressure}]{\text{Catalyst}} \left[CF_2 - CF_2 \right]_n$$

Tetrafluoroethene   Teflon

(c) Polyacrylonitrile

The addition polymerisation of acrylonitrile in presence of a peroxide catalyst leads to the formation of polyacrylonitrile.

$$n\ CH_2 = CHCN \xrightarrow[\text{Peroxide catalyst}]{\text{Polymerisation}} \left[CH_2 - \overset{\displaystyle CN}{\underset{\displaystyle |}{CH}} \right]_n$$

Acrylonitrile   Polyacrylonitrile

Polyacrylonitrile is used as a substitute for wool in making commercial fibres as orlon or acrilan.

15.2.2 Condensation Polymerisation or Step Growth polymerisation

This type of polymerisation generally involves a repetitive condensation reaction between two bi-functional monomers. These polycondensation reactions may result in the loss of some simple molecules as water, alcohol, etc., and lead to the formation of high molecular mass condensation polymers.

In these reactions, the product of each step is again a bi-functional species and the sequence of condensation goes on. Since, each step produces a distinct functionalised species and is independent of each other, this process is also called as step growth polymerisation.

The formation of terylene or dacron by the interaction of ethylene glycol and terephthalic acid is an example of this type of polymerisation.

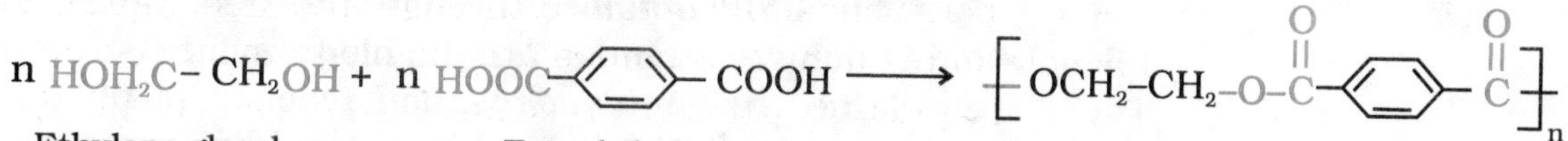

$$n \text{ HOH}_2\text{C}-\text{CH}_2\text{OH} + n \text{ HOOC}-\langle\bigcirc\rangle-\text{COOH} \longrightarrow \left[\text{OCH}_2-\text{CH}_2-\text{O}-\overset{\overset{\text{O}}{\|}}{\text{C}}-\langle\bigcirc\rangle-\overset{\overset{\text{O}}{\|}}{\text{C}}\right]_n$$

Ethylene glycol
(Ethane-1, 2 - diol)

Terephthalic acid
(Benzene-1,4 - di
carboxylic acid)

Terylene or dacron

Some important condensation polymerisation reactions characterised by their linking units are described below:

1. Polyamides

These polymers possessing amide linkages are important examples of synthetic fibres and are termed as nylons. The general method of preparation consists of the condensation polymerisation of diamines with dicarboxylic acids and also of amino acids and their lactams.

Preparation of nylons

(i) **Nylon 6,6:** It is prepared by the condensation polymerisation of hexamethylenediamine with adipic acid under high pressure and at high temperature.

$$n \text{ HOOC}(\text{CH}_2)_4\text{COOH} + n \text{ H}_2\text{N}(\text{CH}_2)_6\text{NH}_2 \xrightarrow[\text{High pressure}]{553\text{K}} \left[\overset{\overset{\text{H}}{|}}{\text{N}}-(\text{CH}_2)_6-\overset{\overset{\text{H}}{|}}{\text{N}}-\overset{\overset{\text{O}}{\|}}{\text{C}}(\text{CH}_2)_4-\overset{\overset{\text{O}}{\|}}{\text{C}}\right]_n$$

Nylon 6,6

Nylon 6, 6 is used in making sheets, bristles for brushes and in textile industry.

(ii) **Nylon 6:** It is obtained by heating caprolactum with water at a high temperature.

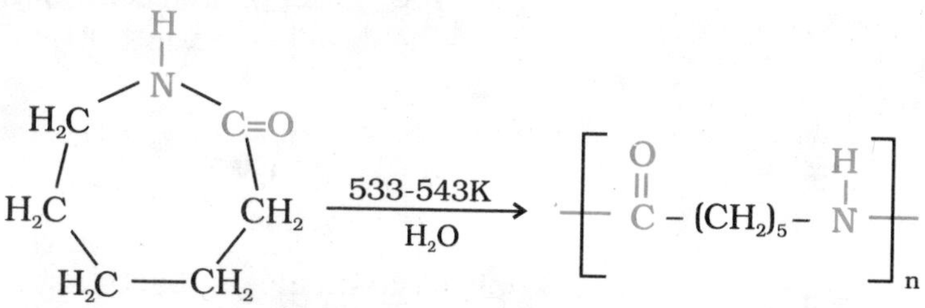

Caprolactam

$$\xrightarrow[\text{H}_2\text{O}]{533\text{-}543\text{K}} \left[\overset{\overset{\text{O}}{\|}}{\text{C}} - (\text{CH}_2)_5 - \overset{\overset{\text{H}}{|}}{\text{N}}\right]_n$$

Nylon 6

Nylon 6 is used for the manufacture of tyre cords, fabrics and ropes.

2. Polyesters

These are the polycondensation products of dicarboxylic acids and diols. Dacron or terylene is the best known example of polyesters. It is manufactured by heating a mixture of ethylene glycol and terephthalic acid at 420 to 460 K in the presence of zinc acetate-antimony trioxide catalyst as per the reaction given earlier. Dacron fibre (terylene) is crease resistant and is used in blending with cotton and wool fibres and also as glass reinforcing materials in safety helmets, etc.

3. Phenol - formaldehyde polymer (Bakelite and related polymers)

Phenol - formaldehyde polymers are the oldest synthetic polymers. These are obtained by the condensation reaction of phenol with formaldehyde in the presence of either an acid or a base catalyst. The reaction starts with the initial formation of o-and/or p-hydroxymethylphenol derivatives, which further react with phenol to form compounds having rings joined to each other through $-CH_2$ groups. The initial product could be a linear product – **Novolac** used in paints.

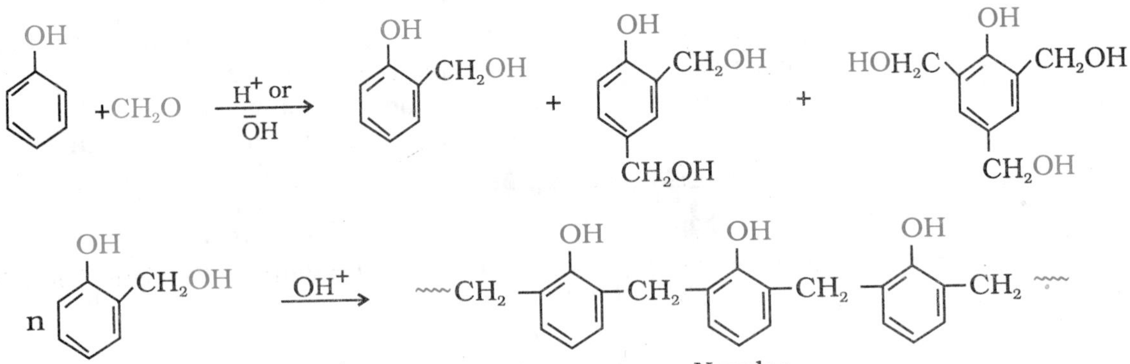

Novolac

Novolac on heating with formaldehyde undergoes cross linking to form an infusible solid mass called **bakelite**. It is used for making combs, phonograph records, electrical switches and handles of various utensils.

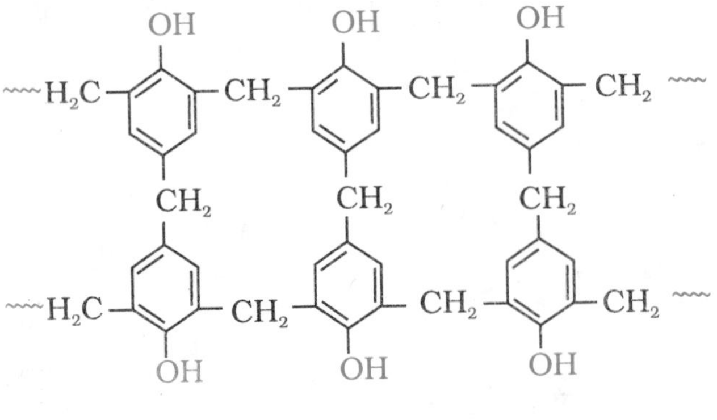

Bakelite

4. Melamine – formaldehyde polymer

Melamine formaldehyde polymer is formed by the condensation polymerisation of melamine and formaldehyde.

Melamine   Formaldehyde   Resin intermediate

Polymerisation

$$\left[HN - \underset{\underset{\displaystyle NH}{\overset{\displaystyle N}{\underset{\displaystyle N \quad N}{\bigtriangleup}}}}{C} - NH - CH_2 \right]_n$$

Melamine polymer

It is used in the manufacture of unbreakable crockery.

Intext Questions

15.3 Write the names of monomers of the following polymers:

$$(i)\ \left[\underset{\overset{\displaystyle |}{\displaystyle H}}{N} - (CH_2)_6 - \underset{\overset{\displaystyle |}{\displaystyle H}}{N} - \underset{\overset{\displaystyle \|}{\displaystyle O}}{C} - (CH_2)_4 - \underset{\overset{\displaystyle \|}{\displaystyle O}}{C} \right]_n \quad (ii)\ \left[\underset{\overset{\displaystyle \|}{\displaystyle O}}{C} - (CH_2)_5 - \underset{\overset{\displaystyle |}{\displaystyle H}}{N} \right]_n \quad (iii)\ \left[CF_2 - CF_2 \right]_n$$

15.4 Classify the following as addition and condensation polymers: Terylene, Bakelite, Polyvinyl chloride, Polythene.

15.2.3 Copolyme-risation

Copolymerisation is a polymerisation reaction in which a mixture of more than one monomeric species is allowed to polymerise and form a copolymer. The copolymer can be made not only by chain growth polymerisation but by step growth polymerisation also. It contains multiple units of each monomer used in the same polymeric chain. For example, a mixture of 1, 3 – butadiene and styrene can form a copolymer.

$$n\ CH_2 = CH - CH = CH_2 \ + \quad \underset{Styrene}{\underset{\displaystyle \bigcirc}{\overset{\displaystyle CH = CH_2}{|}}} \quad \longrightarrow \quad \left[CH_2 - CH = CH - CH_2 - \underset{\overset{\displaystyle |}{\displaystyle \bigcirc}}{CH} - CH_2 \right]_n$$

1, 3-Butadiene   Styrene   Butadiene - styrene copolymer

Copolymers have properties quite different from homopolymers. For example, butadiene - styrene copolymer is quite tough and is a good substitute for natural rubber. It is used for the manufacture of autotyres, floortiles, footwear components, cable insulation, etc.

15.2.4 Rubber

1. Natural rubber

Rubber is a natural polymer and possesses elastic properties. It is also termed as elastomer and has a variety of uses. It is manufactured from rubber latex which is a colloidal dispersion of rubber in water. This latex is obtained from the bark of rubber tree and is found in India, Srilanka, Indonesia, Malaysia and South America.

Natural rubber may be considered as a linear polymer of isoprene (2-methyl-1, 3-butadiene) and is also called as *cis* - 1, 4 - polyisoprene.

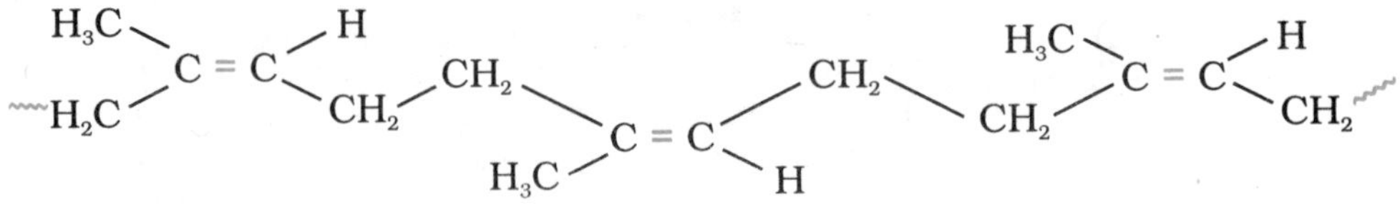

$$\text{Natural rubber structure (cis-polyisoprene)}$$

Natural rubber

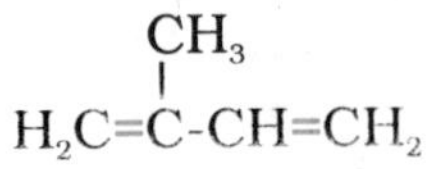

$$\underset{\text{Isoprene}}{H_2C=\overset{\overset{\displaystyle CH_3}{|}}{C}-CH=CH_2}$$

The *cis*-polyisoprene molecule consists of various chains held together by weak van der Waals interactions and has a coiled structure. Thus, it can be stretched like a spring and exhibits elastic properties.

Vulcanisation of rubber: Natural rubber becomes soft at high temperature (>335 K) and brittle at low temperatures (<283 K) and shows high water absorption capacity. It is soluble in non-polar solvents and is non-resistant to attack by oxidising agents. To improve upon these physical properties, a process of vulcanisation is carried out. This process consists of heating a mixture of raw rubber with sulphur and an appropriate additive at a temperature range between 373 K to 415 K. On vulcanisation, sulphur forms cross links at the reactive sites of double bonds and thus the rubber gets stiffened.

In the manufacture of tyre rubber, 5% of sulphur is used as a crosslinking agent. The probable structures of vulcanised rubber molecules are depicted below:

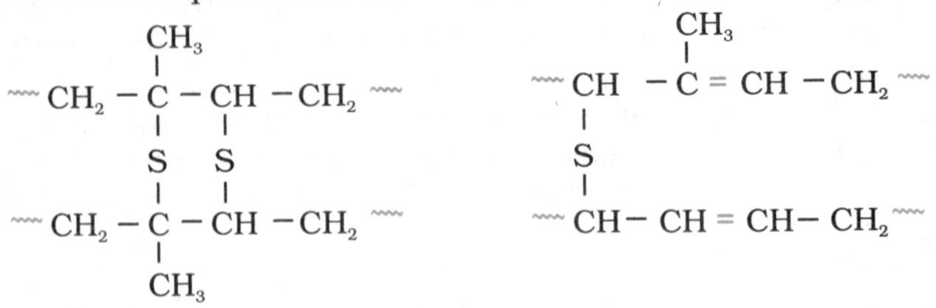

2. Synthetic rubbers

Synthetic rubber is any vulcanisable rubber like polymer, which is capable of getting stretched to twice its length. However, it returns to its original shape and size as soon as the external stretching force is released. Thus, synthetic rubbers are either homopolymers of 1, 3 - butadiene derivatives or copolymers of 1, 3 - butadiene or its derivatives with another unsaturated monomer.

Preparation of Synthetic Rubbers

1. Neoprene

Neoprene or polychloroprene is formed by the free radical polymerisation of chloroprene.

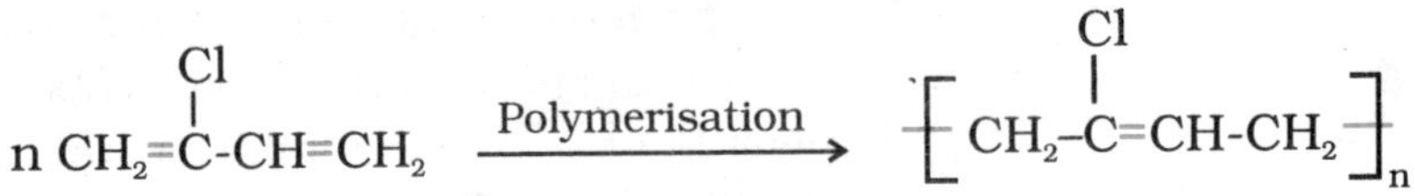

Chloroprene
2-Chloro-1, 3-butadiene

Neoprene

It has superior resistance to vegetable and mineral oils. It is used for manufacturing conveyor belts, gaskets and hoses.

2. Buna – N

You have already studied about Buna-S, in Section 15.1.3. Buna –N is obtained by the copolymerisation of 1, 3 – butadiene and acrylonitrile in the presence of a peroxide catalyst.

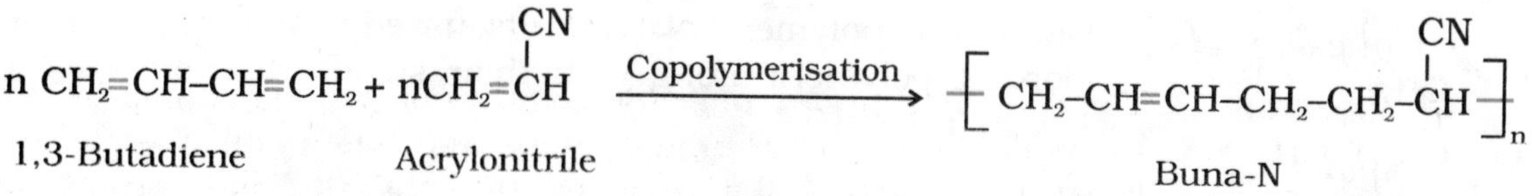

$$n\ CH_2\!\!=\!\!CH\!-\!CH\!\!=\!\!CH_2 + nCH_2\!\!=\!\!\overset{\overset{\displaystyle CN}{|}}{CH} \xrightarrow{\text{Copolymerisation}} \left[CH_2\!-\!CH\!\!=\!\!CH\!-\!CH_2\!-\!CH_2\!-\!\overset{\overset{\displaystyle CN}{|}}{CH} \right]_n$$

1,3-Butadiene   Acrylonitrile   Buna-N

It is resistant to the action of petrol, lubricating oil and organic solvents. It is used in making oil seals, tank lining, etc.

Intext Questions

15.5 Explain the difference between Buna-N and Buna-S.

15.6 Arrange the following polymers in increasing order of their intermolecular forces.
  (i) Nylon 6,6, Buna-S, Polythene.
  (ii) Nylon 6, Neoprene, Polyvinyl chloride.

15.3 Molecular Mass of Polymers

Polymer properties are closely related to their molecular mass, size and structure. The growth of the polymer chain during their synthesis is dependent upon the availability of the monomers in the reaction mixture. Thus, the polymer sample contains chains of varying lengths and hence its molecular mass is always expressed as an average. The molecular mass of polymers can be determined by chemical and physical methods.

15.4 Biodegradable Polymers

A large number of polymers are quite resistant to the environmental degradation processes and are thus responsible for the accumulation of polymeric solid waste materials. These solid wastes cause acute environmental problems and remain undegraded for quite a long time. In view of the general awareness and concern for the problems created by the polymeric solid wastes, certain new biodegradable synthetic polymers have been designed and developed. These polymers contain functional groups similar to the functional groups present in biopolymers.

Aliphatic polyesters are one of the important classes of biodegradable polymers. Some important examples are given below:

1. Poly β-hydroxybutyrate – co-β-hydroxy valerate (PHBV)

It is obtained by the copolymerisation of 3-hydroxybutanoic acid and 3 - hydroxypentanoic acid. PHBV is used in speciality packaging, orthopaedic devices and in controlled release of drugs. PHBV undergoes bacterial degradation in the environment.

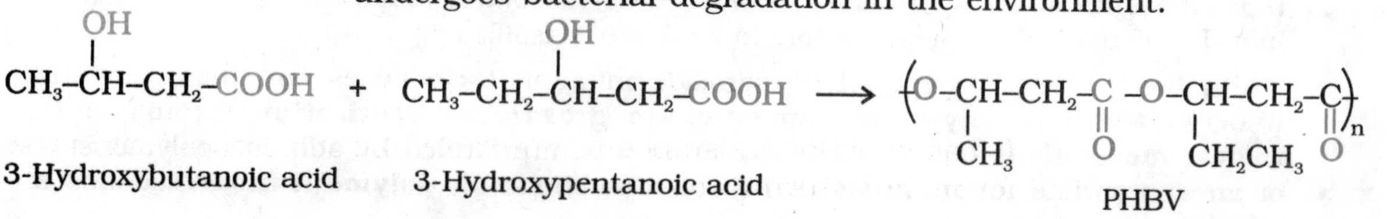

$$CH_3\!-\!\overset{\overset{\displaystyle OH}{|}}{CH}\!-\!CH_2\!-\!COOH \ + \ CH_3\!-\!CH_2\!-\!\overset{\overset{\displaystyle OH}{|}}{CH}\!-\!CH_2\!-\!COOH \longrightarrow \left(O\!-\!\underset{\underset{\displaystyle CH_3}{|}}{CH}\!-\!CH_2\!-\!\underset{\underset{\displaystyle O}{||}}{C}\!-\!O\!-\!\underset{\underset{\displaystyle CH_2CH_3}{|}}{CH}\!-\!CH_2\!-\!\underset{\underset{\displaystyle O}{||}}{C} \right)_n$$

3-Hydroxybutanoic acid   3-Hydroxypentanoic acid   PHBV

2. Nylon 2–nylon 6

It is an alternating polyamide copolymer of glycine (H_2N-CH_2-COOH) and amino caproic acid [$H_2N (CH_2)_5 COOH$] and is biodegradable. Can you write the structure of this copolymer?

15.5 Polymers of Commercial Importance

Besides, the polymers already discussed, some other commercially important polymers along with their structures and uses are given below in Table 15.1.

Table 15.1: Some Other Commercially Important Polymers

Name of Polymer	Monomer	Structure	Uses
Polypropene	Propene	$\left[CH_2-CH\overset{\displaystyle CH_3}{\mid}\right]_n$	Manufacture of ropes, toys, pipes, fibres, etc.
Polystyrene	Styrene	$\left[CH_2-CH\overset{\displaystyle C_6H_5}{\mid}\right]_n$	As insulator, wrapping material, manufacture of toys, radio and television cabinets.
Polyvinyl chloride (PVC)	Vinyl chloride	$\left[CH_2-CH\overset{\displaystyle Cl}{\mid}\right]_n$	Manufacture of rain coats, hand bags, vinyl flooring, water pipes.
Urea-formaldehyle Resin	(a) Urea (b) Formaldehyde	$\left[NH-CO-NH-CH_2\right]_n$	For making unbreakable cups and laminated sheets.
Glyptal	(a) Ethylene glycol (b) Phthalic acid	$\left[OCH_2-CH_2OOC\overset{\displaystyle }{\bigcirc}CO\right]_n$	Manufacture of paints and lacquers.
Bakelite	(a) Phenol (b) Formaldehyde	$\left[\underset{}{\bigcirc}\overset{O-H}{}CH_2\underset{}{\bigcirc}\overset{O-H}{}CH_2\right]_n$	For making combs, electrical switches, handles of utensils and computer discs.

Summary

Polymers are defined as high molecular mass **macromolecules**, which consist of repeating structural units derived from the corresponding **monomers**. These polymers may be of natural or synthetic origin and are classified in a number of ways.

In the presence of an organic peroxide initiator, the alkenes and their derivatives undergo **addition polymerisation** or **chain growth polymerisation** through a **free radical mechanism**. Polythene, teflon, orlon, etc. are formed by addition polymerisation of an appropriate alkene or its derivative. **Condensation polymerisation** reactions are shown by the interaction of bi – or poly functional monomers containing $- NH_2$, $- OH$ and $-$ COOH groups. This type of polymerisation proceeds through the elimination of certain simple molecules as H_2O, CH_3OH, etc. Formaldehyde reacts with phenol and melamine to form the corresponding condensation polymer products. The condensation polymerisation progresses through step by step and is also called as **step growth polymerisation**. Nylon, bakelite and dacron are some of the important examples of condensation polymers. However, a mixture of two unsaturated monomers exhibits **copolymerisation** and forms a **co-polymer** containing multiple units of each monomer. Natural rubber is a *cis* 1, 4-polyisoprene and can be made more tough by the process of **vulcanisation** with sulphur. Synthetic rubbers are usually obtained by copolymerisation of alkene and 1, 3 butadiene derivatives.

In view of the potential environmental hazards of synthetic polymeric wastes, certain **biodegradable polymers** such as PHBV and Nylon-2- Nylon-6 are developed as alternatives.

Exercises

15.1 Explain the terms polymer and monomer.

15.2 What are natural and synthetic polymers? Give two examples of each type.

15.3 Distinguish between the terms homopolymer and copolymer and give an example of each.

15.4 How do you explain the functionality of a monomer?

15.5 Define the term polymerisation.

15.6 Is (NH-CHR-CO)$_n$, a homopolymer or copolymer?

15.7 In which classes, the polymers are classified on the basis of molecular forces?

15.8 How can you differentiate between addition and condensation polymerisation?

15.9 Explain the term copolymerisation and give two examples.

15.10 Write the free radical mechanism for the polymerisation of ethene.

15.11 Define thermoplastics and thermosetting polymers with two examples of each.

15.12 Write the monomers used for getting the following polymers.

(i) Polyvinyl chloride (ii) Teflon (iii) Bakelite

15.13 Write the name and structure of one of the common initiators used in free radical addition polymerisation.

15.14 How does the presence of double bonds in rubber molecules influence their structure and reactivity?

15.15 Discuss the main purpose of vulcanisation of rubber.

15.16 What are the monomeric repeating units of Nylon-6 and Nylon-6,6?

15.17 Write the names and structures of the monomers of the following polymers:

(i) Buna-S (ii) Buna-N (iii) Dacron (iv) Neoprene

15.18 Identify the monomer in the following polymeric structures.

(i) $\left[\begin{array}{c} O \\ \parallel \\ C \end{array} -(CH_2)_8 - \begin{array}{c} O \\ \parallel \\ C \end{array} -NH-(CH_2)_6 -NH \right]_n$

(ii)

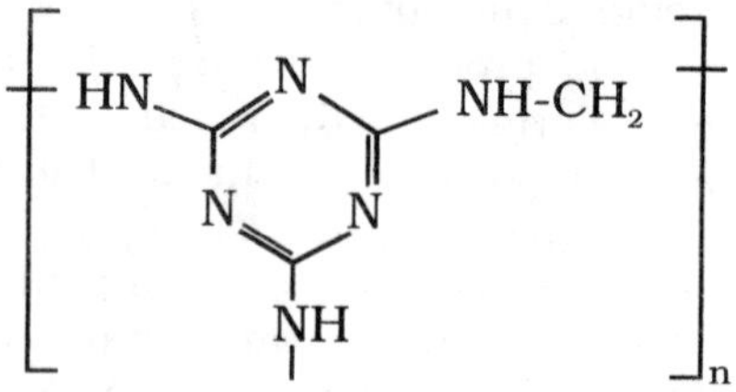

$$\left[\begin{array}{c} HN \diagdown \diagup N \diagdown NH\text{-}CH_2 \\ \diagup \\ N \diagdown \diagup N \\ NH \\ | \end{array}\right]_n$$

15.19 How is dacron obtained from ethylene glycol and terephthalic acid ?

15.20 What is a biodegradable polymer ? Give an example of a biodegradable aliphatic polyester.

Answers of Some Intext Questions

15.1 Polymers are high molecular mass substances consisting of large numbers of repeating structural units. They are also called as macromolecules. Some examples of polymers are polythene, bakelite, rubber, nylon 6, 6, etc.

15.2 On the basis of structure, the polymers are classified as below:
(i) Linear polymers such as polythene, polyvinyl chloride, etc.
(ii) Branched chain polymers such as low density polythene.
(iii) Cross linked polymers such as bakelite, melamine, etc.

15.3 (i) Hexamethylene diamine and adipic acid.
(ii) Caprolactam.
(iii) Tetrafluoroethene.

15.4 Addition polymers: Polyvinyl chloride, Polythene.
Condensation polymers: Terylene, Bakelite.

15.5 Buna-N is a copolymer of 1,3-butadiene and acrylonitrile and Buna-S is a copolymer of 1,3-butadiene and styrene.

15.6 In order of increasing intermolecular forces.
(i) Buna-S, Polythene, Nylon 6,6.
(ii) Neoprene, Polyvinyl chloride, Nylon 6.

Unit 16

Chemistry in Everyday Life

From living perception to abstract thought, and from this to practice.
V.I. Lenin.

Objectives

After studying this Unit you will be able to

- visualise the importance of Chemistry in daily life;
- explain the term 'chemotherapy';
- describe the basis of classification of drugs;
- explain drug-target interaction of enzymes and receptors;
- explain how various types of drugs function in the body;
- know about artificial sweetening agents and food preservatives;
- discuss the chemistry of cleansing agents.

By now, you have learnt the basic principles of chemistry and also realised that it influences every sphere of human life. The principles of chemistry have been used for the benefit of mankind. Think of cleanliness — the materials like soaps, detergents, household bleaches, tooth pastes, etc. will come to your mind. Look towards the beautiful clothes — immediately chemicals of the synthetic fibres used for making clothes and chemicals giving colours to them will come to your mind. Food materials — again a number of chemicals about which you have learnt in the previous Unit will appear in your mind. Of course, sickness and diseases remind us of medicines — again chemicals. Explosives, fuels, rocket propellents, building and electronic materials, etc., are all chemicals. Chemistry has influenced our life so much that we do not even realise that we come across chemicals at every moment; that we ourselves are beautiful chemical creations and all our activities are controlled by chemicals. In this Unit, we shall learn the application of Chemistry in three important and interesting areas, namely – medicines, food materials and cleansing agents.

16.1 Drugs and their Classification

Drugs are chemicals of low molecular masses (~100 – 500u). These interact with macromolecular targets and produce a biological response. When the biological response is therapeutic and useful, these chemicals are called **medicines** and are used in diagnosis, prevention and treatment of diseases. If taken in doses higher than those recommended, most of the drugs used as medicines are potential poisons. Use of chemicals for therapeutic effect is called **chemotherapy**,

16.1.1
Classification of
Drugs

Drugs can be classified mainly on criteria outlined as follows:

(a) On the basis of pharmacological effect

This classification is based on pharmacological effect of the drugs. It is useful for doctors because it provides them the whole range of drugs available for the treatment of a particular type of problem. For example, analgesics have pain killing effect, antiseptics kill or arrest the growth of microorganisms.

(b) On the basis of drug action

It is based on the action of a drug on a particular biochemical process. For example, all antihistamines inhibit the action of the compound, histamine which causes inflammation in the body. There are various ways in which action of histamines can be blocked. You will learn about this in Section 16.3.2.

(c) On the basis of chemical structure

It is based on the chemical structure of the drug. Drugs classified in this way share common structural features and often have similar pharmacological activity. For example, sulphonamides have common structural feature, given below.

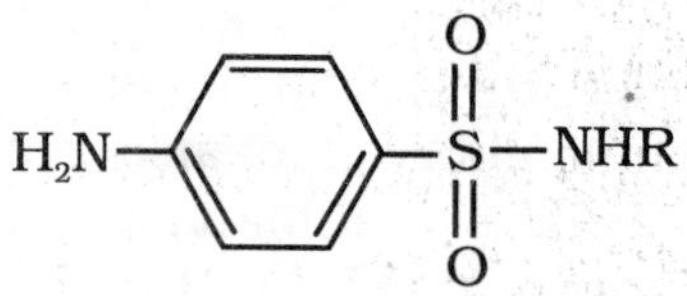

Structural features of sulphonamides

(d) On the basis of molecular targets

Drugs usually interact with biomolecules such as carbohydrates, lipids, proteins and nucleic acids. These are called target molecules or drug targets. Drugs possessing some common structural features may have the same mechanism of action on targets. The classification based on molecular targets is the most useful classification for medicinal chemists.

16.2 Drug-Target
Interaction

Macromolecules of biological origin perform various functions in the body. For example, proteins which perform the role of biological catalysts in the body are called **enzymes**, those which are crucial to communication system in the body are called **receptors**. Carrier proteins carry polar molecules across the cell membrane. Nucleic acids have coded genetic information for the cell. Lipids and carbohydrates are structural parts of the cell membrane. We shall explain the drug-target interaction with the examples of enzymes and receptors.

16.2.1 Enzymes
as Drug
Targets

(a) Catalytic action of enzymes

For understanding the interaction between a drug and an enzyme, it is important to know how do enzymes catalyse the reaction (Section 5.2.4). In their catalytic activity, enzymes perform two major functions:

(i) The first function of an enzyme is to hold the substrate for a chemical reaction. Active sites of enzymes hold the substrate molecule in a suitable position, so that it can be attacked by the reagent effectively.

Substrates bind to the active site of the enzyme through a variety of interactions such as ionic bonding, hydrogen bonding, van der Waals interaction or dipole-dipole interaction (Fig. 16.1).

Fig. 16.1
(a) Active site of an enzyme (b) Substrate (c) Substrate held in active site of the enzyme

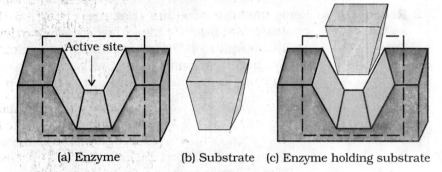

(a) Enzyme   (b) Substrate   (c) Enzyme holding substrate

(ii) The second function of an enzyme is to provide functional groups that will attack the substrate and carry out chemical reaction.

(b) Drug-enzyme interaction

Drugs inhibit any of the above mentioned activities of enzymes. These can block the binding site of the enzyme and prevent the binding of substrate, or can inhibit the catalytic activity of the enzyme. Such drugs are called **enzyme inhibitors.**

Drugs inhibit the attachment of substrate on active site of enzymes in two different ways;

(i) Drugs compete with the natural substrate for their attachment on the active sites of enzymes. Such drugs are called **competitive inhibitors** (Fig. 16.2).

Fig. 16.2
Drug and substrate competing for active site

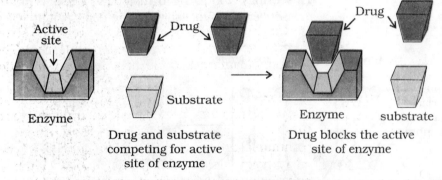

Drug and substrate competing for active site of enzyme

Drug blocks the active site of enzyme

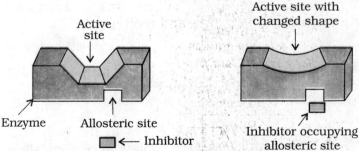

Fig. 16.3: *Non-competitive inhibitor changes the active site of enzyme after binding at allosteric site.*

(ii) Some drugs do not bind to the enzyme's active site. These bind to a different site of enzyme which is called **allosteric site**. This binding of inhibitor at allosteric site (Fig.16.3) changes the shape of the active site in such a way that substrate cannot recognise it.

If the bond formed between an enzyme and an inhibitor is a strong covalent bond and cannot be broken easily, then the enzyme is blocked permanently. The body then degrades the enzyme-inhibitor complex and synthesises the new enzyme.

16.2.2 Receptors as Drug Targets

Receptors are proteins that are crucial to body's communication process. Majority of these are embedded in cell membranes (Fig. 16.4). Receptor proteins are embedded in the cell membrane in such a way that their small part possessing active site projects out of the surface of the membrane and opens on the outside region of the cell membrane (Fig. 16.4).

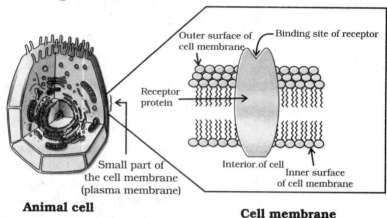

Fig. 16.4
Receptor protein embedded in the cell membrane, the active site of the receptor opens on the outside region of the cell.

Animal cell

Cell membrane

In the body, message between two neurons and that between neurons to muscles is communicated through certain chemicals. These chemicals, known as **chemical messengers** are received at the binding sites of receptor proteins. To accommodate a messenger, shape of the receptor site changes. This brings about the transfer of message into the cell. Thus, chemical messenger gives message to the cell without entering the cell (Fig. 16.5).

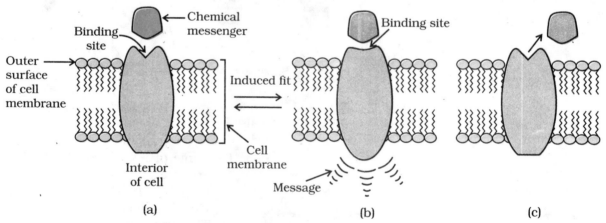

(a)   (b)   (c)

Fig. 16.5: *(a) Receptor receiving chemical messenger*
(b) Shape of the receptor changed after attachment of messenger
(c) Receptor regains structure after removal of chemical messenger.

There are a large number of different receptors in the body ·that interact with different chemical messengers. These receptors show selectivity for one chemical messenger over the other because their binding sites have different shape, structure and amino acid composition.

Drugs that bind to the receptor site and inhibit its natural function are called **antagonists**. These are useful when blocking of message is required. There are other types of drugs that mimic the natural messenger by switching on the receptor, these are called **agonists**. These are useful when there is lack of natural chemical messenger.

16.3 Therapeutic Action of Different Classes of Drugs

In this Section, we shall discuss the therapeutic action of a few important classes of drugs.

16.3.1 Antacids

Over production of acid in the stomach causes irritation and pain. In severe cases, ulcers are developed in the stomach. Until 1970, only treatment for acidity was administration of antacids, such as sodium hydrogencarbonate or a mixture of aluminium and magnesium hydroxide. However, excessive hydrogencarbonate can make the stomach alkaline and trigger the production of even more acid. Metal hydroxides are better alternatives because of being insoluble, these do not increase the pH above neutrality. These treatments control only symptoms, and not the cause. Therefore, with these metal salts, the patients cannot be treated easily. In advanced stages, ulcers become life threatening and its only treatment is removal of the affected part of the stomach.

A major breakthrough in the treatment of hyperacidity came through the discovery according to which a chemical, histamine, stimulates the secretion of pepsin and hydrochloric acid in the stomach. The drug cimetidine (Tegamet), was designed to prevent the interaction of histamine with the receptors present in the stomach wall. This resulted in release of lesser amount of acid. The importance of the drug was so much that it remained the largest selling drug in the world until another drug, ranitidine (Zantac), was discovered.

Histamine

Cimetidine

Ranitidine

16.3.2 Antihistamines

Histamine is a potent vasodilator. It has various functions. It contracts the smooth muscles in the bronchi and gut and relaxes other muscles, such as those in the walls of fine blood vessels. Histamine is also responsible for the nasal congestion associated with common cold and allergic response to pollen.

Synthetic drugs, **brompheniramine (Dimetapp)** and **terfenadine (Seldane),** act as antihistamines. They interfere with the natural action

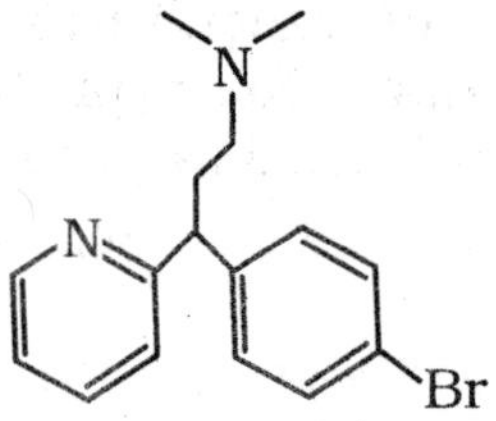

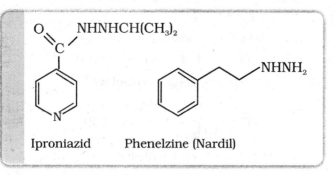

Bromkpheniramine
(Dimetapp, Dimetane)

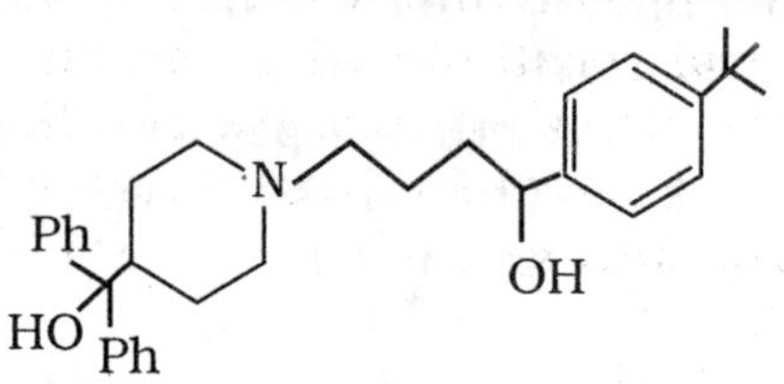

Terfenadine (Seldane)

of histamine by competing with histamine for binding sites of receptor where histamine exerts its effect.

Now the question that arises is, "Why do above mentioned antihistamines not affect the secretion of acid in stomach?" The reason is that antiallergic and antacid drugs work on different receptors.

16.3.3 Neurologically Active Drugs

(a) Tranquilizers

Tranquilizers and **analgesics** are neurologically active drugs. These affect the message transfer mechanism from nerve to receptor.

Tranquilizers are a class of chemical compounds used for the treatment of stress, and mild or even severe mental diseases. These relieve anxiety, stress, irritability or excitement by inducing a sense of well-being. They form an essential component of sleeping pills. There are various types of tranquilizers. They function by different mechanisms. For example, noradrenaline is one of the neurotransmitters that plays a role in mood changes. If the level of noradrenaline is low for some reason, then the signal-sending activity becomes low, and the person suffers from depression. In such situations, **antidepressant drugs** are required. These drugs inhibit the enzymes which catalyse the degradation of noradrenaline. If the enzyme is inhibited, this important neurotransmitter is slowly metabolised and can activate its receptor for longer periods of time, thus counteracting the effect of depression. Iproniazid and phenelzine are two such drugs.

Iproniazid   Phenelzine (Nardil)

Some tranquilizers namely, chlordiazepoxide and meprobamate, are relatively mild tranquilizers suitable for relieving tension. Equanil is used in controlling depression and hypertension.

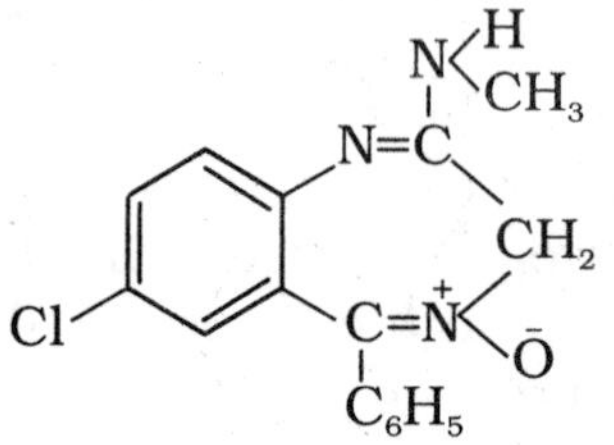

Chlordiazepoxide

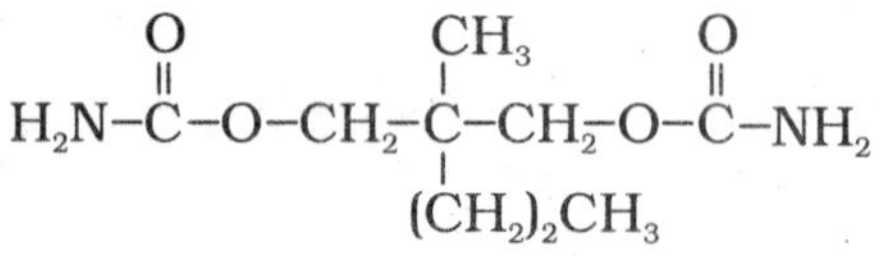

Meprobamate

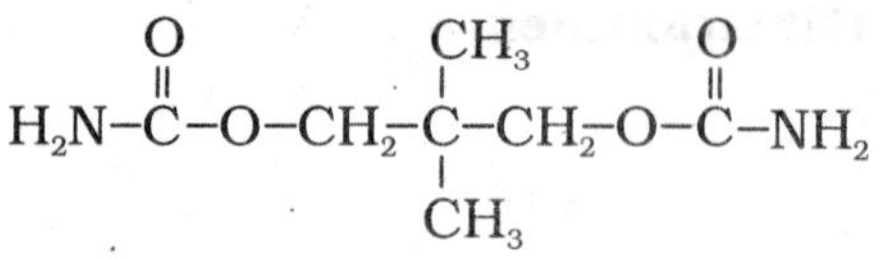

Equanil

Derivatives of barbituric acid viz., veronal, amytal, nembutal, luminal and seconal constitute an important class of tranquilizers. These derivatives are called **barbiturates**. Barbiturates are hypnotic, *i.e.*, sleep producing agents. Some other substances used as tranquilizers are valium and serotonin.

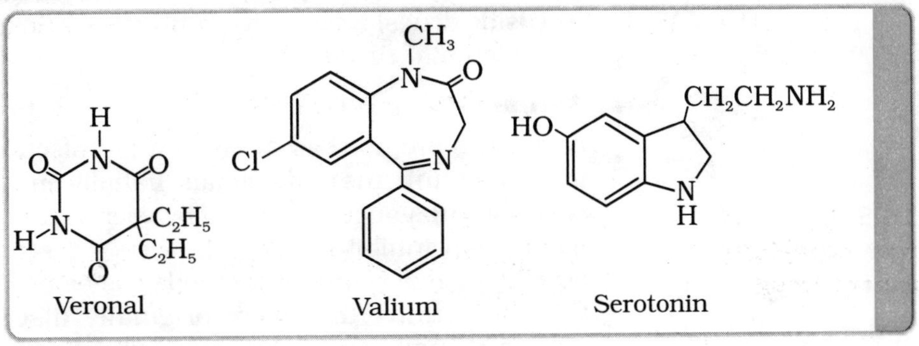

| Veronal | Valium | Serotonin |

(b) Analgesics

Analgesics reduce or abolish pain without causing impairment of consciousness, mental confusion, incoordination or paralysis or some other disturbances of nervous system. These are classified as follows:

(i) Non-narcotic (non-addictive) analgesics

(ii) Narcotic drugs

(i) **Non-narcotic (non-addictive) analgesics:** Aspirin and paracetamol belong to the class of **non-narcotic analgesics**. **Aspirin** is the most familiar example. Aspirin inhibits the synthesis of chemicals known as prostaglandins which stimulate inflammation in the tissue and cause pain. These drugs are effective in relieving skeletal pain such as that due to arthritis. These drugs have many other effects such as reducing fever **(antipyretic)** and preventing platelet coagulation. Because of its anti blood clotting action, aspirin finds use in prevention of heart attacks.

(ii) **Narcotic analgesics:** Morphine and many of its homologues, when administered in medicinal doses, relieve pain and produce sleep. In poisonous doses, these produce stupor, coma, convulsions and ultimately death. Morphine narcotics are sometimes referred to as opiates, since they are obtained from the opium poppy.

These analgesics are chiefly used for the relief of postoperative pain, cardiac pain and pains of terminal cancer, and in child birth.

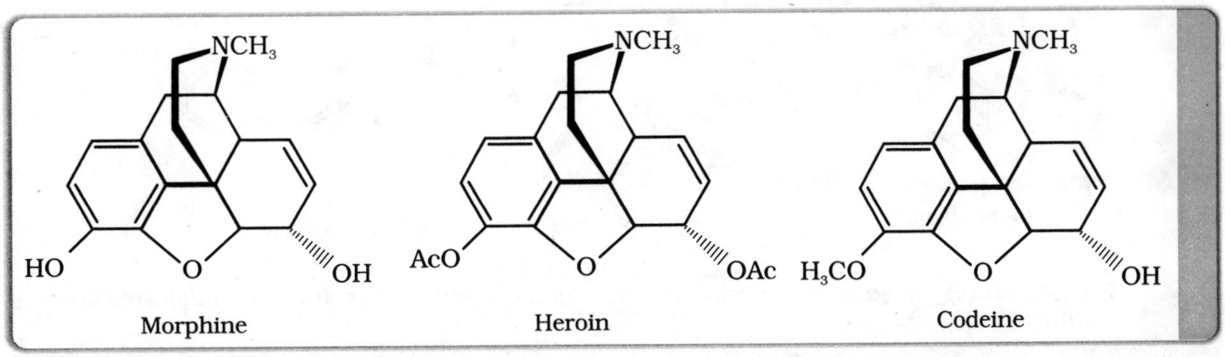

| Morphine | Heroin | Codeine |

Diseases in human beings and animals may be caused by a variety of microorganisms such as bacteria, virus, fungi and other pathogens. An antimicrobial tends to destroy/prevent development or inhibit the pathogenic action of microbes such as bacteria (antibacterial drugs), fungi (antifungal agents), virus (antiviral agents), or other parasites (antiparasitic drugs) selectively. Antibiotics, antiseptics and disinfectants are antimicrobial drugs.

(a) Antibiotics

Antibiotics are used as drugs to treat infections because of their low toxicity for humans and animals. Initially antibiotics were classified as chemical substances produced by microorganisms (bacteria, fungi and molds) that inhibit the growth or even destroy microorganisms. The development of synthetic methods has helped in synthesising some of the compounds that were originally discovered as products of microorganisms. Also, some purely synthetic compounds have antibacterial activity, and therefore, definition of antibiotic has been modified. An antibiotic now refers to a substance produced wholly or partly by chemical synthesis, which in low concentrations inhibits the growth or destroys microorganisms by intervening in their metabolic processes.

The search for chemicals that would adversely affect invading bacteria but not the host began in the nineteenth century. Paul Ehrlich, a German bacteriologist, conceived this idea. He investigated arsenic based structures in order to produce less toxic substances for the treatment of syphilis. He developed the medicine, **arsphenamine**, known as **salvarsan**. Paul Ehrlich got Nobel prize for Medicine in 1908 for this discovery. It was the first effective treatment discovered for syphilis. Although salvarsan is toxic to human beings, its effect on the bacteria, spirochete, which causes syphilis is much greater than on human beings. At the same time, Ehrlich was working on azodyes also. He noted that there is similarity in structures of salvarsan and

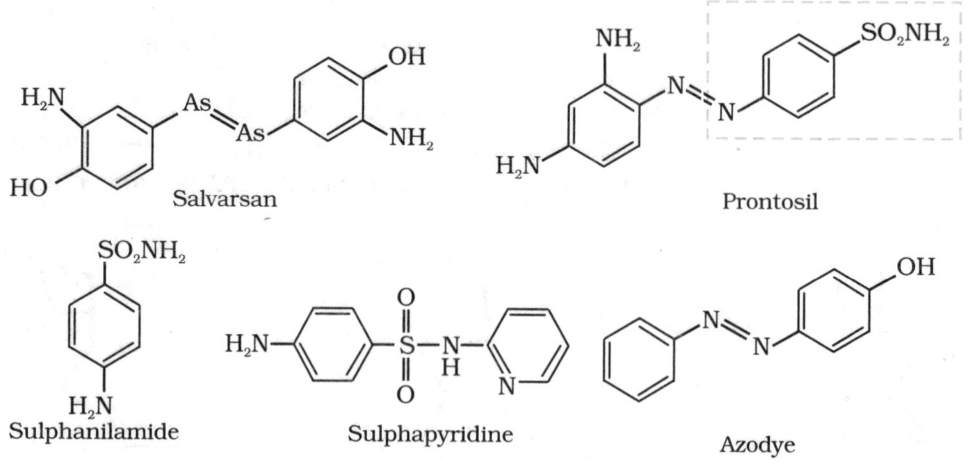

The structures of salvarsan, prontosil azodye and sulphapyridine showing structural similarity.

azodyes. The –As = As– linkage present in arsphenamine resembles the –N = N – linkage present in azodyes in the sense that arsenic atom is present in place of nitrogen. He also noted tissues getting coloured by dyes selectively. Therefore, Ehrlich began to search for the compounds which resemble in structure to azodyes and selectively bind to bacteria. In 1932, he succeeded in preparing the first effective antibacterial agent, **prontosil**, which resembles in structure to the compound, salvarsan. Soon it was discovered that in the body prontosil is converted to a compound called **sulphanilamide**, which is the real active compound. Thus the sulpha drugs were discovered. A large range of sulphonamide analogues was synthesised. One of the most effective is sulphapyridine.

Despite the success of sulfonamides, the real revolution in antibacterial therapy began with the discovery of Alexander Fleming in 1929, of the antibacterial properties of a *Penicillium* fungus. Isolation and purification of active compound to accumulate sufficient material for clinical trials took thirteen years.

Antibiotics have either cidal (killing) effect or a static (inhibitory) effect on microbes. A few examples of the two types of antibiotics are as follows:

Bactericidal	Bacteriostatic
Penicillin	Erythromycin
Aminoglycosides	Tetracycline
Ofloxacin	Chloramphenicol

The range of bacteria or other microorganisms that are affected by a certain antibiotic is expressed as its spectrum of action. Antibiotics which kill or inhibit a wide range of Gram-positive and Gram-negative bacteria are said to be **broad spectrum antibiotics**. Those effective mainly against Gram-positive or Gram-negative bacteria are **narrow spectrum antibiotics**. If effective against a single organism or disease, they are referred to as **limited spectrum** antibiotics. Penicillin G has a narrow spectrum. Ampicillin and Amoxycillin are synthetic modifications of penicillins. These have broad spectrum. It is absolutely essential to test the patients for sensitivity (allergy) to penicillin before it is administered. In India, penicillin is manufactured at the Hindustan Antibiotics in Pimpri and in private sector industry.

Chloramphenicol, isolated in 1947, is a broad spectrum antibiotic. It is rapidly absorbed from the gastrointestinal tract and hence can be given orally in case of typhoid, dysentery, acute fever, certain form of urinary infections, meningitis and pneumonia. *Vancomycin* and *ofloxacin* are the other important broad spectrum antibiotics. The antibiotic *dysidazirine* is supposed to be toxic towards certain strains of cancer cells.

General Sturcture of Pencillin

Chloramphenicol

H.W. Florey and Alexander Fleming shared the Nobel prize for Medicine in 1945 for their independent contributions to the development of penicillin.

(b) Antiseptics and disinfectants

Antiseptics and disinfectants are also the chemicals which either kill or prevent the growth of microorganisms.

Antiseptics are applied to the living tissues such as wounds, cuts, ulcers and diseased skin surfaces. Examples are **furacine**, **soframicine,** etc. These are not ingested like antibiotics. Commonly used antiseptic, dettol is a mixture of **chloroxylenol** and **terpineol**. Bithionol (the compound is also called bithional) is added to soaps to impart antiseptic properties. Iodine is a powerful antiseptic. Its 2-3 per cent solution in alcohol-water mixture is known as **tincture of iodine**. It is applied on wounds. **Iodoform** is also used as an antiseptic for wounds. Boric acid in dilute aqueous solution is weak antiseptic for eyes.

Chloroxylenol   Terpineol   Bithionol

Disinfectants are applied to inanimate objects such as floors, drainage system, instruments, etc. Same substances can act as an antiseptic as well as disinfectant by varying the concentration. For example, 0.2 per cent solution of phenol is an antiseptic while its one percent solution is disinfectant.

Chlorine in the concentration of 0.2 to 0.4 ppm in aqueous solution and sulphur dioxide in very low concentrations, are disinfectants.

16.3.5 Antifertility Drugs

Antibiotic revolution has provided long and healthy life to people. The life expectancy has almost doubled. The increased population has caused many social problems in terms of food resources, environmental issues, employment, etc. To control these problems, population is required to be controlled. This has lead to the concept of family planning. Antifertility drugs are of use in this direction. Birth control pills essentially contain a mixture of synthetic estrogen and progesterone derivatives. Both of these compounds are hormones. It is known that progesterone suppresses ovulation. Synthetic progesterone derivatives are more potent than progesterone. **Norethindrone** is an example of synthetic progesterone derivative most widely used as antifertility drug. The estrogen derivative which is used in combination with progesterone derivative is **ethynylestradiol (novestrol)**.

Norethindrone   Ethynylestradiol (novestrol)

Intext Questions

16.1 Sleeping pills are recommended by doctors to the patients suffering from sleeplessness but it is not advisable to take its doses without consultation with the doctor. Why ?

16.2 With reference to which classification has the statement, "ranitidine is an antacid" been given?

Chemicals are added to food for (i) their preservation, (ii) enhancing their appeal, and (iii) adding nutritive value in them. Main categories of food additives are as follows:

(i) Food colours
(ii) Flavours and sweeteners
(iii) Fat emulsifiers and stabilising agents
(iv) Flour improvers - antistaling agents and bleaches
(v) Antioxidants
(vi) Preservatives
(vii) Nutritional supplements such as minerals, vitamins and amino acids.

Except for chemicals of category (vii), none of the above additives have nutritive value. These are added either to increase the shelf life of stored food or for cosmetic purposes. In this Section we will discuss only sweeteners and food preservatives.

16.4.1 Artificial Sweetening Agents

Natural sweeteners, e.g., sucrose add to calorie intake and therefore many people prefer to use artificial sweeteners. Ortho-sulphobenzimide, also called saccharin, is the first popular artificial sweetening agent. It has been used as a sweetening agent ever since it was discovered in 1879. It is about 550 times as sweet as cane sugar. It is excreted from the body in urine unchanged. It appears to be entirely inert and harmless when taken. Its use is of great value to diabetic persons and people who need to control intake of calories. Some other commonly marketed artificial sweeteners are given in Table 16.1.

Table 16.1: Artificial Sweeteners

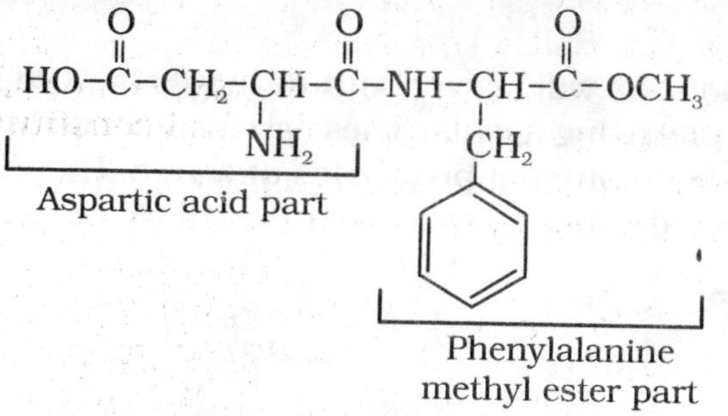

Artificial sweetener	Structural formula	Sweetness value in comparison to cane sugar
Aspartame	$HO-\overset{O}{\overset{\|}{C}}-CH_2-CH-\overset{O}{\overset{\|}{C}}-NH-CH-\overset{O}{\overset{\|}{C}}-OCH_3$ with NH_2 (Aspartic acid part) and CH_2 with phenyl (Phenylalanine methyl ester part)	100
Saccharin	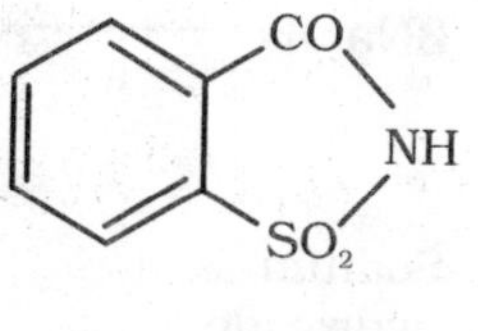 CO NH SO$_2$ ring structure	550
Sucralose	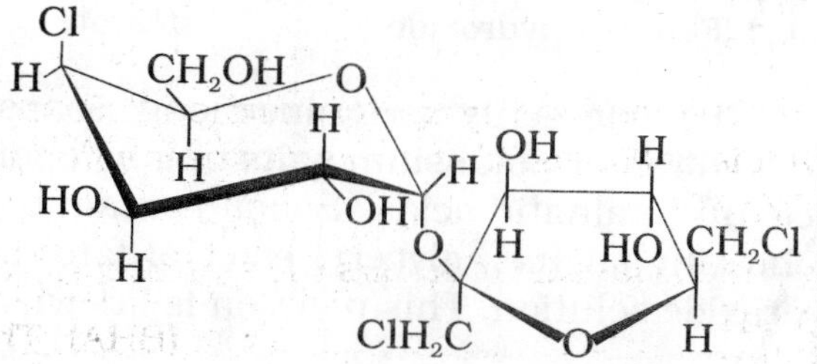 Cl, CH$_2$OH, HO, OH, CH$_2$Cl, ClH$_2$C, HO structure	600

| Alitame | HO$-\overset{\displaystyle O}{\overset{\displaystyle \|}{C}}-CH_2-\underset{\underset{\displaystyle NH_2}{\|}}{CH}-\overset{\displaystyle O}{\overset{\displaystyle \|}{C}}-NH-\underset{\underset{\displaystyle CH_3}{\|}}{CH}-\overset{\displaystyle O}{\overset{\displaystyle \|}{C}}-NH-CH$ S | 2000 |

Aspartame is the most successful and widely used artificial sweetener. It is roughly 100 times as sweet as cane sugar. It is methyl ester of dipeptide formed from aspartic acid and phenylalanine. Use of aspartame is limited to cold foods and soft drinks because it is unstable at cooking temperature.

Alitame is high potency sweetener, although it is more stable than aspartame, the control of sweetness of food is difficult while using it.

Sucralose is trichloro derivative of sucrose. Its appearance and taste are like sugar. It is stable at cooking temperature. It does not provide calories.

16.4.2 Food Preservatives

Food preservatives prevent spoilage of food due to microbial growth. The most commonly used preservatives include table salt, sugar, vegetable oils and sodium benzoate, C_6H_5COONa. Sodium benzoate is used in limited quantities and is metabolised in the body. Salts of sorbic acid and propanoic acid are also used as preservatives.

> *Intext Question*
>
> **16.3** Why do we require artificial sweetening agents ?

16.5 Cleansing Agents

In this Section, we will learn about **detergents**. Two types of detergents are used as cleansing agents. These are soaps and synthetic detergents. These improve cleansing properties of water. These help in removal of fats which bind other materials to the fabric or skin.

16.5.1 Soaps

$$CH_2 - O - \overset{\displaystyle O}{\overset{\displaystyle \|}{C}} - C_{17}H_{35}$$
$$CH - O - \overset{\displaystyle O}{\overset{\displaystyle \|}{C}} - C_{17}H_{35} + 3NaOH \longrightarrow 3C_{17}H_{35}COONa + \begin{matrix} CH_2-OH \\ | \\ CH-OH \\ | \\ CH_2-OH \end{matrix}$$
$$CH_2 - O - \overset{\displaystyle O}{\overset{\displaystyle \|}{C}} - C_{17}H_{35}$$

| Glyceryl ester of stearic acid (Fat) | Sodium hydroxide | Sodium stearate | Glycerol (or Glycerine) |

Soaps are the detergents used since long. Soaps used for cleaning purpose are sodium or potassium salts of long chain fatty acids, e.g., stearic, oleic and palmitic acids. Soaps containing sodium salts are formed by heating fat (*i.e.*, glyceryl ester of fatty acid) with aqueous sodium hydroxide solution. This reaction is known as **saponification**.

In this reaction, esters of fatty acids are hydrolysed and the soap obtained remains in colloidal form. It is precipitated from the solution by adding sodium chloride. The solution left after removing the soap contains glycerol, which can be recovered by fractional distillation. Only sodium and potassium soaps are soluble in water and are used for cleaning purposes. Generally potassium soaps are soft to the skin than sodium soaps. These can be prepared by using potassium hydroxide solution in place of sodium hydroxide.

Types of soaps

Basically all soaps are made by boiling fats or oils with suitable soluble hydroxide. Variations are made by using different raw materials.

Toilet soaps are prepared by using better grades of fats and oils and care is taken to remove excess alkali. Colour and perfumes are added to make these more attractive.

Soaps that float in water are made by beating tiny air bubbles before their hardening. *Transparent soaps* are made by dissolving the soap in ethanol and then evaporating the excess solvent.

In *medicated soaps*, substances of medicinal value are added. In some soaps, deodorants are added. *Shaving soaps* contain glycerol to prevent rapid drying. A gum called, rosin is added while making them. It forms sodium rosinate which lathers well. *Laundry soaps* contain fillers like sodium rosinate, sodium silicate, borax and sodium carbonate.

Soap chips are made by running a thin sheet of melted soap onto a cool cylinder and scraping off the soaps in small broken pieces. *Soap granules* are dried miniature soap bubbles. *Soap powders* and *scouring soaps* contain some soap, a scouring agent (abrasive) such as powdered pumice or finely divided sand, and builders like sodium carbonate and trisodium phosphate. Builders make the soaps act more rapidly. The cleansing action of soap has been discussed in Unit 5.

Why do soaps not work in hard water?

Hard water contains calcium and magnesium ions. These ions form insoluble calcium and magnesium soaps respectively when sodium or potassium soaps are dissolved in hard water.

$$2C_{17}H_{35}COONa + CaCl_2 \longrightarrow 2NaCl + (C_{17}H_{35}COO)_2Ca$$

Soap   Insoluble calcium stearate (Soap)

These insoluble soaps separate as scum in water and are useless as cleansing agent. In fact these are hinderance to good washing, because the precipitate adheres onto the fibre of the cloth as gummy mass. Hair washed with hard water looks dull because of this sticky precipitate. Dye does not absorb evenly on cloth washed with soap using hard water, because of this gummy mass.

16.5.2 Synthetic Detergents

Synthetic detergents are cleansing agents which have all the properties of soaps, but which actually do not contain any soap. These can be used both in soft and hard water as they give foam even in hard water. Some of the detergents give foam even in ice cold water.

Synthetic detergents are mainly classified into three categories:
(i) Anionic detergents (ii) Cationic detergents and (iii) Non-ionic detergents

(i) *Anionic Detergents:* Anionic detergents are sodium salts of sulphonated long chain alcohols or hydrocarbons. Alkyl hydrogensulphates formed by treating long chain alcohols with concentrated sulphuric acid are neutralised with alkali to form anionic detergents. Similarly alkyl benzene sulphonates are obtained by neutralising alkyl benzene sulphonic acids with alkali.

$$CH_3(CH_2)_{10}CH_2OH \xrightarrow{H_2SO_4} CH_3(CH_2)_{10}CH_2OSO_3H \xrightarrow{NaOH(aq)} CH_3(CH_2)_{10}CH_2O\overset{-}{S}\overset{+}{O_3Na}$$

Lauryl alcohol　　　　Lauryl hydrogensulphate　　　　Sodium laurylsulphate
(Anionic detergent)

$$CH_3(CH_2)_{11}- \bigcirc \xrightarrow{H_2SO_4} CH_3(CH_2)_{11}- \bigcirc -SO_3H \xrightarrow{NaOH(aq)} CH_3(CH_2)_{11}- \bigcirc -\overset{-}{S}\overset{+}{O_3Na}$$

Dodecylbenzene　　　　Dodecylbenzenesulphonic acid　　　　Sodium dodecylbenzenesulphonate

In anionic detergents, the anionic part of the molecule is involved in the cleansing action. Sodium salts of alkylbenzenesulphonates are an important class of anionic detergents.

They are mostly used for household work. Anionic detergents are also used in toothpastes.

(ii) *Cationic Detergents*: Cationic detergents are quarternary ammonium salts of amines with acetates, chlorides or bromides as anions. Cationic part possess a long hydrocarbon chain and a positive charge on nitrogen atom. Hence, these are called cationic detergents. Cetyltrimethylammonium bromide is a popular cationic detergent and is used in hair conditioners.

$$\left[CH_3(CH_2)_{15} - \overset{\displaystyle CH_3}{\underset{\displaystyle CH_3}{N}} - CH_3 \right]^{+} Br^{-}$$

Cetyltrimethyl ammonium bromide

Cationic detergents have germicidal properties and are expensive, therefore, these are of limited use.

(iii) *Non-ionic Detergents:* Non-ionic detergents do not contain any ion in their constitution. One such detergent is formed when stearic acid reacts with polyethyleneglycol.

$$CH_3(CH_2)_{16}COOH + HO(CH_2CH_2O)_nCH_2CH_2OH \xrightarrow{-H_2O} CH_3(CH_2)_{16}COO(CH_2CH_2O)_nCH_2CH_2OH$$

Stearic acid　　　　Polyethyleneglycol

Liquid dishwashing detergents are non-ionic type. Mechanism of cleansing action of this type of detergents is the same as that of soaps. These also remove grease and oil by micelle formation.

Main problem that appears in the use of detergents is that if their hydrocarbon chain is highly branched, then bacteria cannot degrade this easily. Slow degradation of detergents leads to their accumulation. Effluents containing such detergents reach the rivers, ponds, etc. These persist in water even after sewage treatment and cause foaming in rivers, ponds and streams and their water gets polluted.

These days the branching of the hydrocarbon chain is controlled and kept to the minimum. Unbranched chains can be biodegraded more easily and hence pollution is prevented.

Intext Questions

16.4 Write the chemical equation for preparing sodium soap from glyceryl oleate and glyceryl palmitate. Structural formulae of these compounds are given below.

(i) $(C_{15}H_{31}COO)_3C_3H_5$ – Glyceryl palmitate

(ii) $(C_{17}H_{32}COO)_3C_3H_5$ – Glyceryl oleate

16.5 Following type of non-ionic detergents are present in liquid detergents, emulsifying agents and wetting agents. Label the hydrophilic and hydrophobic parts in the molecule. Identify the functional group(s) present in the molecule.

$$C_9H_{19} - \bigcirc - O(CH_2CH_2O)_xCH_2CH_2OH$$

$(x = 5 \text{ to } 10)$

Summary

Chemistry is essentially the study of materials and the development of new materials for the betterment of humanity. A **drug** is a chemical agent, which affects human metabolism and provides cure from ailment. If taken in doses higher than recommended, these may have poisonous effect. Use of chemicals for therapeutic effect is called **chemotherapy**. Drugs usually interact with biological macromolecules such as carbohydrates, proteins, lipids and nucleic acids. These are called **target molecules**. Drugs are designed to interact with specific targets so that these have the least chance of affecting other targets. This minimises the side effects and localises the action of the drug. Drug chemistry centres around arresting microbes/destroying microbes, preventing the body from various infectious diseases, releasing mental stress, etc. Thus, drugs like analgesics, antibiotics, antiseptics, disinfectants, antacids and tranquilizers are used for specific purpose. To check the population explosion, antifertility drugs have also become prominent in our life.

Food additives such as **preservatives, sweetening agents, flavours, antioxidants, edible colours** and **nutritional supplements** are added to the food to make it attractive, palatable and add nutritive value. Preservatives are added to the food to prevent spoilage due to microbial growth. Artificial sweeteners are used by those who need to check the calorie intake or are diabetic and want to avoid taking sucrose.

These days, **detergents** are much in vogue and get preference over soaps because they work even in hard water. Synthetic detergents are classified into three main categories, namely: **anionic, cationic** and **non-ionic,** and each category has its specific uses. Detergents with straight chain of hydrocarbons are preferred over branched chain as the latter are **non-biodegradable** and consequently cause environmental pollution.

Exercises

16.1 Why do we need to classify drugs in different ways ?

16.2 Explain the term, target molecules or drug targets as used in medicinal chemistry.

16.3 Name the macromolecules that are chosen as drug targets.

16.4 Why should not medicines be taken without consulting doctors ?

16.5 Define the term chemotherapy.

16.6 Which forces are involved in holding the drugs to the active site of enzymes ?

16.7 While antacids and antiallergic drugs interfere with the function of histamines, why do these not interfere with the function of each other ?

16.8 Low level of noradrenaline is the cause of depression. What type of drugs are needed to cure this problem ? Name two drugs.

16.9 What is meant by the term 'broad spectrum antibiotics' ? Explain.

16.10 How do antiseptics differ from disinfectants ? Give one example of each.

16.11 Why are cimetidine and ranitidine better antacids than sodium hydrogencarbonate or magnesium or aluminium hydroxide ?

16.12 Name a substance which can be used as an antiseptic as well as disinfectant.

16.13 What are the main constituents of dettol ?

16.14 What is tincture of iodine ? What is its use ?

16.15 What are food preservatives ?

16.16 Why is use of aspartame limited to cold foods and drinks ?

16.17 What are artificial sweetening agents ? Give two examples.

16.18 Name the sweetening agent used in the preparation of sweets for a diabetic patient.

16.19 What problem arises in using alitame as artificial sweetener ?

16.20 How are synthetic detergents better than soaps ?

16.21 Explain the following terms with suitable examples
  (i) cationic detergents
  (ii) anionic detergents and
  (iii) non-ionic detergents.

16.22 What are biodegradable and non-biodegradable detergents ? Give one example of each.

16.23 Why do soaps not work in hard water ?

16.24 Can you use soaps and synthetic detergents to check the hardness of water ?

16.25 Explain the cleansing action of soaps.

16.26 If water contains dissolved calcium hydrogencarbonate, out of soaps and synthetic detergents which one will you use for cleaning clothes ?

16.27 Label the hydrophilic and hydrophobic parts in the following compounds.

(i) $CH_3(CH_2)_{10}CH_2O\overset{-}{S}O_3\overset{+}{N}a$

(ii) $CH_3(CH_2)_{15}\overset{+}{N}(CH_3)_3\overset{-}{B}r$

(iii) $CH_3(CH_2)_{16}COO(CH_2CH_2O)_nCH_2CH_2OH$

Answers to Some Intext Questions

16.1 Most of the drugs taken in doses higher than recommended may cause harmful effect and act as poison. Therefore, a doctor should always be consulted before taking medicine.

16.2 This statement refers to the classification according to pharmacological effect of the drug because any drug which will be used to counteract the effect of excess acid in the stomach will be called antacid.

16.5

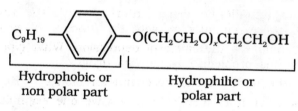

C_9H_{19} —〈benzene ring〉— $O(CH_2CH_2O)_xCH_2CH_2OH$

Hydrophobic or non polar part   Hydrophilic or polar part

UNIT 11

11.1   (i) 2,2,4-Trimethylpentan –3-ol   (ii) 5-Ethylheptane –2, 4-diol

     (iii) Butane –2,3-diol   (iv) Propane –1,2,3,-triol

     (v) 2- Methylphenol   (vi) 4-Methylphenol

     (vii) 2,5 – Dimethylphenol   (viii) 2,6-Dimethylphenol

     (ix) 1-Methoxy-2-methylpropane   (x) Ethoxybenzene

     (xi) 1-phenoxyheptane   (xii) 2 –Ethoxybutane

11.2   (i)
$$CH_3-\underset{\underset{OH}{|}}{\overset{\overset{CH_3}{|}}{C}}-CH_2-CH_3$$

(ii) 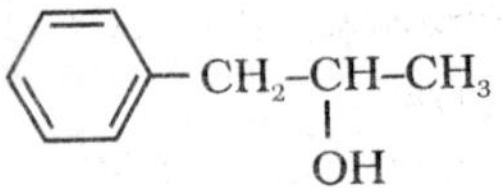 $C_6H_5-CH_2-\underset{\underset{OH}{|}}{CH}-CH_3$

(iii) $HOCH_2-CH_2-\underset{\underset{CH_3}{|}}{\overset{\overset{OH}{|}}{C}}-CH_2-\underset{\underset{CH_3}{|}}{\overset{\overset{OH}{|}}{C}}-CH_3$

(iv) 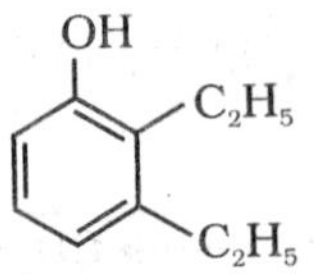 (benzene ring with OH, C_2H_5, C_2H_5)

(v) $C_2H_5-O-CH_2-CH_2-CH_3$

(vi) $CH_3-CH-\underset{\underset{OC_2H_5}{|}}{CH}-\underset{CH_3}{}-CH_2-CH_3$

(vii) (cyclohexyl)–CH_2OH

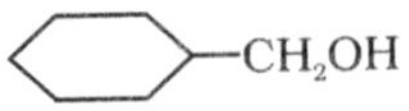

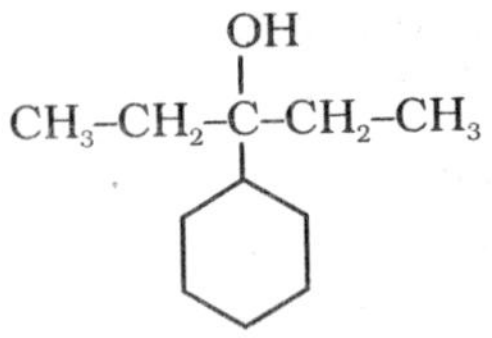

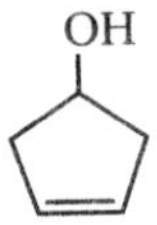

(viii) $CH_3-CH_2-\underset{\underset{(cyclohexyl)}{|}}{\overset{\overset{OH}{|}}{C}}-CH_2-CH_3$

(ix) (cyclopentene with OH)

(x) $CH_3-CH_2-\underset{\underset{CH_2Cl}{|}}{CH}-CH_2-CH_2-OH$

11.3 (i) (a) $CH_3CH_2CH_2CH_2CH_2OH$, Pentan-1-ol;

     (b) $CH_3-CH_2-\underset{\underset{CH_3}{|}}{CH}-CH_2-CH_2-OH$, 2-Methylbutan-1-ol;

     (c) $CH_3-\underset{\underset{CH_3}{|}}{\overset{\overset{CH_3}{|}}{C}}-CH_2OH$, 2,2-Dimethylpropan-1-ol

     (d) $CH_3-CH_2-CH_2-\underset{\underset{OH}{|}}{CH}-CH_3$, Pentan-2-ol

     (e) $CH_3-CH_2-CH_2-\underset{\underset{OH}{|}}{CH}-CH_3$, Pentan-2-ol

     (f) $CH_3-\underset{\underset{CH_3}{|}}{CH}-\underset{\underset{OH}{|}}{CH}-CH_3$, 3-Methylbutan-2-ol

     (g) $CH_3-CH_2-\underset{\underset{CH_3}{|}}{\overset{\overset{CH_3}{|}}{C}}-OH$, 2-Methylbutan-2-ol

11.4   Hydrogen bonding in propanol.

11.5 Hydrogen bonding between alcohol and water molecules.

11.8 o-Nitrophenol is steam volatile because of intramolecular hydrogen bonding.

11.12 **Hint:** Carryout sulphonation followed by nucleophilic substitution.

11.13 (i)

$$\text{(styrene CH=CH}_2\text{)} \xrightarrow{\text{H}^+/\text{H}_2\text{O}} \text{CH(OH)CH}_3$$

(ii)

CH$_2$Cl (on benzene) + NaOH $\longrightarrow$ CH$_2$OH (on benzene) + NaCl

(iii) $CH_3(CH_2)_4Cl + NaOH \longrightarrow CH_3(CH_2)_4OH + NaCl$

11.14 Reaction with (i) sodium and (ii) sodium hydroxide.

11.15 Due to electron withdrawing effect of nitro group and electron releasing effect of methoxy group.

11.20 (i) Hydration of Propene.

(ii) By nucleophilic substitution of –Cl in benzyl chloride using dilute NaOH.

(iii) $C_2H_5MgBr + HCHO \rightarrow C_2H_5CH_2OMgBr \xrightarrow{H_2O} C_2H_5CH_2OH$

(iv) $CH_3MgBr + CH_3COCH_3 \longrightarrow CH_3-\underset{\underset{CH_3}{|}}{\overset{\overset{CH_3}{|}}{C}}-OMgBr \xrightarrow{H_2O} CH_3-\underset{\underset{CH_3}{|}}{\overset{\overset{CH_3}{|}}{C}}-OH$

11.23 (i) 1-Ethoxy-2-methylpropane.

(ii) 2-Chloro-1-methoxyethane.

(iii) 4-Nitroanisole.

(iv) 1-Methoxypropane.

(v) 1-Ethoxy-4,4-dimethylcyclohexane.

(vi) Ethoxybenzene.

UNIT 12

12.2 (i) 4-Methylpentanal

(ii) 6-Chloro-4-ethylhexan-3-one

(iii) But-2-enal

(iv) Pentane-2,4-dione

(v) 3,3,5-Trimethylhexan-2-one

(vi) 3,3-Dimethylbutanoic acid

(vii) Benzene –1,4-dicarbaldehyde

12.3 (i) $H_3C-\underset{\underset{CH_3}{|}}{CH}-CH_2-\overset{\overset{O}{\|}}{C}-H$

(ii) $O_2N-\text{C}_6\text{H}_4-\overset{\overset{O}{\|}}{C}-CH_2-CH_3$

(iii) $H_3C-\text{C}_6\text{H}_4-\overset{\overset{O}{\|}}{C}-H$

(iv) $H_3C-\underset{\underset{O}{\|}}{C}-CH=\underset{\overset{CH_3}{|}}{C}-CH_3$

(v) $H_3C-\overset{\overset{O}{\|}}{C}-CH_2-\underset{\underset{Cl}{|}}{CH}-CH_3$

(vi) $H_3C-CH-\underset{\underset{C_6H_5}{|}}{\overset{\overset{Br}{|}}{CH}}-CH_2-\overset{\overset{O}{\|}}{C}-OH$

(vii) 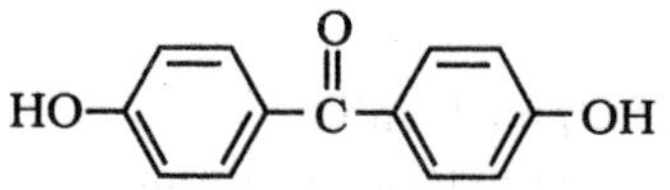 HO—⟨benzene⟩—C(=O)—⟨benzene⟩—OH   (viii) $H_3C-C\equiv C-CH=CH-C(=O)-OH$

12.4 (i) Heptan-2-one   (ii) 4-Bromo-2-methylhexanal   (iii) Heptanal

(iv) 3-Phenylprop-2-enal   (v) Cyclopentanecarbaldehyde   (vi) Diphenylmethanone

12.5 (i) 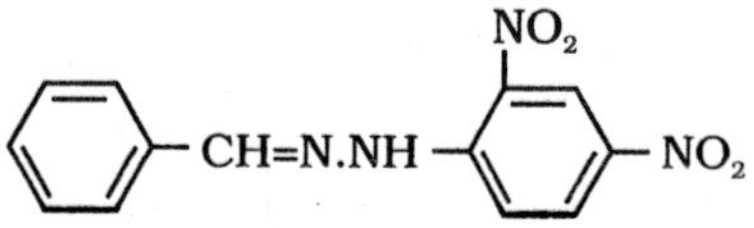 ⟨benzene⟩—CH=N.NH—⟨2,4-dinitrophenyl, NO₂ / NO₂⟩

(ii) 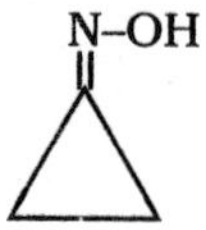 cyclopropane with =N—OH

(iii) $CH_3-CH\langle^{OCH_3}_{OCH_3}$

(iv) 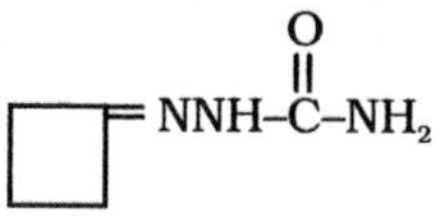 cyclobutane =NNH—C(=O)—NH₂

(v) 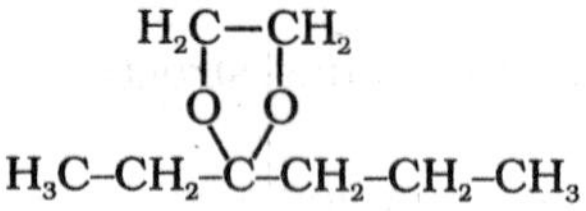 $H_3C-CH_2-C(\text{dioxolane } H_2C-CH_2, O, O)-CH_2-CH_2-CH_3$

(vi) 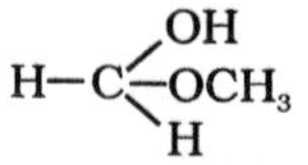 $H-C\langle^{OH}_{OCH_3}$ with H below

12.6 (i) 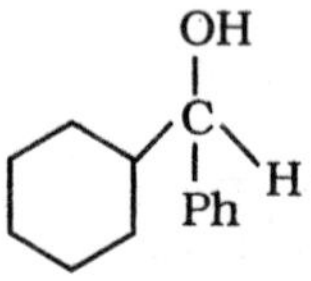 cyclohexane—C(OH)(Ph)(H)

(ii) 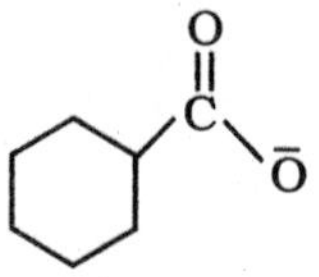 cyclohexane—C(=O)—O⁻

(iii) 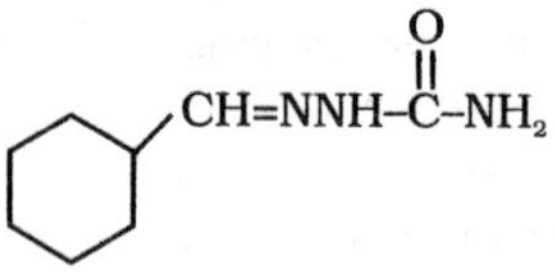 cyclohexane—CH=NNH—C(=O)—NH₂

(iv) 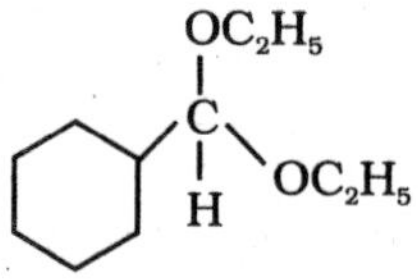 cyclohexane—C(H)(OC₂H₅)(OC₂H₅)

(v) 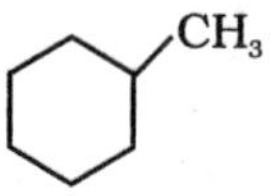 cyclohexane—CH₃

12.7 (ii), (v), (vi), (vii): Aldol condensation. (i), (iii), (ix) Cannizaro reaction. (iv), (viii) Neither.

12.10 2-Ethylbenzaldehyde (draw the structure yourself).

12.11 (A) $CH_3CH_2CH_2COOCH_2CH_2CH_2CH_3$, butyl butanoate.

(B) $CH_3CH_2CH_2$ COOH   (C) $CH_3CH_2CH_2CH_2OH$. Write equation yourself.

12.12 (i) Di-tert-butyl ketone < Methyl tert-butyl ketone < Acetone < Acetaldehyde

(ii) $(CH_3)_2CHCOOH$ < $CH_3CH_2CH_2COOH$ < $CH_3CH(Br)CH_2COOH$ < $CH_3CH_2CH(Br)COOH$

(iii) 4-Methoxybenzoic acid < Benzoic acid < 4-Nitrobenzoic acid < 3,4-Dinitrobenzoic acid.

12.17 (i) 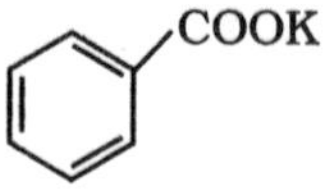 benzene—COOK

(ii) 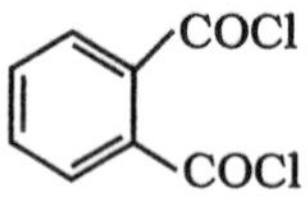 benzene with COCl / COCl (ortho)

(iii) $C_6H_5CH=NNHC(=O)-NH_2$

(iv) $C_6H_5COCl-AlCl_3$

(v) 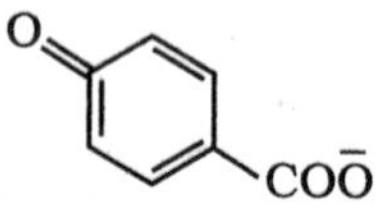 O=⟨cyclohexadiene⟩=COO⁻

(vi) 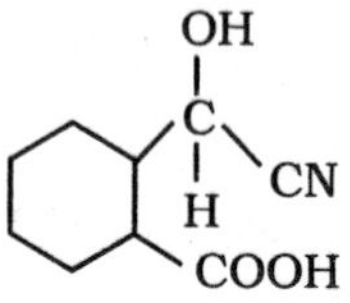 cyclohexane with C(OH)(CN) and COOH

(vii) $C_6H_5CH=C-CHO$ with CH_3 below

(viii) $CH_3CH(OH)CH_2COOC_2H_5$ (ix) 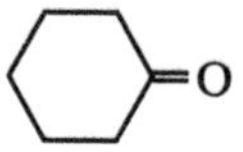 cyclohexane=O

(x) 1. BH_3; 2. $H_2O_2/\bar{O}H$; 3. PCC   (xi) 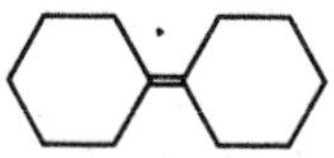 bicyclohexylidene

12.19 The compound is methyl ketone and its structure would be: $CH_3COCH_2CH_2CH_3$

UNIT 13

13.1 (i) 1-methylethanamine   (ii) Propan-1-amine

    (iii) N-methyl-2-methylethanamine   (iv) 2-methylpropan-2-amine

    (v) N-methylbenzamine or N-methylaniline   (vi) N-Ethyl-N-methylethanamine

    (vii) 3-Bromoaniline or 3-Bromobenzenamine

13.4 (i) $C_6H_5NH_2 < C_6H_5NHCH_3 < C_2H_5NH_2 < (C_2H_5)_2NH$

    (ii) $C_6H_5NH_2 < C_6H_5N(CH_3)_2 < CH_3NH_2 < (C_2H_5)_2NH$

    (iii) (a) p-nitroaniline < aniline < p-toluidine

        (b) $C_6H_5NH_2 < C_6H_5NHCH_3 < C_6H_5CH_2NH_2$

    (iv) $(C_2H_5)_3N > (C_2H_5)_2NH > C_2H_5NH_2 > NH_3$ (v) $(CH_3)_2NH < C_2H_5NH_2 < C_2H_5OH$

    (vi) $C_6H_5NH_2 < (C_2H_5)_2NH < C_2H_5NH_2$

UNIT 15

15.1 Polymer is a high molecular mass macromolecule consisting of repeating structural units derived from monomers.

Monomer is a simple molecule capable of undergoing polymerisation and leading to the formation of the corresponding polymer.

15.2 Natural polymers are high molecular mass macromolecules and are found in plants and animals. The examples are proteins and nucleic acids.

Synthetic polymers are man-made high molecular mass macromolecules. These include synthetic plastics, fibres and rubbers. The two specific examples are polythene and dacron.

15.4 Functionality is the number of bonding sites in a monomer.

15.5 Polymerisation is a process of formation of a high molecular mass polymer from one or more monomers by linking together of repeating structural units with covalent bonds.

15.6 Since the unit $-(NH-CHR-CO)_n$ is obtained from a single monomer unit, it is a homopolymer.

15.7 On the basis of molecular forces present between the chains of various polymers, the classification of polymers is given as follows.

(a) Elastomers (b) Fibres (c) Thermoplastics and (d) Thermosetting plastics.

15.8 In addition polymerisation, the molecules of the same or different monomers add together to form a large polymer molecule. Condensation polymerisation is a process in which two or more bi-functional molecules undergo a series of condensation reactions with the elimination of some simple molecules and leading to the formation of polymers.

15.9 Copolymerisation is a process in which a mixture of more than one monomeric species is allowed to polymerise. The copolymer contains multiple units of each monomer in the chain. The examples are copolymers of 1,3-butadiene and styrene and 1, 3-butadiene and acrylonitrile.

15.10

$$C_6H_5-C-O-O-C-C_6H_5 \longrightarrow 2C_6H_5-C-\dot{O} \longrightarrow 2C_6\dot{H}_5$$
phenyl radical

$$C_6\dot{H}_5 + CH_2=CH_2 \longrightarrow C_6H_5-CH_2-C\dot{H}_2$$

$$C_6H_5-CH_2-\dot{C}H_2 + CH_2=CH_2 \longrightarrow C_6H_5-CH_2-CH_2-CH_2-CH_2$$

chain termination

$$C_6H_5+(CH_2-CH_2)_n CH_2-CH_2-CH_2-CH_2+(CH_2-CH_2)_n C_6H_5$$
Polythene

15.11 A thermoplastic polymer can be repeatedly softened on heating and hardened on cooling, hence it can be used again and again. The examples are polythene, polypropylene, etc.

A thermosetting polymer is a permanent setting polymer as it gets hardened and sets during moulding process and cannot be softened again. The examples are bakelite and melamine-formaldehyde polymers.

15.12 (i) The monomer of polyvinyl chloride is $CH_2=CHCl$ (vinyl chloride).
(ii) The monomer of teflon is $CF_2=CF_2$ (tetrafluoroethylene).
(iii) The monomers involved in the formation of bakelite are HCHO (formaldehyde) and C_6H_5OH (phenol).

15.14 From the structural point of view, the natural rubber is a linear cis-1,4- polyisoprene. In this polymer the double bonds are located between C_2 and C_3 of isoprene units. This cis-configuration about double bonds do not allow the chains to come closer for effective attraction due to weak intermolecular attractions. Hence, the natural rubber has a coiled structure and shows elasticity.

15.16 The monomeric repeat unit of Nylon-6 polymer is:
$[NH–(CH_2)_5–CO]$
The monomeric repeat unit of Nylon-6,6 polymer is derived from the two monomers, hexamethylene diamine and adipic acid.
$[NH–(CH_2)_6–NH-CO–(CH_2)_4–CO]$

15.17 The names and structures of monomers are:

Polymers	Monomer Names	Monomer Structures
(i) Buna-S	1,3-Butadiene	$CH_2=CH–CH=CH_2$
	Styrene	$C_6H_5CH=CH_2$
(ii) Buna-N	1,3- Butadiene	$CH_2=CH–CH=CH_2$
	Acrylonitrile	$CH_2=CH\ CN$
(iii) Neoprene	Chloroprene	$CH_2=\overset{\overset{\textstyle Cl}{\textstyle \vert}}{C}–CH=CH_2$
(iv) Dacron	Ethylene glycol	$OHCH_2–CH_2OH$
	Terephthalic acid	COOH—⟨phenyl⟩—COOH

15.18 The monomers forming the polymer are:
(i) Decandioic acid $HOOC–(CH_2)_8–COOH$ and Hexamethylene diamine $H_2N(CH_2)_6\ NH_2$

(ii)

and HCHO

15.19 The following are the equations for the formation of Dacron.

$$n\ HOCH_2CH_2OH + nHOOC—⟨phenyl⟩—COOH \longrightarrow \left\{ O–CH_2CH_2O–CO—⟨phenyl⟩—CO \right\}_n$$

Ethylene glycol   Terephthalic acid   Dacron

INDEX

SUPPLEMENTARY MATERIAL

UNIT XIV: *Biomolecules*

14.5 HORMONES

Hormones are molecules that act as intercellular messengers. These are produced by endocrine glands in the body and are poured directly in the blood stream which transports them to the site of action.

In terms of chemical nature, some of these are steroids, e.g., estrogens and androgens; some are poly peptides for example insulin and endorphins and some others are amino acid derivatives such as epinephrine and norepinephrine.

Hormones have several functions in the body. They help to maintain the balance of biological activities in the body. The role of insulin in keeping the blood glucose level within the narrow limit is an example of this function. Insulin is released in response to the rapid rise in blood glucose level. On the other hand hormone glucagon tends to increase the glucose level in the blood. The two hormones together regulate the glucose level in the blood. Epinephrine and norepinephrine mediate responses to external stimuli. Growth hormones and sex hormones play role in growth and development. Thyroxine produced in the thyroid gland is an iodinated derivative of amino acid tyrosine. Abnormally low level of thyroxine leads to hypothyroidism which is characterised by lethargyness and obesity. Increased level of thyroxine causes hyperthyroidism. Low level of iodine in the diet may lead to hypothyroidism and enlargement of the thyroid gland. This condition is largely being controlled by adding sodium iodide to commercial table salt ("Iodised" salt).

Steroid hormones are produced by adrenal cortex and gonads (testes in males and ovaries in females). Hormones released by the adrenal cortex play very important role in the functions of the body. For example, glucocorticoids control the carbohydrate metabolism, modulate inflammatory reactions, and are involved in reactions to stress. The mineralocorticoids control the level of excretion of water and salt by the kidney. If adrenal cortex does not function properly then one of the results may be Addison's disease characterised by hypoglycemia, weakness and increased susceptibility to stress. The disease is fatal unless it is treated by glucocorticoids and mineralocorticoids. Hormones released by gonads are responsible for development of secondary sex characters. Testosterone is the major sex hormone produced in males. It is responsible for development of secondary male characteristics (deep voice, facial hair, general physical constitution) and estradiol is the main female sex hormone. It is responsible for development of secondary female characteristics and participates in the control of menstrual cycle. Progesterone is responsible for preparing the uterus for implantation of fertilised egg.

UNIT XVI: *Chemistry in Everyday Life*

16.4.3 Antioxidants in Food

These are important and necessary food additives. These help in food preservation by retarding the action of oxygen on food. These are more reactive towards oxygen than the food material which they are protecting. The two most familiar antioxidants are butylated hydroxy toluene (BHT) and butylated hydroxy anisole (BHA). The addition of BHA to butter increases its shelf life from months to years.

Sometimes BHT and BHA along with citric acid are added to produce more effect. Sulphur dioxide and sulphite are useful antioxidants for wine and beer, sugar syrups and cut, peeled or dried fruits and vegetables.